RUN
SMARTER

Run Smarter: Evidence-Based Guidance and Expert Opinions to Help You Survive & Thrive as a Runner

Copyright © 2022 by Brodie Sharpe.

ISBN: 978-0-6455207-0-5 (Paperback)
978-0-6455207-1-2 (ePub)

Typesetting and formatting: Minhajul Islam
Cover design: Verity Casey
Copyediting: Paige Rundle and Gillian Bronte

EVIDENCE-BASED GUIDANCE AND EXPERT OPINIONS
TO HELP YOU SURVIVE & THRIVE AS A RUNNER

RUN

SMARTER

BRODIE SHARPE

TABLE OF CONTENTS

PART ONE:
PREVENTING INJURY

PART TWO:
INCREASING PERFORMANCE

PART ONE

PREVENTING INJURY

INTRODUCTION

The Run Smarter Book aims to serve runners of all abilities and to explain every important facet of training in an engaging and straightforward manner. As a physiotherapist and running coach, I have dedicated my career to educating runners on injury reduction, injury rehabilitation and running performance. After becoming a recreational runner in my mid twenties, I quickly developed a passion for treating every runner looking for guidance.

As my passion and understanding of running related injuries grew, more runners would contact me seeking help. Over a few years, I learned the common patterns that lead to injury and the typical mistakes and misconceptions widely considered fact but contradictory to evidence based research. I realised this knowledge gap and created the Run Smarter Podcast tailored to educating runners of all abilities. Alongside my solo-recorded episodes, where I deliver foundational injury-prevention principles, I also had the pleasure of interviewing world class health professionals, running coaches and researchers, providing correct information to the running population. This information inevitably extended to publishing blogs through my website and social media channels.

The birth of the podcast also gave rise to my own business, the Run Smarter Physiotherapy Clinic, which allows me to support runners one-on-one with in-person or online physiotherapy consults. Directing my business to this specific niche market has put me in a unique position to assess, treat and chat with thousands of runners in a short amount of time. My proficient understanding of injuries and the everyday struggles runners face allows me to deliver evidence based advice.

With my goal to educate as many runners as possible, I decided to branch out of the podcast space and tackle the monstrous task of writing the Run Smarter Book. This book, in two distinct parts, aims to convey running related guidance using easy-to-understand language and practical advice. Part One details universal principles that will help reduce injury risk, while Part Two is designed to build your running performance safely. Each chapter will help reveal missing pieces in your training and list practical takeaways to implement. However, if you read the book cover to cover, you can always revisit sections of the book that become more relevant as your running goals change and new obstacles present themselves.

Both parts of the book follow a fictional character Pete throughout his running journey. Pete is a composite character based on many runners I encountered throughout my physiotherapy and running career. Each chapter details Pete's journey as he builds upon his running IQ and strives for higher running feats. Pete's journey will lead into a deeper dive on a specific running topic, including published research, expert opinions, relevant podcast quotes, and practical lessons.

Spending my career educating runners, I have learned that large volumes of content delivered in one method will not resonate with everyone. To help this situation, I have included a dot-point summary at the end of each chapter to highlight the key lessons and takeaways. I have also included different analogies within the book to help runners who might not pick up on the concepts straight away. Hopefully, you find these useful.

The Start of My Run Smarter Journey

In late 2019, I worked as a private practice physiotherapist treating anyone who walked through the door. However, 2019 was a big career change for me. I was leaving my safe employee role and venturing out on my own to start a niche online physiotherapy clinic tailored for runners. Based on the level of enjoyment I had when treating runners, I decided to dedicate my entire career to treating only this demographic. I knew my work life would be more fulfilling if I spent it doing things that built up my energy levels rather than depleting them. To this day, my business decisions revolve around the same question. Will this generate or deplete my energy levels?

Accompanying this business decision was my idea to launch a podcast. I wanted to release solo episodes along with interviews to teach runners of all abilities the most fundamental, effective, evidence based principles to help them survive and thrive. Even though I wanted to have clients pay me to help them, I still wanted to deliver as much free content as possible without holding anything back. The way I saw it, if runners were willing to educate themselves with my information and execute the lessons they had learned, I had done my job.

However, if a runner was gaining information through my content and still needed assistance, I wanted to be the first person they thought of contacting for help. To this day, I still receive feedback from runners saying I am doing myself a disservice because they are overcoming their injuries by just listening to my podcast and reading my content. In my eyes, that means I am serving my purpose, and in this book, I aim to continue that approach.

Starting a podcast is a steep learning curve. I thought of the title 'Run Smarter' easily because I knew of the positive impact runners could have if they took the time to educate themselves with the right information. Next came the podcast logo, audio equipment and recording software. These steps took a lot more thought and patience. However, long before I thought of the podcast title, I already knew what my first episode would contain. Episode number one was released on the 12th of January 2020 and was titled *Adaptation Education.*

It was clear that this had to be the first piece of information in the runner's ears because understanding the key principles of the adaptation process is crucial before learning any other complex topic.

CHAPTER ONE

ADAPTATION EDUCATION

L ike many of us in our thirties, Pete got up one morning and took a good, hard look at himself. He wasn't getting any younger, his 40th birthday was rapidly approaching, and as a father of two boys, he knew he needed to change his lifestyle and set a better example. He had been at the pub with his mates the night before and had really noticed a difference between those who were fit and those who weren't. He knew which side he wanted to align himself with.

The first step was to get a medical check from his doctor. Pete had his weight, height, heart rate, and blood pressure recorded. Based on his results, his doctor advised Pete to make a lifestyle change to reduce the risk of severe health consequences later in life. The first recommendation was to engage in regular physical activity. Having run recreationally in high school, Pete decided to give it a try.

Driving home from the doctor's office, numerous questions kept circling in his head.

How fit will I be after years of inactivity?
Am I too old to start?
What running route should I take?
Is running on grass better?

Should I avoid hills?

How far should I run?

Which pair of running shoes are the best?

Can I find a way to run without my neighbours seeing me?

After stewing with his thoughts all day, he decided to jog around the quiet streets once night fell. Running in the dark was a safe strategy for Pete, as he was embarrassed to be seen by others. He headed up to his bedroom and sifted through his shoe drawer. The best pair of shoes he could find were old running shoes he had worn when playing sports with his kids. They were old with significant wear and tear, but they were comfortable. With the street lamps being the only light illuminating the streets, Pete was ready to attempt this first run.

Pete recalled some stretches from his high school days and spent a few minutes going through the routine. He didn't want to get injured during his first run, so he tried to take every precaution. First, he bent over with straight legs reaching for his toes, then grabbed his foot from behind and pushed it into his glutes. Lastly, he held onto a light post and swung each leg side to side, back and forth.

Pete was all set. He started jogging on the spot for a few seconds to ensure his body was ready and then set out with a conservative jog. Initially, he was insecure and had his eyes peeled for any nosey neighbours. In addition, he felt an unusual sensation coming from his stomach. Never before had Pete felt his belly flop while running, but it served as a reminder to get into shape. Two minutes into his jog, Pete's effort levels became increasingly uncomfortable. He felt his breath rate climb, which quickly turned into distressing gasps for air. Concurrently, Pete's calves started to burn. He thought this running attempt was pathetic. Frankly, he was shocked at how hard it was but figured he just needed to push through the discomfort.

His calves elevated from a mild burn to an intense scream. Suddenly, the warning signs in Pete's body were too loud to ignore. The urge to stop overwhelmed him and he had no choice but to stop and collapse. He could hardly hold his arm steady as he read the stopwatch. His heart sank as the watch displayed a time of 3 minutes and 22 seconds.

Looking back down the street, Pete could still see his mailbox. It was a humiliating defeat, but at least there was no one to witness his demoralising reality check. Looking on the bright side, Pete recognised he needed to start somewhere. After a few minutes, he had his breath under control, and the burning in his calves simmered down to a mild tightness. He repeated two more rounds of three minute efforts before walking home. Each round of jogging ended in the same result, his need for air spiralled out of control, and his calves burning was too great to ignore. He decided to persist with running for two more weeks. By then, if running still made him miserable, he would seek out another fitness alternative. He knew the beginning would always be the least enjoyable, like any new task.

Over the next four weeks, Pete would find a consistent groove. He'd run three days per week and a little further with each attempt. Not only were distances increasing, but the level of effort was decreasing. His calves were still sore after running, but his breathing was under control. Alongside his physical improvements were his evergrowing confidence levels. No longer were his runs hidden by night, he would even chat about his new hobby to his friends and work colleagues. Surprising everyone, including himself, he was starting to enjoy the feeling of running.

The same routine was followed week after week. Every Tuesday and Thursday after work, Pete would set off on an evening jog. On weekends, he'd squeeze in a long run around family commitments. His running duration would range from 20 to 40 minutes at an easy to moderate intensity. As disciplined as Pete was to keep this easy effort level, he couldn't resist picking up speed in the final minutes. He even downloaded a fitness tracking app to calculate his weekly mileage.

Throughout the next six weeks, Pete was still seeing improvements but then realised that the rate of progression started to plateau. It was time to change something in his routine to keep seeing further improvement. Chatting with some work colleagues who were keen runners, Pete was advised to run a similar weekly mileage but to spread it across more days in the week. By increasing the frequency, the body has more opportunities to develop and adapt to the demands of running. Once this became a part of Pete's regular routine, he could then gradually increase the distance. Pete decided to run 20 minutes on Monday, Wednesday, Thursday, Saturday and Sunday.

MON	TUE	WED	THU	FRI	SAT	SUN	TOT.
			Original Routine				
	30 mins		20 mins			40 mins	90 mins
			New Routine				
20 mins		20 mins	20 mins		20 mins	20 mins	100 mins

Implementing this new running strategy worked wonders for Pete's fitness and confidence. He continued to run five easy days per week, each run ranging from 20 to 30 minutes. Pete was slowly losing weight, his calves were less stiff, and most importantly, he was maintaining a high level of enjoyment.

Run Smarter Lesson 1

The people who say 'running just isn't for me' will usually try running for a few weeks and hate the entire experience. Like Pete's first attempt, they are discouraged by their lack of ability and often move on to another form of exercise. Once someone breaks through this trial period, the body will adapt and meet the demands of running. Around the six week mark, runners will usually reach a level of fitness that enables them to run at a comfortable, steady state. In other words, consistency will give most beginner runners the ability to run continuously at a low intensity, without the need to stop and gasp for air.

The body is quite extraordinary in this regard. If you try something outside your normal routine, it triggers a physiological response. If this trigger is carried out on a regular basis, your body will physiologically change the inner structures to make that task easier. For example, elite swimmers will develop large shoulders to push through the water. Compare this to endurance cyclists who develop a thin upper body but strong legs. Elite endurance runners on the other hand, tend to develop a lightweight body with stiff, strong tendons that can absorb the ground reaction force and propel forward efficiently.

I remember this process vividly. I started running recreationally in 2015 at the age of 25. After playing competitive basketball into my mid-twenties, I had a decent fitness level, but that career had ended, and I was looking for my next fitness challenge. Coincidentally, my sister had decided to train for a half marathon and asked if I would join her. The stars aligned, so I agreed.

At this stage, my body was adapted to suit the demands of basketball which involved short sprinting, jumping and pivoting. Once

I started my recreational running journey, I quickly discovered it was not ready for low intensity, endurance-based exercise. Whenever I attempted a slow, steady run, my calves would be screaming. To make matters worse, my natural running style involved contact with my midfoot which further increased the demand on my calves. As a result, after every run, my calves were extremely sore, and I constantly felt the urge to stretch for temporary relief.

Slowly but surely, my body adjusted to meet these low intensity demands. After six weeks, my calves had adapted and the urge to stretch after a run slowly dissipated. Symptoms were even decreasing as my weekly mileage picked up. The tricky thing is that most runners are not very patient. It takes time and discipline to allow the adaptation process to take full effect. Hence, the first of three key ingredients for adaptation is patience. Steady progress with sensible training parameters will let the body do its thing.

Adaptation ingredient number 1 = Patience

The Adaptation Sweet Spot

While having the patience to build the necessary components is crucial, it is just as important to provide the right training load. Training loads could encompass the running duration, speed and elevation, but will also apply to other exercise loads, cross training and strength training. There are three phases of adaptation to consider:

1. Underloading phase: For adaptation to occur, the body needs to be triggered with enough stimulus. Your body will already have the capacity to tolerate small exercise bouts without any strain. For example, jogging on the spot for 30 seconds or walking for 20 minutes. In addition, elite athletes who have already adapted to high volumes of training may require

a larger stimulus to trigger the adaptation response. In this case, even a 30 minute low intensity run may fall within the underloading phase. For these examples, the load will still be applied, but there isn't enough demand to challenge the body and trigger the adaptation response.

2. Overloading phase: Just as easily as you can underload the body, you can also overload the body. While there is a certain minimum threshold to trigger an adaptation response, there is also a threshold that surpasses the body's ability to adapt. Operating in this phase dramatically increases your risk of injury and will be discussed in detail in the next chapter.

3. The adaptation sweet spot: This phase surpasses the minimum threshold to trigger the adaptation response and is necessary if your goal is to physiologically improve at a physical task. It also falls short of overloading the body and acts as the perfect middle ground.

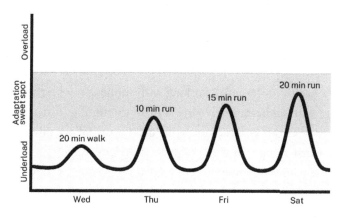

Let's imagine Pete decided to run 60 minutes every single day. This trend would most likely exceed Pete's healthy adaptation zone and increase the likelihood of injury. If, however, Pete decided to only walk 20 minutes for the first three weeks without progressing, he would risk falling shy of the minimum threshold load required for adaptation. As a result, there would be no adaptation trigger, and the body would not see improvements.

Finding Your Adaptation Sweet Spot

Every person will have a different adaptation zone. For this reason, it is common to see someone develop an overuse injury while trying to mimic the training schedule of a more experienced runner. The frustrating part about finding your adaptation zone is the inability to directly measure capacity. Instead, based on specific pieces of information, one needs to make an educated guess.

For instance, you can roughly gauge your capacity limits based on your fitness history. When I work with new runners, I ask about their gym experience, history with team sports, injury history and other fitness routines. It is also essential to investigate how recent these routines have been. In Pete's case, his capacity limits were relatively low due to several years of inactivity, so a conservative start would be recommended.

As a health professional working with runners, my best advice is to start with embarrassingly slow and short running distances. From there, you can consistently build up. If you follow this approach, the worst thing that could happen is underloading yourself for the first few weeks. However, with regular progression, you will quickly find your adaptation zone and your body will build up from there. Runners often make mistakes because they underestimate how much impact is involved when running until an overload injury develops.

Adaptation ingredient number 1 = Patience

Adaptation ingredient number 2 = Train within the adaptation sweet spot

Insight into Adaptation Hacking

Your running 'frequency' refers to the number of running sessions you undertake per week. As mentioned earlier, adaptation is crucial for a runner to handle greater running loads. In addition, optimising your running frequency will give your body the best opportunity to adapt. Simply put, you are spending more time within your adaptation zone, triggering the exercise response and reaping the reward.

When you transition from rest to exercise, your body embraces the change and begins adapting. But importantly, your body also loves variety. If you wake up the body by changing from rest to a low intensity run, it will initially be excited about this change. However, it only takes a few minutes for this initial excitement to wear off. While your cardiovascular system may embrace the challenge of a long distance run, other structures like your bones have already become bored and numb to the stimulus. If you run the following day, however, the excitement returns.

In Pete's new weekly adjustment, he now has five opportunities to excite the body and trigger an adaptation response compared to the original three. Keep in mind that Pete's adjustment was made without creating an abrupt change in weekly volume. Frequency is the key to adaptation and is the third and final ingredient.

Adaptation ingredient number 1 = Patience
Adaptation ingredient number 2 = Train within the
adaptation sweet spot
Adaptation ingredient number 3 = Frequency is the key

Adaptation Optimisation = Patience + Adaptation Sweet Spot + Frequency

One non-running example that can illustrate adaptation optimisation is my goal to increase my bench press. For six months I had remained stagnant on my bench press progression. I was doing 3 sets of 15 repetitions at 27 kilograms for each dumbbell. This load pushed me to my maximum and resulted in three days of muscle soreness. I had recovered by day four which was followed by two rest days before repeating the same exercise on day seven. This routine meant I was only doing chest press once per week and it never got easier.

Based on my understanding of adaptation, I decided to try a new tactic and reduced the weights and repetitions. My next set would be 3 sets of 12 repetitions and I would reduce each dumbbell by four kilograms. This was nowhere near as challenging and left me with only one day of mild soreness. However, since I wasn't incapacitated for the majority of the week, I could repeat the process three days later. I then scheduled my bench press every four to five days with regular progressions.

After two months of dedication, I had surpassed my previous weight with less soreness. This example shows that backing off the intensity and increasing the overall frequency can allow you to hit your adaptation zone more often and see enhancements in performance.

Bench Press Progression

	OLD ROUTINE		NEW ROUTINE
WEEK 1	3x15 2x27kg DBs		3x12 2x23kg DBs
			3x12 2x23kg DBs
WEEK 2	3x15 2x27kg DBs		
			3x10 2x25kg DBs

WEEK 3	3x15 2x27kg DBs		3x10 2x25kg DBs
WEEK 4	3x15 2x27kg DBs		3x15 2x25kg DBs
			3x15 2x25kg DBs
WEEK 5	3x15 2x27kg DBs		3x12 2x27kg DBs
WEEK 6	3x15 2x27kg DBs		3x15 2x27kg DBs
			3x10 2x30kg DBs

Chasing the Adaptation Sweet Spot

The illustration below highlights the effects of the adaptation zone when these three ingredients are applied. Over time as the body gets stronger, the adaptation zone continues to rise. It is still important, however, that as this process occurs, higher training loads stay within the sweet spot.

For example, think of a runner who progresses over two years and runs multiple marathons per year. Initially, a 20 minute run may have hit the adaptation sweet spot perfectly. However, as the body adapts to higher loads over several months or years, 20 minutes of running will not suffice. In this example, the athlete will need to continue chasing the sweet spot over time if the goal is to progress into a stronger, more resilient runner.

Understanding these adaptation principles will assist any runner in their decision making process. It helps reveal the cause of an injury and assists in future training plans. Each subsequent chapter will add layers of complexity to this principle, but comprehending this chapter alone will give you a huge advantage and a significant step towards reducing the risk of injury.

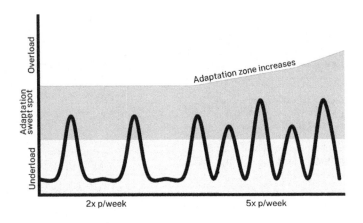

Consider Your Body as an Iceberg

Imagine an iceberg floating in the ocean. Think of this iceberg as your body and its ability to tolerate load. The size of your iceberg is very important. Too small and it can become susceptible to damage, but a large iceberg will prove resistant and unshakable when subjected to high training forces. When in a vulnerable state, harsh conditions such as waves can crack the surface or break off small pieces, resulting in pain and injury.

Imagine a wave colliding with your iceberg. When this process happens, water partially covers the wall of ice and trickles down the face. Moments after impact, the water freezes in place and makes a small contribution to the overall size of the iceberg. So, in this context, being hit with a wave has its benefits, but you want to nurture your iceberg and the surroundings carefully. With enough patience and the right sized waves arriving at an ideal frequency, your iceberg can grow to meet even the hardest conditions. We will revisit this iceberg analogy throughout part one of the book with added complexity.

Chapter 1 Summary

1. Your body will adapt to specific demands if you consistently train within your adaptation sweet spot.

2. Underloading your body will not trigger the body to adapt.

3. As the progression continues, your training demands will also need to progress. Keep chasing your ever-growing adaptation zone.

4. The key ingredients to adaptation include training within your adaptation sweet spot, with high frequency, and patience.

Action Items

1. If unsure of your starting point, start at an embarrassingly slow, short distance and gradually build from there.

2. Reflect on your training frequency and assess whether a change in frequency can optimise your adaptation without a spike in weekly volume.

3. Practice the art of patience. Getting fit and strong takes time.

CHAPTER TWO

STRESS SCIENCE AND LOAD MANAGEMENT

N ow that Pete was completing longer distances comfortably, he decided to check out his local Parkrun. Parkrun is a free, weekly, timed, five kilometre community event hosted in various locations worldwide. At the event, he spotted various local running clubs, parents pushing prams and people walking dogs. With five minutes until the start, a volunteer appeared to cover proceedings. When she asked for a show of hands for all newcomers, Pete curled up into his invisible shell but managed enough courage for a half raised hand. The volunteer offered a warm welcome to all the new participants and a rush of claps and cheers filled the air. Pete even felt a few encouraging pats on his back. Suddenly, he was out of his shell and puffing his chest out proudly.

After an enthusiastic group countdown, Pete was off around the five kilometre track of his local wetlands. He was initially surprised at the number of runners he was overtaking and fell in love with the friendly crowd and positive energy of the community. He also took note of the number of runners checking their pace on their watches and thought that would be a great tool if he were to take running seriously. Later that Saturday, he received a Parkrun email that contained his race time alongside his overall position in the race. He was pleased with his results which heightened his excitement and accountability to improve.

Parkrun Results

Total time: 27 minutes 50 seconds
Average pace: 5 minutes 34 seconds
Overall position: 151/273
Age and gender category: 21/49

The next day, after shopping for a brand new smartwatch, Pete decided to look up other local fun runs. While his plans were to keep attending Parkrun, he also needed a bigger challenge with a longer distance. Within five minutes of searching, he found a local 14 kilometre race in seven weeks.

Every weekend, Pete planned to increase his distance by one kilometre and keep weekday runs between 20 and 40 minutes. He calculated the weekly training plan on a piece of paper to ensure there were no spikes in volume.

WEEK	MON	TUE	WED	THU	FRI	SAT	SUN
1	20 mins		30 mins	20 mins		20 mins	9km
2	20 mins		30 mins	20 mins		30 mins	10km
3	20 mins		30 mins	30 mins		30 mins	11km
4	20 mins		40 mins	30 mins		30 mins	12km
5	20 mins		40 mins	30 mins		30 mins	13km
6	Buffer		Buffer		Buffer		Buffer
7							14km race

As the weeks rolled on Pete had a minor dilemma. He was getting bored with the same loop and a different route would be better suited for the gradual increase in distance. After looking online, he found a perfect 10 kilometre loop that detached itself from his usual track and reattached itself towards the end.

Sunday, with his new watch plus perfect weather conditions, Pete noticed a slight uptick in speed. This wasn't a bad thing. After all, the majority of his weekend runs had been an easy intensity, and the occasional uptick in pace was working well. Approaching the three kilometre mark, he turned onto a single dirt track to begin his new extended loop. Off in the distance, he noticed a significant, steady incline. The hill was a welcoming challenge, and he bounded up it hearing the dirt shuffle under his feet with each stride.

Running over the crest and thumping downhill, he was surprised by how good he felt. The five kilometre notification chimed on his watch. A one kilometre split of 4 minutes and 50 seconds, his best split ever. One more kilometre of dirt trail remained before attaching onto the loop home, ticking off 10 kilometres.

Curling around a final bend Pete approached another hill. This one looked more challenging. He guessed it was about 400 metres and noticeably steeper. He realised his previous splits were quicker than expected because of the subtle decline. Now after running slightly downhill for several kilometres something had to change, and that change was now staring Pete in the face. Feeling in the best form of his life, Pete decided to take the challenge head on. He felt the incline rise under his feet as he worked his legs like pistons. Halfway up the slope, his calves started burning. The last time he had felt this sensation was during his first week of running. Even though his controlled breathing turned into uncontrollable panting, and his pace started to slow, Pete was determined to continue until he reached the top.

As the ground under his feet started to level, Pete knew he had conquered the beast. The elevation completely levelled out and he transitioned into a walk and eventually halted to catch his breath. The screaming in his legs started to soften and with his hands on his knees, he pushed in as much air as he could until his heart rate lowered. After two minutes, he kicked back into a jog and finished the last four kilometres. A surge of exhaustion and satisfaction flowed through his body. However, later that day, walking around the house he noticed a mild tightness forming in his right achilles.

The tightness didn't surprise him, considering the challenging run he had just completed. He decided to monitor symptoms over the next few hours. The following morning, he stepped out of bed and almost collapsed at the sharp pain stabbing his achilles. After months of flying high, Pete had his first reality check.

Run Smarter Lesson 2

This chapter explores the complexities of stress applied to the body, particularly when running. The previous chapter introduced the adaptation zone in its simplest form, highlighting the aim to train within the adaptation sweet spot. However, life is rarely simple. Instead, there are many intrinsic and extrinsic factors influencing the load on the body and the body's ability to handle the load.

Load Versus Capacity

There is a considerable distinction between applied load and tissue capacity that athletes of any ability need to understand to reduce injury risk. The first element to consider is load, which can be defined as a stimulus applied directly to the body. Several factors can amplify the load placed on the body including:

- Increasing the repetitions or weight when strength training
- Increasing the range of movement or speed when resistance training
- Increasing your running speed
- Increasing your weekly mileage
- Changing from a flat running surface to hill running

With these examples, there is an increasing demand on the body to either absorb or produce force. The load application can be considered over a short duration, (within one training session, for example), but can also be accumulated over days and weeks. This is why tracking your training load across different timescales is important.

The next variable to consider is the body's capacity to handle the load. In a sense, each ligament, muscle, tendon and bone within the body holds a level of capacity. In other words, they will reach a limit after which the likelihood of injury increases. For decades, it has been suggested that the balance between external load and tissue capacity plays a significant causative role in injury amongst athletes. For example, when training for a marathon, the idea is to slowly challenge the body with greater loads and over time, the body adapts to these higher loads, raising its overall capacity.

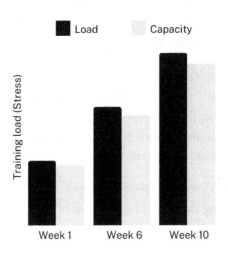

Standard Training Plan

The above depiction relates to the load and capacity of the body as a whole. However, you can also apply this concept to individual tissues. Suppose your weekly mileage holds steady at 15 kilometres per week but you decide to incorporate interval running sessions. Even though the mileage hasn't changed, the load increases and challenges the capacity of each joint, muscle and tendon. If there is a large discrepancy between load and capacity, it will significantly increase your likelihood of injury. This load versus capacity relationship is constantly played out through every tissue within the body when running, strength training and cross training.

Running 15 Kilometres per Week (Slow)

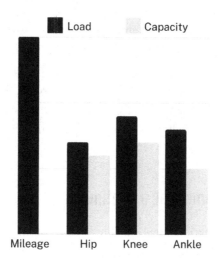

Running 15 Kilometres per Week (Fast)

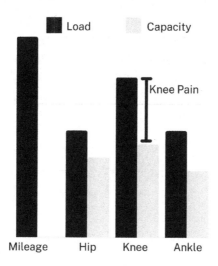

To add further complexity, while the external load may be easy to measure, your internal capacity can constantly fluctuate without warning. You may easily tolerate a 10 kilometre run one week but struggle with the same load the next week. The main lifestyle factors that influence your body's ability to tolerate load include sleep, nutrition, downtime and stress management. If these areas of life are negatively affected, so too will your ability to recover from a training session. If your body hasn't fully recovered, the capacity will reduce and create a similar discrepancy between load and capacity as detailed above. We will discuss these circumstances in more detail in Chapter seven.

Load Management as a Continuum

While the adaptation zone is a simple concept, in reality achieving balance is more complex. There is no simplified threshold level that sends a runner straight into injury territory or, on the other side, keeps them out. Instead, there are a series of escalating stress phases, situated between a theoretical safe zone and injury. These phases are described by researcher Chris Bramah, starting with acute fatigue before progressing to microscopic tissue damage, macroscopic tissue damage, tissue failure and eventually, injury. While these phases were originally detailed in a book chapter written by Chris Bramah [1], he did lay out each phase in detail in episode 230 of the Run Smarter Podcast [2].

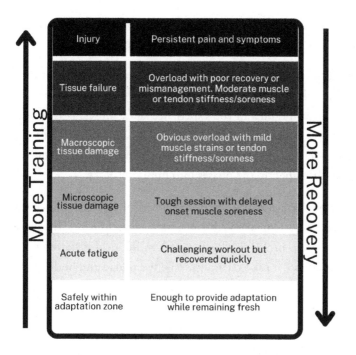

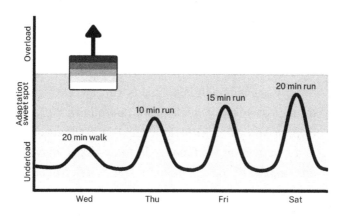

While dipping your toes into these phases has its risks, it is still encouraged. After all, challenging your capabilities and testing your physiological limits is fun, rewarding and sometimes necessary for athletic development. In other words, you risk a painfully slow progression if you train entirely within the safe zone.

While it is important to occasionally venture into riskier domains, it is equally important to recover adequately from hard training sessions. If you train and you experience acute muscle fatigue, recovery needs to follow otherwise the adaptation process will not happen. If recovery is inadequate, you risk accumulating load and sending yourself higher up the phases into injury territory.

Torbjorn Soligard was the lead author of an Olympic committee consensus statement titled 'How Much is Too Much?' [3] The consensus meeting ran in 2015, where experts in the field reviewed the scientific evidence for the relationship between load and health outcomes in sports. The statement explained:

> "The aim of load management is to optimally config-ure training, competition and other loads to maximise adaptation and performance with minimal risk of injury. Load management, therefore, comprises the appropriate prescription, monitoring and adjustment of external and internal loads".

> "Poorly managed training loads can increase injury risk through a variety of mechanisms operating either at a tissue level or at a whole-athlete level. At a tissue level, training and competition load may lead to excessive microdamage and injury if the magnitude (intensity, frequency and duration) of loading is beyond the tissue's current load bearing capacity or if the recovery between loading cycles is insufficient".

Realistic Demands of Running

Most runners vastly underestimate how strong they should be to endure a long run. With the relationship between load and capacity so vital to injury prevention, it is equally as important that runners appreciate the muscle forces applied to their bodies during the running action. When you strike the ground, you encounter a certain ground reaction force that the body needs to tolerate. When running, each bone, tendon and muscle needs to either absorb impact or produce force for forward momentum. Tim Dorn and colleagues published a paper illustrating these particular forces during various running speeds [4]. These are the main takeaways runners should understand:

1. The accumulation of ground reaction forces: Dorn's paper reveals that the ground reaction force during each step while running is more than 2.5 times your body weight while travelling at 3.5 metres per second. Some recreational runners may run slower, but this principle is still important. Imagine a runner who weighs 70 kilograms. For each strike on the ground, the ground reaction force would peak at 175 kilograms. Accumulating this throughout a run emphasises the loads placed on the body:

    *   70kg runner generating 175kg of force per step
    *   180 steps per minute = 31,500kg per minute
    *   30 minute run = 945,000kg of load on the body

This accumulation will also vary based on terrain, hills, carrying gear, running fatigue and several other factors. I believe this is why injuries are so prevalent in the sport of running compared to sports such as cycling that aren't subject to large ground reaction forces.

2. The propulsion phase: Even when travelling at slower speeds, your calf complex, particularly your soleus muscle, produces a force over 6.5 times your body weight for every step. The calf will use this amount of force during the 'push off' phase when the need for propulsion is at its highest. This will increase when reaching speeds up to seven metres per second and running uphill. This is a huge demand placed on the calf and achilles and your body needs to be prepared.

3. The stance phase: As a runner impacts the ground, entering the early stance phase, the front of the thigh and muscles surrounding the hips need to work extremely hard to absorb the ground reaction forces while concurrently maintaining an upright posture. Dorn's paper suggests that the quadriceps and hip muscles work over four times your body weight.

4. The swing phase: Particularly during the late swing phase, your hamstrings are required to contract to slow down the fast swinging motion of the lower leg. Slowing down this momentum allows for steady, predictable foot placement to begin the stance phase. Even during this open swing phase where the ground doesn't play a role, the hamstring is still required to work double your body weight when travelling at three metres per second. Another important muscle during this phase is your primary hip flexors called the iliopsoas. The demand in both these muscles climbs exponentially with the introduction of faster speeds and this is why hamstring tendinopathies and hip flexor issues are so prevalent when workout intensity is increased.

The Impact of Running

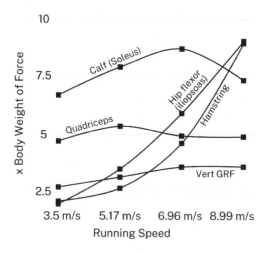

The posterior tibialis tendon is another example of a structure experiencing a high demand when running. Running parallel to the achilles, it continues behind the ankle bone on the big toe side and attaches underneath the foot. When your foot strikes the ground, the ankle begins to pronate. Despite the harsh criticism pronation has received, this ankle movement plays a crucial role in helping to slow down the rate of the ground reaction force experienced by the body. Imagine slapping your flat, rigid hand on a concrete path versus hitting the ground with a loose, rolling hand. During this pronation phase, the posterior tibialis tendon needs to activate while lengthening to slow down the foot 'slap' against the ground.

Imagine your grandmother walking beside you, and she suddenly trips and begins falling over. You throw out your arms and catch her but don't have the strength to stop her fall completely. Your best and safest option is to slow down her descent and soften her impact as much as possible. While you and your grandmother slowly descend to the ground, you are under constant strain. The posterior tibialis tendon operates similarly during the pronation phase of running.

All the examples above are but a shortlist of muscle groups generating and accumulating an enormous load during the running cycle. Therefore, any decision to change a running variable should be made with the above information in mind. If you decide to increase your distance, speed or terrain, ensure the challenge comes in the right dosage.

I often ponder why the prevalence of running injuries is so high. Each chapter will reveal another element that may contribute to an injury, but the nature of recreational running in itself is a factor. The fact is, recreational running is open ended and limitless. There are no boundaries set for how fast or how far to run. Therefore, the loads subjected to the body are entirely dependent on the judgements of the runner. A common career progression is from a five kilometre to a ten kilometre run. After that, a runner will strive for a half marathon, then a marathon and beyond. Alternatively, a runner might decide on a favourite distance and try to finish faster or compete in a race with difficult terrain.

Overall, we strive to better ourselves and push our limits, but simultaneously, we are flirting with the boundary lines of what our bodies can handle. It isn't like a game of basketball that ends in 40 minutes and will always end in 40 minutes. The limitless nature of recreational running is why we as runners need to be extra careful, realistic, and respectful of the demands running places on our bodies.

Objectively Monitoring Load

Since the load versus capacity relationship closely ties in with preventing injury, the sensible decision would be to start tracking the values for each. The external loads placed on the body can be measured in different ways, including speed, distance, elevation and weekly mileage, many of which are available from common GPS tracking devices. In addition to tracking the above data, these devices can contain accelerometers and gyroscopes to gather cadence and vertical distribution information. For a beginner runner, calculating the distance covered during a workout and the total weekly mileage is a great starting point.

Once you are familiar with this process, you may decide to include a metric that accounts for intensity levels. This can include your rate of perceived exertion or RPE over a certain training duration. Your RPE can be ranked out of ten and then multiplied by the workout minutes to calculate a total training impulse or TRIMP.

RATE OF PERCEIVED EXERTION (RPE) SCALE	
10	Max Effort: Almost impossible to keep going, out of breath, unable to talk
9	Very hard: Can barely breathe, can only speak a few words
7–8	Vigorous: Borderline uncomfortable, can speak a sentence
4–6	Moderate: Somewhat comfortable but becoming more challenging
2–3	Light: Feels like you can maintain for hours, can carry out a conversation
1	Very Light: Hardly any exertion, but more than sleeping

RPE = Average perceived intensity for a particular training session.
TRIMP = RPE x minutes of workout

Assigning a TRIMP score to your workout or calculating it across an entire week factors in your body's response to exercise and can increase the accuracy of the load versus capacity relationship. For instance, if you are not sleeping well and getting adequate rest, your workouts will be perceived as harder. This will raise your effort levels and spike your TRIMP score. Below is an example of the difference when factoring in internal training loads, which will be discussed in more detail in Chapter 12.

Workout: 10 kilometre Run at a 5 minute per Kilometre Pace

When well recovered:
RPE = 5
Minutes = 60
Total TRIMP = 300

During poor sleep recovery:
RPE = 8
Minutes = 65
Total TRIMP = 520

The above examples are rudimentary but easy to implement and understand. When assessing a runner with an injury, it is useful to identify if there were any training errors present. Looking at the overall mileage is my first point of investigation. If there is no obvious cause, then training intensity or change in terrain is the next point of investigation. In most runners, these two steps would identify a primary cause of injury. Once identified, we can move forward to ensure the same training error doesn't occur and that rehabilitation is tailored for the identified weak link. If there are still no training errors, the next round of questioning focuses on factors that may influence recovery or load capacity.

Objectively Measuring Capacity

Unlike measuring external forces on the body, it is extremely difficult to calculate capacity. Chief amongst them is the fact that capacity is constantly changing. Calculating the load of a future training session can be easy. For example, if you choose to run for 30 minutes at an RPE of four, you know your TRIMP for that session will be 120.

Conversely, it is extremely difficult to predict your future capacity and ensure you'll tolerate a certain training load.

While predicting your capacity to tolerate load is difficult, you can take an educated guess based on past performances and certain capacity testing. Here are four examples:

1. Strength capacity tests: Various tests within a gym setting can provide one piece to the capacity puzzle and help runners understand strong and weak points. For example, practitioners can attach dynamometers to various body parts and display a force reading when instructed to contract a certain muscle group.

   Another way of testing strength is by conducting exercises such as squats, lunges, deadlifts, and calf raises. A one repetition max test will provide clear data on your maximum strength but is not recommended for runners not experienced in lifting heavy weights. Instead, an eight or ten repetition max will be safer. Lastly, power based tests can assess force production over time. Examples include a vertical hop test or a horizontal jump test.

2. Weekly mileage tolerance: Looking back over your past successful running weeks can provide another piece to the capacity puzzle. In other words, if you can successfully tolerate an 80 kilometre week, you'll hold greater capacity than another runner who is only completing 30 kilometres. This same principle applies to weekly elevation and weekly TRIMP scores.

3. Tolerance to speed: Running fast demands more from the body. The ground reaction forces climb along with the demands to absorb and produce force. Keeping track of your

recent successful speed attempts can be helpful retrospective data for estimating your current and future capacity. Fast interval sessions, strides, time trials and shorter races are examples of speed efforts you can use.

4. Wellbeing and health measures: As previously mentioned, certain lifestyle factors can hinder recovery and, therefore, load tolerance. Tracking your sleep, nutrition and stress levels can work as a constant monitoring system. If these domains are optimal, then capacity should reflect past performances. If hindered over a short or long period of time, then past performance may be less accurate.

Listening to your body may reveal telling signs of under-recovery. Warning signs can include higher perceived effort levels during low intensity exercise, or unusual signs of fatigue, stiffness and soreness.

Past successful fitness metrics can paint a picture of current capacity, but runners can also learn a lot from their unsuccessful past performances. For instance, if a 35 kilometre week was successful, but a jump to 40 kilometres resulted in injury, this may reveal capacity limits. The same can be said when jumping from a weekly TRIMP score of 800 to 950. While these examples are simplistic and will have several other factors potentially influencing the outcome, it will still be a lesson. In this case, once the runner is symptom free, they should recognise this exposed limit and take extra care to plan accordingly.

Abrupt Load Changes and Injury Rates

Based on the understanding of load versus capacity, it would make sense that changes in training loads that are too abrupt would result in injury. However, the multifactorial nature of overuse injuries has created debate and confusion in the available literature. For example, Fredette and colleagues published a 2020 systematic review on running injuries and training parameters [5]. They aimed to link a recent injury with training metrics such as running volume, intensity, frequency or other recent changes.

However, the 36 articles they gathered, totalling over 23,000 runners, returned conflicting results. This review identified eleven articles containing data about recent training changes, and only five included studies that reported a correlation between injury and an increase in running distance. For example, Rasmus Nielsen and colleagues found that novice runners who progressed their running distance by more than 30% over a two week period seem to be more vulnerable to running related injuries than runners who increased their running distance by less than 10% [6].

Conversely, Fredette found five other studies that found no association between recent changes in training and the incidence of injury. Overall they concluded:

> *"Our findings show conflicting evidence about the role of specific training parameters (distance, duration, frequency, intensity), as well as the influence of recent changes in training on the onset of running-related injuries".*

> *"In our opinion, the persistence of conflicting results over the years speaks to a lack of consistent definitions and reporting guidelines in the field of running-related injuries. In addition, the relationship between training parameters and injuries is certainly more complex than looking at training parameters in isolation".*

There are several potential reasons for this discrepancy. Firstly, the definition of 'injury' changes from paper to paper. Another could relate to the delay of some injuries when a change is made. Chris Bramah talked about this particular effect in a book titled '*The Science and Practice of Middle and Long-distance Running*'. He states:

> "With running, several studies have reported injury onset to occur following a sudden or rapid change to weekly running volume and/or training intensity. Often, however, the onset of injury in relation to the change in training can be delayed, with injuries occurring up to four weeks after the initial change in training". [1]

Another reason for these conflicting results can stem from running related injuries being so multifactorial. As we have already discussed, load capacity is ever changing and difficult to measure. Therefore, overuse injuries can arise with the absence of load changes if the tolerance to handle load is diminished and undetected.

From personal experience, I can almost always identify a mechanical reason behind my injuries. Patellofemoral pain, also known as runner's knee, was my first injury while training with my sister for our first half marathon. Looking back, it was an increase in both weekly mileage and speed that exceeded my knee's capacity. In fact, this was an old injury that I had been managing throughout my basketball career. It must have been my weakest link because it was the first warning sign I was doing too much.

My next significant injury was proximal hamstring tendinopathy. After 10 months of distance running, I decided to change my routine and give sprint distance triathlons a go. At the time, my body could easily handle slow running beyond 20 kilometres but did not hold the capacity for short running sprints and fast cycling intervals. As a result, my hamstring flared up and would be persistent throughout the entire triathlon season. Over my athletic career, I have also developed plantar fasciitis, low back pain and a pes anserine tendinopathy. I can attribute every instance or particular flare-up to the load versus capacity model.

One abrupt change that we haven't yet considered is the change in footwear. One of my favourite papers that highlights an obvious abrupt change in footwear is by Matthew Salzler and colleagues [7]. They recruited 14 runners who were previously running in traditional running shoes and fitted them with five toed barefoot shoes. In addition to these new shoes, was an educational pamphlet on the recommended transition guidelines. The researchers discovered that 12 out of 14 runners sustained an injury during the follow up period. Ten of these injuries involved the foot or calf complex. More importantly, when questioning the runners afterwards, the researchers learned that not one runner complied with all industry recommended guidelines for the transition into minimalist shoes.

This is a prime example of an abrupt load that exceeds capacity, as minimalist shoes require a high demand on the foot, ankle and calf complex. A combination of training errors created a recipe for disaster resulting in 86% of the group developing an injury. First, these runners were accustomed to traditional shoes. Second, it forced their bodies to adapt to five finger barefoot running shoes, which are the most extreme form of barefoot shoes. Third, all runners displayed a lack of patience and diligence in the transition process.

A similar pattern occurred with Pete and his training. Rather than an abrupt change in footwear, it was the combination of factors that exceeded his limits. If Pete were to encounter each variable individually, his training loads might have remained within his zone of adaptation. Think back to work by Tim Dorn's depiction of each muscle group when running at different speeds. The achilles is a continuation of the soleus, which produces force over six times your body weight every step. In Pete's case, combine this load with a longer duration, increased speed, and uphill terrain, and the overall accumulation of load is abrupt and severe, dramatically increasing the likelihood of injury.

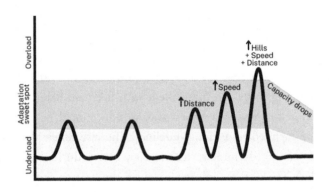

Protecting Your Iceberg from Overload

The first chapter explains the goal of building your iceberg as big as possible. This happens when waves collide with the iceberg, and water freezes in place. In this analogy, you have the power to control all elements of the wave including the size, frequency and speed of its arrival. This is similar to running when you have complete control over your running distance, speed and training frequency. If you want your iceberg to grow, the waves will need to be at the ideal height, and approach at the right speed. A big wave can break pieces off and damage its structural integrity, while small waves have a minimal contribution.

Regarding the frequency of waves, it would seem irresponsible to barrage your iceberg constantly without allowing the water enough time to settle and freeze. It is all about finding the right balance and being patient enough to let your iceberg grow.

Within this scenario, understanding the impact of load and capacity becomes crucial. If you could accurately measure the magnitude of the wave and its force on the iceberg, it would give you a significant advantage in fostering the right conditions for growth. Just as importantly is gathering intel on the current status of your iceberg and its ability to handle incoming waves. If both of these measurements are dialled in and checked regularly, the odds of structure deterioration are significantly low.

Chapter 2 Summary

1. The load versus capacity relationship centres around all running related and overuse injuries.

2. Understanding and measuring loads placed on the body will help direct your training away from abrupt changes.

3. Equally important, is understanding and monitoring your body's ability to tolerate current and future loads.

4. Abrupt changes can occur within sessions, or be spread over several weeks.

5. Overloading the body over short periods of time is still encouraged, however, adequate recovery needs to follow.

Action Items

1. Begin monitoring external loads by calculating your total weekly mileage.

2. If you're looking for more detail and accuracy, track your TRIMP score per session and per week.

3. You may also want to constantly monitor your sleep, nutrition, and stress levels, and make adjustments in your training if these markers are suboptimal.

CHAPTER THREE

DETECTING AND MANAGING EARLY SIGNS OF INJURY

Pete felt stupid! Reflecting on his last run, he obviously overworked himself. The soreness was mild during the day, so mild that sometimes he could hardly notice it. However, mornings were a stark reminder that he still needed recovery time. Most mornings, he rated his pain severity at three out of ten. However, after a warm shower, his symptoms dropped to zero.

Later that day, after a symptom free afternoon, he decided to test out the achilles. After a gentle warm-up, he cautiously set off at his regular slow pace. Within ten seconds, he had a heightened awareness of the achilles tendon. He wasn't limping, but a pain level of two out of ten ached in the background. These symptoms didn't alarm him, and he decided to persevere. To Pete's surprise, his background aches improved within three minutes of running. The reduction of pain was a relief, and symptoms seemed to disappear for the remainder of the run. Still erring on the side of caution, he decided to stop at 20 minutes rather than his usual 30 minute mid week session.

The next day, Pete's alarm woke him from a restful night's sleep. With the success of last night's run, he was relieved to see his achilles pain abolished once and for all. However, standing up from the bed he experienced a familiar, but more severe sharp stabbing pain. He couldn't make sense of it. He went to sleep pain free after his run. Now, the symptoms were worse than the days prior. He placed his pain at a four out of ten. Not horrible, but the worst it had been in four days.

Pete limped throughout the morning, and like always, the pain subsided. After a warm shower, his symptoms settled to a background ache of one out of ten. His morning panic seemed like an over reaction as symptoms continued to improve throughout the day. He was eager to continue running, as symptoms didn't appear to be worsening and he didn't want to lose all the fitness he had built up. He decided to persevere with running and continue to monitor his symptoms.

The following week, he resumed a five kilometre run three times per week. He was sensible and maintained a slow speed throughout. Another decision he made was to avoid hills and keep to his regular loop. On weekends, his long run would stretch to seven kilometres. With each attempt, Pete encountered mild symptoms, but as the weeks continued, his morning symptoms gradually worsened. The pain severity elevated, and the irritability lasted longer into the morning.

The worsening symptoms were so gradual that Pete hardly noticed the trend. Even more gradual were his symptoms while running. What once took three minutes of running to settle symptoms now extended beyond five, six and seven minutes. Because the symptoms remained mild, and the gradual progression of symptoms went undetected, there was no level of concern in Pete's mind. The pain free running was simply a green light to continue.

Run Smarter Lesson 3

I often say that the overall goal to eradicate injury is an unrealistic expectation. Those who aim to improve their running with zero injury risk better have their fingers and toes crossed. There are plenty of smart training decisions you can make to significantly reduce the risk of injury, but in reality, it's hard to imagine a scenario in which the injury risk is zero. This is especially the case for runners looking to build upon their current performance or capacity. Running accumulates high, repetitive loads on the body, and when considering the multifactorial nature of running related injuries, symptoms are likely to appear occasionally.

There is hope. Understanding how to interpret early, mild symptoms accurately along with implementing an early, effective management plan can in most cases abolish symptoms without the need for major training disruption. Troubleshooting early symptoms effectively without loss of fitness is my definition of injury prevention. Granted, implementing smarter training decisions is of utmost importance and if new symptoms arise frequently, perhaps the current training approach requires rethinking.

Training smarter to reduce risk of injury
+
Accurately interpreting injury symptoms
+
Early implementation of effective management
+
Return to activity without fitness loss
=
True injury prevention

Early symptoms can arise from a new or old injury, and if you are proactive in these early stages, minimal intervention is required. For example, in early 2021 my girlfriend and I went on a road trip along the coast of Victoria and New South Wales. While my girlfriend gets involved in running occasionally, her biggest passion is hiking. For several days in a row, we would walk along beaches and hike through national parks, exploring all nature had to offer. Halfway into our two week trip, I realised my plantar fasciitis symptoms were starting to surface during my first steps in the morning. While I had been running modest amounts during our trip I was sure the primary reason was the mountain walking and stair climbing.

My plantar fasciitis initially arose several years prior, not from running, but from a change in footwear while working. At that time, I changed my work footwear to a hard sole dress shoe and that, combined with long hours of standing at work, overloaded the fascia. Not ignoring these mild morning symptoms, I proactively took several action steps to manage the fascia. First, I made sure to wear my most supportive footwear during our hikes. Second, I began slow, heavy, single leg heel raises to load the fascia. I decided to do these exercises every second day. Luckily, I brought my 16 kilogram kettlebell on the trip, which served me well.

The next day I reduced my daily walking by 30%. The following morning, my symptoms had significantly improved, and every day after that, the symptoms never returned. I can think of several personal examples and countless experiences from running clients that involved early symptom detection and minimal intervention, resulting in complete resolution.

Accurately Interpreting Symptoms

One of the key ingredients for managing the early onset of symptoms is accurately interpreting pain signals. While it may seem straightforward that pain equals danger and no pain equals no danger, the complex nature of pain can sometimes result in confusion.

For instance, like Pete's experience, it is a common experience for mild tendinopathies to have a warm-up effect. While this isn't the case with every tendinopathy presentation, most will experience discomfort at the onset of exercise, which dramatically reduces when the body and tendons warm up. With a mild pathology, symptoms can even dissipate to the point of becoming pain free throughout the remainder of the activity. Like Pete, if misinterpreted, this could create a green light to continue exercising when in fact, it could further develop the pathology.

Firstly, if symptoms arise the injured site may still handle a certain amount of exercise. As the book has already discussed, it is our job to find a new adaptation zone for the injured area. But a new adaptation zone may not necessarily be pain free. Depending on the injury, low levels of discomfort can still be beneficial and if interpreted correctly, can be more productive than exercising with zero pain.

When is it Okay to Run with Pain?

For most running related injuries, including lower limb tendinopathies, patellofemoral pain, shin splints and plantar fasciitis, exercise can resume provided symptoms remain lower than a four out of ten on the pain scale. In most cases, these guidelines apply to continuous running, walk-run intervals, cross training and strength training. However, like Pete's achilles symptoms, some injuries can elicit a warm-up effect and steer the runner in the wrong direction. It is this reason why a runner must assess symptoms outside of running to accurately interpret whether the injury is tolerating the current management plan. Runners need to consider four main timeframes for accurate interpretation:

1. Assess symptoms during running: Symptoms starting higher than a four may indicate that the injured site is not ready for

running. Most severe, irritable injuries will not pass this test. If symptoms start below a four but elevate to unacceptable levels throughout the run, this is a reflection of your current running capacity. While most mild tendinopathy symptoms ease throughout the run, some severe tendinopathies return later in the running session. Other injuries such as shin splints, ITB syndrome and patellofemoral pain can also elevate throughout the run if the pathology is severe enough.

Clients often ask me what constitutes a four on the pain scale. This is tough to answer and everyone's perception of pain is different. For instance, someone may rate a five out of ten for a pain sensation what another may rate as a three. For this reason, I like to assign some additional characteristics to use as a guide. Here is a table separating the acceptable pain levels from unacceptable:

PAIN SCALE	
1	Acceptable: Mild tightness or soreness that comes and goes throughout a run. It isn't bothersome and doesn't raise any concern.
2	Acceptable: Slightly more concerning, may even present as constant symptoms without reprieve.
3	Acceptable: Slightly worse pain but confidence absorbing forces when landing and producing forward propulsion without hesitation or compensation.
4	Unacceptable: Pain levels increase enough that confidence levels diminish, and hesitation with absorption and producing forces required for running.
5	Unacceptable: Pain levels elevated to the point that compensations occur, including limping and adjusting foot placement.

2. Assess symptoms later in the day: The hours following a bout of exercise present a good opportunity to reassess for symptom aggravation. In most cases, symptoms are considered acceptable if they remain below a four out of ten for the remainder of the day or quickly return to baseline. Baseline symptoms refer to the everyday, non-irritated pain levels.

3. Assess symptoms the next day: Most body structures, including tendons, require close to 24 hours to process the workload. If you have ever experienced a tendinopathy or plantar fasciitis, you'll be familiar with elevated pain levels the following morning. If you are experiencing levels of pain above baseline the following morning, chances are you exceeded your capacity the day before. This could have included your running distance or a combination of the entire daily load.

Assessing symptoms the next day is tricky because runners need to trial an exercise bout and wait until the next day before interpreting acceptable loads. However, implementing a conservative distance initially will help the process. You may even choose to include walking intervals. For example, one minute of running followed by two minutes of walking repeated ten times. If symptoms are more severe or stubborn, I recommend an embarrassingly slow and short run. You can then reassess symptoms the following day and, depending on symptoms, make the subsequent adjustment.

4. Assess symptoms week by week: While the first three periods of time focus on short term effects, this last guideline analyses symptom behaviour across a longer trend. Some mild injuries pass all three tests but remain symptomatic for months because rehabilitation and load management are ineffective. On top of all the previous timescales, an injury should be

having a measurable improvement week by week. If an injury fails this guideline, action should be taken immediately.

In addition, an injury may improve week by week, only because the runner continuously retreats to safer exercise dosages, leading them to misinterpret the improvement of their injury. For example, they are reducing their weekly mileage, backing off speedwork and avoiding hills. Pain levels may reduce week by week but recovery is not occurring. In fact, it may be counterproductive as the injury's capacity diminishes alongside the retreat to safety. Do not fool yourself. Observe each pain rule fairly and objectively.

From a recovery standpoint, all four timescales should fall within acceptable pain boundaries. This behaviour of symptoms proves that the injury is tolerating your current load management plan. Remember, these are general guidelines only. Because of the complexities and subjective nature of pain, you should follow these guidelines with caution. For example, stress fractures require serious intervention and complete rest from the injured site. After the appropriate healing time frame, it is medically advised to return to exercise symptom free. Other exceptions may include compartment syndrome, nerve related injuries, chronic pain management, vascular related symptoms and other pain behaviours outside common overuse injuries.

How do these four guidelines apply to Pete's scenario? Once Pete gave himself the green light to exercise, he decided to keep running loads consistent. He avoided speedwork and hills while keeping to a similar distance. This running dosage was similar to or less than his training loads before the injury, so there was reason to believe that these dosages were safe. However, once Pete's achilles flared up, his overall capacity to tolerate load through the achilles diminished.

Thus, future training sessions which would usually fit comfortably within the adaptation zone were now mildly exceeding it.

Since he was constantly exceeding this adaptation sweet spot, the overall capacity continued to drop. (Remember, if you overload a structure beyond its capacity, symptoms become worse, more sensitive and less tolerant of future training loads). Consequently, the casual five kilometre run three times per week created an increasing gap between the applied load and adaptation zone as the capacity for the achilles to tolerate load gradually dropped. As a result, Pete continued to experience pain and symptoms gradually worsened. If Pete were to closely track his symptoms during a run and the next day, he would recognise this trend and intervene. More obviously, Pete's symptoms were not improving week by week, indicating the load management plan needed to change.

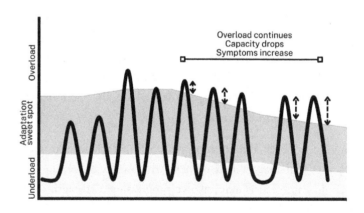

Increase Accuracy of Interpretation by Isolating Variables

When working with runners, I am constantly presented with a diversity of injuries of different severities, irritabilities and pain behaviours. My role as the therapist is to identify the current adaptation zone of the symptomatic structure. Most of my initial judgements require an educated guess based on the level of fitness and tolerance pre-injury, the behaviour of symptoms with recent loading attempts, and the results of strength and capacity tests such as step-ups, heel raises and hopping.

Once suitable training loads begin, symptoms must be accurately documented so the athlete and rehabilitation team can decide whether to modify or progress training. For example, suppose a runner had mild hamstring pain and is currently running 10 kilometres with only two out of ten pain the next day. In that case, my initial advice may be to continue running at the same volume while implementing some strengthening exercises. If the same runner had severe pain and after a 10 kilometre run was experiencing pain at six out of ten, my decision might involve reducing the mileage and lighter rehabilitation exercises.

Throughout the rehabilitation process, it is often helpful to separate the factors that may benefit or harm the area. Concerning factors that could cause harm may involve progressing a strength exercise, reintroducing a higher running dosage and excessive injury loading outside of exercise. Take severe achilles pain as an example. Once symptoms have settled, it would not be wise to reintroduce hills on the same day you progress the level of difficulty of heel raises in case there is a flare-up 24 hours later. In this scenario, the athlete and the therapist would find difficulty in identifying the cause of the increased symptoms. Was it the hills, the exercises or the combination of both?

While combining two potentially aggravating factors could result in a puzzling flareup, it is also useful to isolate potential remedies. Treatment options for achilles pain could involve a change in footwear, manual therapy, massage, stretches and rehabilitation exercises. While a runner wouldn't complain if the injury improves with all these options, it would be valuable and more efficient to separate these variables. It involves becoming a scientist and running your own small experiments until you are happy and confident with the outcome. Each methodical step grants the ability to accurately interpret symptoms and leads to more effective rehabilitation.

Earlier I shared my plantar fasciitis troubleshooting during a road trip. My first encounter with plantar fasciitis was not so simple. In fact, it took five months to overcome. Rather than overloading my fascia through running, I irritated my foot with a change in footwear. In particular, I was wearing new hard-soled work shoes combined with increased standing volumes. Paying attention to the 24 hour rule, I discovered that long days on my feet at work correlated with increased symptoms the following day.

At its worst, my morning pain level would spike at five out of ten and last for ten minutes. Throughout the day, an ache would hover at three out of ten. Strangely, on the days I would run, this would not worsen my morning pain. Documenting the symptoms across each timescale meant that my running speed and mileage weren't contributing to the pathology. Therefore, I continued to run. It wasn't until I changed my work habits that I could start the healing process and notice improvements. Here is a list of my modifications:

- Insert soft gel-based heel insoles into work shoes

- Shift body weight away from my heels when standing still and treating patients
- Taking my shoes off when conducting Pilates classes
- Sit when eating lunch or typing treatment notes

I highly recommend writing or typing your symptoms daily to help identify a trend, because most people are poor at recollecting accurate information beyond one to two days. If you have elevated pain in the mornings, write down the duration of pain in addition to its severity.

After two weeks of changing work habits, my morning symptoms settled to a two out of ten lasting less than 30 seconds. This improvement was an encouraging sign to determine the effectiveness of my plan. If I didn't document the behaviour of my injury, the rate of progress would have been too gradual to detect and I would have been unable to make accurate adjustments in my treatment.

Assessment Tests to Predict Future Injury

Some exciting findings have come from Eric Hegedus and colleagues about injury prediction [11]. They conducted a study to try and identify any strength, flexibility, or movement tests that predict injury. Eleven performance tests were issued to over 359 sporting athletes during their pre-season screening across three years. Each test was categorised into five constructs: active motion, power, hip stability, flexibility and motor control.

The motor control construct observed athletes during a single leg and double leg squat. Rather than test how many they could do, assessors would score an athlete based on the quality of movement. Each was tested with bodyweight only and required the athlete to maintain parallel arms pointing upward. The squat involved feet spread hip width apart.

Several quality checkpoints were listed but mainly involved the overall depth of the squat, posture and leg alignment. In other words, if the knees drifted inward towards the midline during the test, their quality would rank lower. Another common movement fault was athletes bending too much through their lower back to compensate for lack of ankle and hip mobility. Here is a statement from the Hegedus paper:

> *"Our construct of motor control, which consisted of the single-leg squat test for the left and right lower extremity and the unloaded full squat, predicted non-traumatic injuries". "Good motor control was associated with a 59% decrease in the odds for a non-traumatic overuse injury".*

I interviewed Eric on the Run Smarter Podcast to discuss the findings of this paper. Episode 219 was titled '*Predicting Future Injuries and Early Detection*' [12], and I asked Eric why he believes his paper has produced these results. He shared his thoughts:

> *"The number one thing I see in distance runners is gluteus medius weakness. When you're standing on one leg, it is the job of the gluteus medius to keep the knee from buckling to the midline. So what we would see is poor strength or poor motor control".*
>
> *"The other thing that I see is a lack of ankle mobility. If you run out of the ability to flex your ankle during a squat, you pronate your foot which collapses your arch and your knee also collapses to the midline".*

To the uninitiated, buckling of the knee may signal poor knee strength. In fact, as Eric explained, the knee is drifting towards the midline during a double or single leg squat because of either a distal cause from ankle immobility, a proximal cause from hip weakness, or motor control issues. While the findings of this paper are impressive, it still begs the question of how close we are to predicting injury confidently. These tests may provide some correlation to injury, but the multitude of factors involved in an injury occurring seem incomprehensible. While talking to Eric, I used this as a good opportunity to hear his thoughts and I asked him straight up, can we have confidence in predicting injuries. Here is his response.

> "Do I believe we can predict running injuries? Yes. Do I believe that technology is allowing us to get closer and closer to certain things? Yes. If you ask me today as we sit here on your podcast that when I look at a runner and I gather all this data about muscle soreness, stress, fatigue and all the other stuff, how confident am I that you're going to get injured based on the data that I am gathering? I'd say 30–50%".

Warning Signs that an Injury is Approaching

Eric Hegedus and his research help correlate physical movement to injury risk. But just as useful would be some early injury warning signs. After all, a runner will need to push the boundaries and challenge their capabilities on occasion to improve running qualities. Playing it safe and training conservatively will reduce injury risk, but progression will be slow or non-existent. While pushing the boundaries, challenging limitations and training for races, are there any measures runners could track to know if an injury is around the corner? Eric provided some key insight on this matter. He stated:

> *"This is early data but we sort of think to combine things like fatigue, stress, sleep quality and muscle soreness. If you examine those four things very closely and all these things are bad, an injury is coming for you". "Those tend to be the ones that you can monitor pretty easily and if those are off you're heading down a path that you're more likely to get injured".*

Eric's response makes sense based on our current understanding of the injury. Remember, most running related injuries will involve an imbalance in load versus capacity. All of these four components can reveal a pattern of overtraining or under-recovery. While sleep quality can be tracked with wearable technology, fatigue, stress and muscle soreness can be tracked with subjective data, questionnaires and listening to your body.

Tuning in to how your body feels and responding to training is a skill that can develop over time. Just as importantly, when all four of these health measures are tracking poorly, it requires having the sensibility to adjust your training loads until each domain improves. Tracking each area is redundant if you do not take action.

Early Management of Injuries

This chapter explained the importance of accuracy when interpreting symptoms and trying to find your new injury adaptation zone, highlighting the need to isolate key variables and gradually build the load. However, there may be a few added tips to accelerate this process. Consider the discussion of frequency in Chapter one. A higher frequency provides more opportunities throughout the week for your body to recognise the training stimulus, react to the stimulus and in turn, adapt.

You can also harness the power of a high frequency schedule when recovering from most running related injuries. A prime example comes from a 2019 study conducted by Jean-Francois Esculier and colleagues [13]. They collected 69 runners with at least three months of runner's knee and randomly allocated each runner to one of three groups.

Group one:
Education only

Group two:
Education + strengthening

Group three:
Education + running technique modifications

After four weeks, they collected pain and function questionnaires from all participants to see which treatment had the biggest impact. Surprisingly, all groups showed a significant improvement in knee questionnaires and reported a significant decrease in pain. In addition to all three groups improving, they all improved at the same rate and continued to show similar improvements after 20 weeks.

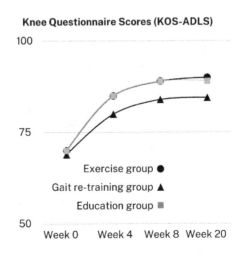

Knee Questionnaire Scores (KOS-ADLS)

Exercise group ●
Gait re-training group ▲
Education group ■

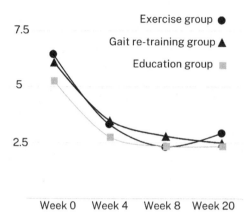

Knee Pain while Running

It is important to factor in the body's natural healing ability in these studies. However, these participants experienced ongoing pain for three months before participating in this study, making natural healing an unlikely proposition. These findings highlight the importance of education when managing an injury, as each group received identical education. The education delivered covered three main areas:

1. Education on acceptable pain levels: Similar to the information provided earlier in this chapter, each runner was told they could continue running and exercising but pain levels needed to remain below a three out of ten. Additionally, symptoms needed to return to baseline within 60 minutes after exercise and without elevated symptoms the following morning. These guidelines cover the first three time periods listed above, excluding week-by-week improvements.

2. Education on running variables: So runners didn't run the risk of overload, they were instructed to avoid running hills

and speed work. These particular variables may spike knee loads and will be hard to manage acceptable pain levels if incorporated.

3. Education on running frequency: Participants were advised to spread their current running mileage across extra running days. If they were previously running two or three days per week, they were asked to run four to five times per week. Like Pete in the first chapter, their overall running distance remained the same, essentially spreading their weekly dosage across more days.

This high frequency training gives your body more opportunities to adapt whether you are injured or not. Incorporating walking intervals can also be extremely helpful if you find it hard to manage acceptable pain levels during a slow, short, frequent run. In some cases, depending on the severity and irritability of the injury, short yet frequent walk-run intervals may promote healing quicker than continuous running.

For example, in late 2020, I developed irritable forefoot pain after a speed session followed by weighted single leg heel raises. After a few short days of rest, I reintroduced shorter and slower running. The pain didn't increase, but being honest with myself, I realised it wasn't getting better week by week. Fearing a stress fracture, I booked in for an MRI. Frustratingly, the MRI waitlist was four weeks. I sidelined my running, not wanting to run on a potential stress fracture. After a frustrating wait, the MRI cleared me of a stress fracture and only revealed minor swelling.

Alongside foot strengthening exercises, I implemented a walk-run plan. I started with 30 seconds of running and two minutes of walking for ten rounds. Most runners would be appalled by this minuscule running attempt, but my symptoms were stable at this dosage, and it allowed me to run with a high weekly frequency. Within two weeks, I was back to 15 minutes of continuous pain free running. With this strategy, I was definitely seeing improvements week by week.

My Walk-run Program

WEEK 1	10 x (30sec run /2 min walk) 10 x (45sec run /2 min walk) 8 x (1 min run /2 min walk) 9 x (1 min run /1 min walk) 10 x (1 min run /1 min walk)
WEEK 2	5 x (2 min run /1 min walk) 5 x (3 min run /1 min walk) Run 3 min, 5 min, 3 min (1 min walk between) Run 5 min, 10 min, 5 min (2 min walk between) Run 15 minutes continuous

Monitoring Your Iceberg for Damage

If you are subjecting your iceberg to waves frequently, it is important to catch any early signs of damage. To do this, you'll need to inspect all areas and all angles. More importantly, you'll need to know what to look out for. For example, you could see a minor crack in the surface of the ice and believe it is nothing to worry about.

In the unfortunate circumstance that a serious injury develops, instead of focussing the attention on the capacity of the entire body, honing on an adaptation sweet spot of the injured area will be helpful. In other words, you can have an iceberg that represents the entire body or if injured, can have an iceberg that represents a specific muscle, tendon or joint. In Pete's case, he now has to manage his right achilles iceberg and determine its current capacity to tolerate load.

Depending on the location and size of the crack in your iceberg, you must carefully and deliberately assign a wave of a sensible size. If water never reaches the crack, then nothing will happen. If the wave has too much force behind it, you risk greater damage. The frequency of the arriving waves to the damaged site should also be considered because finding an ideal frequency of waves helping to heal the cracks will accelerate the healing process.

Over time, once the crack shows significant signs of healing, the next step would be to gradually introduce challenging waves to assess the reaction. If this process is done with careful progression, it will eventually reach a point when the crack can tolerate a wave at the same rate as the rest of the ice.

Chapter 3 Summary

1. Trying to train with zero injury risk is unrealistic, but resolving symptoms quickly without disruption to training is a great outcome.

2. Running while injured may be acceptable if there are low levels of pain and the pain returns to baseline quickly.

3. You can help decipher treatment effectiveness more accurately by isolating rehabilitation variables.

4. An injury may be looming if you are negatively impacted by fatigue, stress, sleep quality, and muscle soreness concurrently.

Action Items

1. Administer a double leg and single leg squat with arms raised. Assess the quality of movement as an injury prevention measure.

2. Take immediate action with an early sign of injury. The earlier it is implemented, the minimal the change that is required.

3. Early intervention may include reducing weekly mileage or dialling back speed workouts.

4. If injured and not seeing improvements week by week, change your management approach or seek medical advice.

CHAPTER FOUR

SEPARATING FACT FROM FICTION

Pete's concern began to heighten and the running green light had now turned an alarming amber. Today's Sunday 40 minute run was a harsh reminder that his achilles symptoms were not getting better. The run started with an annoying three out of ten pain. Initially, these symptoms would settle within five minutes, but now, Pete's warm-up took over 15 minutes. To make matters worse, instead of the warm-up eliminating symptoms completely, one out of ten pain remained throughout the entire run.

Pete was hoping to have fully recovered by now. His 14 kilometre race was only three weeks away, and a sense of urgency started to build. He needed to take action but didn't know where to start. After his post-run shower, he limped into the study and turned on his computer. He opened up his search browser for treatment ideas. He typed in 'achilles pain in runners' and pressed enter. Immediately, he came across three reputable websites and wrote down their recommendations. His list consisted of:

- Stretch and foam rolling the calf daily

- Strengthen the calf muscles with eccentric exercises
- Ice for 10 minutes several times a day
- Apply anti-inflammation creams
- Take anti-inflammatory medicine such as ibuprofen
- Self massage the area until symptoms settle

Now armed with an arsenal of treatment remedies, Pete started to feel a lot better. With hope in sight, he continued his search. However, his optimism turned to confusion when a lot of contradictory information surfaced. Another website mentioned applying heat rather than ice and another highlighted stretching and foam rolling as a waste of time. Instead of looking at opinion pieces, his attention turned to research publications. He uncovered a peer reviewed paper strongly advising people against anti-inflammatory medication if they have a tendon injury. The report mentioned that this class of medication is inappropriate and likely to be harmful to tendon structure.

Finding running specific advice, Pete read varying opinions on running versus not running when managing tendon pain. Other topics involved changing running techniques and comments on correct running shoes. This filled him with confusion and frustration as he glanced down at his list of ideas. He didn't know what to believe anymore. He even came across a startling blog that mentioned the possibility of achilles tendon pain requiring surgery. Alarm bells were now flashing red.

Luckily, during Pete's search, he came across a local physiotherapist who seemed to specialise in running related injuries. Without a second thought, he booked an appointment. It was time to seek professional help.

Run Smarter Lesson 4

When I ask runners what they want most, it will usually be one of two things. First, it is to overcome their current injury, and second to reduce their likelihood of a future injury. We are desperate for the correct information to set us on the right path. Unfortunately, there is rarely a straightforward solution. The individual components of each injury, mixed with the inner complexities of the runner, means the perfect solution for you may not be the right solution for another.

Not only are we constantly looking for a simple solution, but we are also looking for a quick fix. But why is it so difficult to find the correct information? I believe it stems from a combination of six elements.

Six Reasons Behind Treatment Misinformation

1. Online content producers need eyeballs and clicks: The need for a quick fix gives websites and companies a chance to grab your attention. Not only are clickbait titles promising instant results, but they suggest unconventional treatments that create intrigue. Creators design titles to pique your curiosity and start reading. For example, when I searched '*how to treat achilles pain*', I encountered blogs and videos titled '*fix achilles tendonitis in eight simple moves*' and '*how to fix achilles tendonitis in three to five minutes*'. In other words, it is not about evidence based research. It's about grabbing attention.

2. Patient placebos: Posting questions to online forums or online groups while inviting others to respond is also a cause for confusion. A posted question asking for achilles treatments will return a wide array of responses. Everything from shoe changes, orthotics, acupuncture, stretching and strengthening.

You may also encounter comments that contradict one another. Some people may report that orthotics worsened their condition or acupuncture had no effect. But why?

Through groundbreaking research into pain science, we know that treatment effects can vary depending on the patient's belief, overall experience and context of the situation. This individual outcome is known as the placebo effect. If you have a strong belief in its effectiveness, it will increase the likelihood of being effective. For example, imagine that acupuncture cured your friend's achilles pain. You make a booking with the same acupuncturist believing this is the answer. During your consultation, you are impressed by your therapist's physical appearance and level of knowledge. After the acupuncture session, the therapist answers all your questions with reassurance and optimism. The overall outcome is likely to provide a positive impact.

Conversely, if the experience was underwhelming and mixed with a therapist's rude and condescending behaviour, it has less likelihood of returning a similar benefit. The physical treatment is identical, but the belief, experience and context have dictated the outcome.

3. Therapist placebos: Health professionals conducting the treatment can also fall victim to the placebo effect. It may not be the treatment itself that is effective, but the ability to enhance the patient's belief that it will work. Take the prescription of orthotics as an example. Very rarely are orthotics provided to a patient in isolation. A health professional will assess the patient, identify an underlying cause for symptoms, explain the benefits of orthotics for this specific condition and share past success stories before providing the orthotics.

The patient's belief in orthotics changes throughout this process, and therefore, the outcome changes. But this doesn't only affect the client. The therapist will witness the orthotic's benefit, reinforcing their belief in its effectiveness. This leads to a likelihood of recommending the treatment to other patients in the future. While orthotics are used as an example, the same can apply to massage therapy, dry needling, shock-wave therapy and many other services.

To be clear, orthotics can still be a justified, evidence based treatment approach. After all, most of these treatments can provide real benefits with low to no risk. However, there will always be placebo effects unless research designs a double-blinded clinical trial.

4. Misinterpreting treatment benefits: In the previous chapter, it was recommended that injured runners isolate treatment variables to better understand their benefits. When this doesn't happen, it opens up the possibility of misinterpretation. In a simple scenario, if an injured runner presented to a health professional with an overuse injury, their experience would look something like this:

Patient treatment = Education + Load modification + strength rehabilitation + (Treatment B)

'Treatment B' could be a wide array of treatment options such as massage, cupping, dry needling, joint mobilisation, ice packs, heat bags, taping, orthotics prescription, stretches, foam rolling or a change in running shoes. In most cases, education, load management and active rehabilitation can have long term benefits on their own, but if the patient is misled to believe that treatment B was the magic ingredient to recovery, this could solidify a false belief.

One of the most common running related injuries is pain around the kneecap. Like most other running injuries, this predominantly relates to mechanical overload such as doing too much too soon. If a therapist prescribes a management plan for this runner, they would undoubtedly educate the runner about their injury. They would also advise a reduction in running mileage and strength exercises such as step-ups and squats. Imagine this injured runner also adds ITB foam rolling twice a day based on a friend's recommendation. If the above course of treatment is followed, symptoms will likely improve. In the future, when encountering other runners with a similar injury, this individual will swear by foam rolling twice a day as the cure when in fact it was more likely the other ingredients that resulted in the cure.

Runners can also be misled by the narrative of a certain treatment. Commonly, runners are told that their glute muscles are 'weak', 'switched off', 'lazy', 'not firing' or 'dead'. When applied to an injury, they are told these lazy glutes are responsible for muscle imbalance and the likely cause of their pain. Like most injuries, the prescribed treatment is often load modification and strengthening exercises. After four weeks, when the pain has settled and the runner is back to pain free running, they are sold on the belief that their glutes were not activating correctly.

In reality, the cause may have simply been a training error that was solved through load modifications and strengthening. While it may appear there is no harm done in this example, an ongoing concern may persist with the runner. For instance, they may try to consciously activate their glutes while running in fear of them switching off. Also, they may be upset if they cannot feel their glutes muscles firing during a workout. This 'switched off glute muscle' narrative may persist beyond the injury which is often an unhelpful and unnecessary belief.

Seven years into my physiotherapy career, a middle-aged male came to me with horrible knee pain. He wasn't a runner but developed pain around his kneecap after a heavy day of manual labour. Over several months, he was told by medical professionals that his kneecap is positioned incorrectly and there was a risk of the kneecap 'falling out of place' if he didn't abide by his rehabilitation. This threatening language created high levels of fear and anxiety. When I greeted this man in the reception area, he stood up with angst. His face winced and he grasped his knee with both hands as he stood up. As we walked into the clinic room to discuss his situation, he described his severe ongoing knee pain and the need to hold his kneecap every time he stood up. If he didn't support the knee, he feared dislocation.

My session with this man involved a lot of education and reassurance. I advised that the likely cause for the initial pain was from an overloaded joint. I rationalised that the shape of his knee was unchanged throughout adulthood, and before this injury, he was functioning normally. After answering all his questions, I prescribed knee strengthening exercises, including half squat holds for 15 seconds with his back against the wall. The man failed to attend his appointment the following week, so I called him to follow up. He reported a significant improvement and was very happy with his progress. Another call two weeks later and he reported a complete recovery.

These examples highlight the importance of helpful versus unhelpful narratives. So, when asking for a simple treatment remedy on social media, you'll commonly see these beliefs surface. Be respectful and open minded with other opinions and take reported miracles with a grain of salt.

5. The lag in published research: I graduated from university in 2012, and since then, the change in clinical practice has been dramatic. Clinical trials and robust research are constantly published to help optimise the care provided by health professionals. Recent research can help a therapist better understand injury causality, treatment effectiveness, injury prevention insights or ways to enhance performance. As more research surfaces, so do our clinical opinions and guidance. In fact, when I was a student, my lecturer said that 50% of what they are currently teaching would be redundant in five years. The tricky part is no one knows which 50% will be redundant.

Not only is medical practice ever evolving, but the lag from publication to clinical practice moves at a snail's pace. A paper from the Journal of the Royal Society of Medicine reported a 17 year lag between scientific discovery and the implementation into clinics [14]. Since the release of this paper in 2011, the accessibility to research has vastly improved but remains an important factor.

When publishing an informative blog on the internet, the content remains unchanged unless the author edits or deletes it. With the rapidly emerging science, outdated information far outweighs the recent breakthroughs. For example, since the early 2000s, the term 'tendinitis' was classified as inaccurate due to the continued understanding of tendon pathology. The term 'itis' refers to inflammation as the primary source of pain and dysfunction, and research shows that inflammation is rarely present in tendon pathology. The term 'tendinopathy' was then globally adopted as the most appropriate term. Still to this day, the term 'tendinitis' is circulating on the internet along with other outdated terminology, treatment recommendations, and myths that have been busted by science decades ago.

6. Poor regulation: Companies discovered a long time ago that science sells. Whether the company is selling shoes, supplements or recovery devices, they have the freedom to use cherry picked evidence or poorly designed studies for advertising. These advertising claims do not fall under the same scrutiny or regulations as medical institutions or medical grade devices. For example, a home based massage tool can claim to assist in blood flow, flexibility and help relieve delayed onset muscle soreness (DOMS) without anyone holding them accountable.

So, in Pete's case, when looking for answers online, he finds himself swimming in a sea of helpful information, mixed with misleading details, without knowing the difference. It is almost impossible for a recreational runner to decipher fact from fiction, especially if the facts change over decades. But, having a team of trusted, credible individuals can be a good start. After all, the job of a credible health professional is to keep their finger on the pulse of emerging evidence and changes in injury consensus. I advise you to find a small group of people, websites and social media accounts that aren't gimmicky and tend to focus on transparent, up to date information. The willingness of a health professional to change their opinion on a topic is a good sign of a trusted source. This requires humility and dedication to seek the truth.

In the case of online groups offering contradictory treatment options, approach some ideas that resonate with you and see if they improve symptoms. Provided there isn't a high cost or high risk, you can always try them out and if ineffective, move on to another suggestion. For those options with high price points and associated risks, consult a member of your trusted rehabilitation team.

Top Running Misconceptions

Below is a list of common myths or unhelpful beliefs I see when working with runners. Most of which will be covered in greater detail throughout the book but might be useful to list in one place. Most of these misconceptions were considered standard practice when I graduated in 2012. Over time, as new research emerges, our understanding has grown, and the consensus has shifted. When reading the information in this book, I caution the reader as future consensus may change based on future publications.

1. "Running is bad for your knees": The knee is the most common site of injury in runners, but as we have already discussed, training smarter will significantly reduce that risk. Some people believe the repetitive nature of running deteriorates the knee joint and surrounding structures on a more severe scale. To this day, I hear stories of some health professionals and doctors suggesting that running causes wear and tear within the knee joints, eventually evolving into osteoarthritis. This message has spread into the running community and is accepted as a fact by many.

   The joints were once thought of as a part of a car. Car parts have a certain mileage or expiry date before they need to be serviced or replaced. If you reduce your mileage, you will preserve the finite mileage. Translated to running, generating a high ground reaction force step by step, session by session, year by year will eventually show signs and symptoms of degeneration. Contrary to this narrative was a paper published by David Hunter in the Rheumatology journal titled

'*Osteoarthritis: Time for us All to Shift the Needle*' [15]. In his paper, Hunter explains that structures within the knee joint are not like a part of a car but like any other tissue in the body that adapts if the balance between load and recovery is optimal. Hunter declared that:

> "'*Osteoarthritis is no longer a cartilage-centric disease, and archaic terms such as wear and tear and degenerative are now considered inaccurate*".

This archaic understanding still ripples through the general public and creates a lot of fear. Samantha Bunzli and colleagues interviewed people awaiting a joint replacement and asked them about their understanding of the condition [16]. Here is what they found:

> *All participants believed that their knee osteoarthritis was 'bone on bone' and most believed it was caused by 'wear and tear'. Most believed that loading the knee could further damage their 'vulnerable' joint and all believed that their pain would deteriorate over time. Many believed that physiotherapy and exercise interventions would increase pain and could not replace lost knee cartilage".*

Contrary to a knee joint deteriorating from running, it has been shown that pounding the pavement within sensible limits actually triggers and stimulates cartilage growth. I spoke with Dr Kevin Maggs on episode 32 of the Run Smarter Podcast to disseminate this osteoarthritis information [17]. The title was '*Knee OA Misconceptions*', and Kevin Maggs stated:

"We have pretty good evidence that cartilage actually adapts to mechanical load, and the evidence is pretty overwhelming that the people who exercise and people who run actually have a lot less knee osteoarthritis pain and symptoms".

Kevin refers to the 2017 systematic review, which looked at the prevalence of hip and knee osteoarthritis in a population of over 125,000 [18]. The aim was to determine the likelihood of osteoarthritis in runners versus non runners. Interestingly, they discovered 10% of non runners had osteoarthritis while only 3.5% of runners had osteoarthritis. In other words, you are three times more likely to suffer from knee or hip osteoarthritis if you are a non runner.

These findings fit our current understanding of the condition. Runners are hitting the ground regularly, which helps joint health. Additionally, runners are likely to have healthier lifestyle habits such as maintaining good body weight and strong muscles surrounding the knee.

2. "I'm always injured because I don't stretch enough": This belief is extremely unhelpful, particularly for runners who do not like stretching. In my experience, runners who don't like stretching will never prioritise it, and when injured, this belief redirects their focus away from factors that may play a significant role. For instance, they could believe not stretching increases injury risk, but they constantly over train or under-recover.

Research can help bust this myth. David Behm and colleagues released a systematic review in 2015 analysing the acute effects of muscle stretching on injury incidence across the active population [19]. They stated that pre-activity stretching might only benefit events containing a 'sprinting' component and not endurance based running activities.

This finding has been shown in other studies such as Baxter and colleagues who suggest that long term stretching may help with muscle tendon unit compliance. But for endurance running, these effects are not clinically beneficial [20].

Once again, overuse injuries follow a load versus capacity relationship, which stretching rarely influences. When a runner talks to me about their running and mentions they are injured because they do not stretch, I often ask about their training philosophy and the running loads at the time of injury. More often than not, they can self identify a training error that was irrelevant to their flexibility status.

3. "I need release work because I am constantly stiff": If you are challenging your capabilities within training, there will often be soreness the following day. This delayed onset muscle soreness or DOMS is beneficial and necessary for muscular development. However, if this trend continues without adequate recovery, the soreness will persist and become counterproductive.

One should be careful when interpreting the signs of stiffness caused by exercise. When your body is recovering from a workout and is in a state of soreness, stretching the muscle group produces soreness. The rationale and understanding go like this:

"Stretching my muscles creates soreness"
"Therefore, my muscles must be stiff"
"Therefore, they need to be released"

Release work includes massage therapy, dry needling, foam rolling, massage balls, thera guns and other similar passive treatments. These treatments can help symptoms but are often short lived. I believe the temporary relief primarily comes from a pain inhibition effect and a placebo effect. The least likely effect is the 'release' of a muscle, tendon or ligament.

In reality, the muscles are not stiff but sore due to the training load. If your body is showing prolonged or persistent soreness, attention should turn away from 'release work' and towards enhancing recovery or reducing training loads.

In Chapter one, I shared my experience with constant calf soreness as a new recreational runner. In my mind, my calves felt tight and I would seek out any pain relieving method. Stretching would provide relief for less than 60 seconds, but I persisted. However, once my body adapted to long distance running and I balanced my training intensity, the sensation of tightness dissipated. I still encourage release work if you can justify the benefits, however, as an athlete, you need to understand its short term benefits. If your body is constantly sore, adjust your training to find the right balance.

Some runners are obsessed with releasing their iliotibial band also known as the ITB. This is a thick, fibrous structure that attaches to the outside of your hip bone, runs along the outer part of your thigh and connects below your knee. Because it is a fibrous band, it doesn't contain any muscular properties. Unlike muscles like your hamstrings or calves, the ITB cannot contract and relax, and instead offer rigid support for the hips and knee when standing on one leg.

While stretching and foam rolling an ITB may accompany symptom relief, it is most certainly not stretching or releasing the band. The structure and formation are too thick and offer no give during even the most methodical routines [21]. Even though the ITB does not have the same properties as a muscle, it can still be subjected to stress and strain from any other structure within the body. So, if you are experiencing ITB soreness, closely inspect your training loads and recovery methods.

4. "Your flat feet require stability": Before looking at the research, a lot of these myths make logical sense. One of the most common I see is the need for a stability shoe, orthotics or other support for those runners with low arches or flat feet. The rationale follows the theory that if your foot excessively collapses when walking and running, it accentuates pronation of the ankle, creating malalignment and, therefore, increasing the likelihood of injury.

   While stability shoes and orthotics may offer benefits and symptom relief for some, it seems the treatment response is independent of foot shape. Details are covered in Chapter 14, but in brief, orthotics do not 'realign', 'correct posture' or 'reduce pronation' despite the narrative and marketing statements.

   One of the largest studies on this topic comes from Rasmus Nielsen and colleagues who investigated if foot postures changed the rate of injury in runners wearing neutral shoes [22]. The authors categorised 927 runners into five categories.

   • Highly supinated
   • Supinated
   • Neutral
   • Pronated
   • Highly pronated

They then assigned neutral shoes to each runner and observed their running, along with their injury occurrence over one year. After one year of observation, they concluded:

"No significant differences in distance to first running-related injury was found between highly supinated, supinated, pronated and highly pronated feet when compared with neutral feet. In contrast, pronated feet sustained significantly fewer injuries per 1,000 kilometres of running than neutral feet".

This paper helps support the idea that pronation is a protective movement and is essential for reducing the risk of running related injuries. However, it seems that pronation as a protective motion is not linear, and those with excessive pronation may not receive added benefits.

The confusion stems from the assumption that a stability shoe or orthotic will act as an anti-pronation device. Foot posture is only one piece of the complex puzzle to tackle but training habits and shoe selection also play a large role. If you are sensible with your training and wear comfortable running shoes you are significantly reducing your risk of injury.

5. "Your injury is caused by a tilted pelvis": Discoveries of a twisted, tilted or uneven pelvis can be extremely threatening to athletes. Upon assessment, runners are commonly diagnosed with some form of hip malalignment or leg length discrepancy which is then highlighted as a cause of symptoms. The prescribed treatment is often manual therapy or adjustments to correct the discrepancy and on occasion, stretches or strengthening exercises to iron out any imbalance.

What practitioners fail to discuss is the prevalence of discrepancy in the general, asymptomatic population. Research shows that up to 90% of the population have some form of leg length discrepancy with the average discrepancy placed around five millimetres [23]. The evidence suggests that, for most people, anatomic leg length inequality does not appear to be clinically significant until the magnitude reaches around 20 millimetres. The prevalence of a discrepancy this large is around 1 in every 1,000.

In reality, the body does an amazing job at adapting to minor imperfections, especially for discrepancies that have been present throughout the athlete's life. So when injured, the primary focus should be on changes in load and the absence of abrupt changes rather than handing our control over to a false, disempowering narrative.

Chapter 4 Summary

1. Many biases contribute to the spread of misinformation.

2. Be open to individuality. One treatment may not be effective for everyone.

3. In most cases, gold standard treatment requires education, load management and strength rehabilitation.

4. Be sceptical of quick fix promises, and administer supplementary treatments on a trial and error basis provided they are accompanied by evidence based, long term treatment options.

Action Items

1. Find a small group of health professionals, websites and social media accounts that focus on transparent, up to date information.

CHAPTER FIVE

RUNNING TECHNIQUE TO REDUCE INJURY RISK

P ete had never seen a physiotherapist before. The unknown made him uneasy. Upon entering the clinic he met Daniel, a physiotherapist and running coach who was happy to guide him on the path to recovery.

Daniel asked Pete various questions about the time of the injury such as changes in distance, speed, terrain, footwear and the behaviour of the achilles symptoms. He was impressed with the thorough assessment. Next, Daniel directed him through several loading activities. A single leg heel raise progressed into a double leg jump and lastly, into a single leg hop. Throughout each test, Daniel would ask for the severity of the pain.

Once complete, Daniel inspected Pete's running technique on a treadmill. After a five minute warm-up, he was cruising at his normal fluent stride. After two minutes of running, Daniel turned off the treadmill and walked with Pete back into the treatment room. He explained to Pete that his achilles tendon seemed to be undergoing a reaction in response to his long hilly run. Simply, the event exceeded the tendon's capacity, and now it was struggling to find an acceptable load that didn't perpetuate symptoms.

The first action step was to update Pete's training plan to prevent any future overload. Secondly, Daniel assigned a home based rehabilitation exercise designed to gradually increase the tendon's capacity. He drew up an exercise called eccentric single leg heel raises which involved a double leg heel raise off the edge of a step followed by a slow single leg descent on the affected side. If bodyweight heel raises became too easy, then a weighted backpack should be added.

Regarding the treadmill assessment, Daniel explained that Pete's posture and running technique were fine. However, he did comment that Pete's cadence was a bit low. It was hovering around 150 steps per minute.

Daniel explained that running cadence referred to the number of steps a runner took per minute. While the running speed does not heavily influence cadence, it does rely on the size of the steps. He advised that it would be beneficial for Pete to take shorter, quicker steps. Daniel continued to explain that there was no perfect number every runner should reach, but there was a recommended range for most runners of between 165 and 185 steps per minute.

Pete informed Daniel of his upcoming race. They spent a few minutes writing down the risks and rewards and decided it wasn't worth the risk. Pulling the pin was a kick in the guts for Pete, but the silver lining was a new management plan which he was excited to start. Daniel recommended that Pete return in a few days' time, if the achilles showed signs of improvement, then additional elements would be added to the recovery plan.

Physiotherapy Instructions

Previous Running Schedule

MON	TUE	WED	THU	FRI	SAT	SUN
5k		5k		5k		40min run

New Running Schedule

MON	TUE	WED	THU	FRI	SAT	SUN
Rehab	3k	Rehab	3k	Rehab	5k	Rehab

Running instructions:

- Run at a slow, conservative speed
- Avoid running uphill
- Run to a metronome at 165 beeps per minute

Strength exercises:

- Eccentric single leg heel raises
- 3x12 each side
- Twice per day on non running days

14 kilometre Race Risk and Reward List

REWARD	RISK
Achieving my 1st 14k race	Exacerbating symptoms
The joy of completing my goal	Delaying recovery by weeks/months
	Potential for another injury

Run Smarter Lesson 5

Running techniques are highly variable between runners. I am amazed at the different forms and strategies I witness during a run around my local parkland. I see the same breed of dogs all running the same and birds flying the same. However, for some reason, we as a species have decided to adapt interesting variations into a seemingly straightforward task. Whether it is our various arrangement of body sizes, levels of mobility, strength and stability or type of footwear, I rarely see two runners adopting the same running action. With such variety, are there some characteristics that increase the likelihood of injury?

Categorising Running Techniques

Before diving into the relevance of each running characteristic, it is necessary to place certain characteristics into categories. These categories involve the action of a certain body part in a certain phase of the running action. The first important element to analyse is the foot at initial contact. More specifically, what part of the foot makes contact with the ground. Even though runners strike the ground with subtle differences, there are three main categories:

1. Rearfoot striker: An initial contact with the heel of the foot.
2. Midfoot striker: An initial contact with a flat foot.
3. Forefoot striker: An initial contact with the heel off the ground.

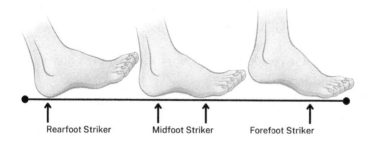

Rearfoot Striker   Midfoot Striker   Forefoot Striker

Runners often discover foot strike recommendations and statements criticising a rearfoot strike. Some claims can be outlandish and suggest that all runners avoid contact with their heels because it is inefficient and will lead to injury. Interestingly, a study by Peter Larson and colleagues looked at the prevalence of each category during the Manchester City Marathon [24]. They filmed, observed, and categorised 936 distance runners, most of whom would be considered recreational or of sub-elite ability. The researchers decided to record the runners at the 10 kilometre marker. This would allow each runner plenty of time to warm up into their fluent stride and before a point of fatigue, in which foot strike may change.

The data collection revealed 89% of runners were rear foot strikers, 3.5% as midfoot strikers and less than 2% as forefoot strikers. The remainder exhibited a foot strike asymmetry. These findings illustrate the high prevalence of heel striking throughout the running population. Additionally, the paper discovered no significant relationship between foot strike patterns and race times.

The second, lesser known category is a runner's step width. This phase is easily categorised during mid stance when the foot is directly under the hips. To help imagine the relationship between step width and running mechanics, I find it helpful to visualise running on a painted line along an athletics track or a line within the middle of a treadmill belt. With this visualisation, you can then separate a runner's step width into three categories.

1. Wide step width: The left foot contacts the left side of the line.
2. Narrow step width: The left foot contacts the middle of the line.
3. Cross over step width: The left foot contacts the right side of the line.

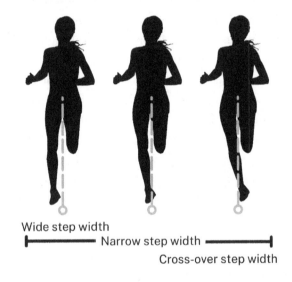

Wide step width

|————————— Narrow step width ——————|

Cross-over step width

Each of these categories are important because it will paint a picture of the loads generated throughout the body. With different loads comes different demands required by the muscles, tendons and joints. As you can appreciate from Chapter two, running accumulates high loads on the body overall and these subtle differences may result in large fluctuations in load across different techniques.

Like Pete's experience, some health professionals may look at your running technique to gain deeper insights. Categorising initial contact and step width simplifies a running technique, but more specific joint angles may be valuable. While this takes a trained eye and expertise to decipher, some other insightful observations may include:

At initial contact:

1. Ankle dorsiflexion.
2. Presence of an overstride pattern.

At mid stance:

1. Contralateral hip drop.
2. Degree of knee flexion.
3. Ankle plantarflexion.

At push-off:

1. Hip extension.
2. Ankle plantarflexion.
3. Big toe extension.

During the swing phase:

1. Knee flexion.
2. Ankle dorsiflexion.
3. Heel whip angles.

Other observations:

1. Spine posture.
2. Arm swing.

Running Techniques to Reduce Injury Risk

The debate correlating running technique to injury rate continues between health professionals and researchers. Large, robust studies seem inconclusive, while other smaller studies reveal some intriguing results.

For example, an extensive systematic review by Linde Ceyssens and colleagues was released in 2019 titled 'Biomechanical Risk Factors Associated with Running-Related Injuries' [25]. After an extensive search for all previously published papers on this topic, their search only yielded 13 high quality and three moderate quality papers. It is an interesting finding that such little, high quality research is available. The paper commented:

> "Despite the common belief that biomechanical factors greatly influence running-related injury risk, only a limited body of high-quality research, with significant heterogeneity in study populations, methodologies and outcome variables, was identified".

Essentially, the authors hoped to find a better volume of high quality research on this topic. Since they could not achieve this, the reader should be sceptical and not consider these findings as absolute.

Hip Adduction and Knee Rotation

After reviewing each paper in the systematic review, it seems limited evidence has emerged linking certain populations to specific injuries. Firstly, the paper found limited evidence for greater peak hip adduction in female recreational runners developing knee pain and ITB syndrome. Running traits such as brushing knees together may indicate a less ideal hip adduction angle. Interestingly, one paper found hip adduction not related to injury risk in a mixed-sex population of cross country runners. So while limited evidence may reveal a small connection, the debate continues.

Ceyssens' work also found limited evidence linking greater peak knee internal rotation in female recreational runners developing iliotibial band syndrome. However, the difference between groups was relatively small and is questionable in detecting such a small change in rotation in a clinical setting.

Hip Drop, Posture and Overstride

While encompassing a large systematic review returns low confidence linking mechanics to injury, other one-off studies are worth mentioning such as a paper by Chris Bramah and colleagues looking for pathological gait patterns [26]. These authors analysed the running mechanics of 72 injured runners and 36 healthy runners on a treadmill. To be included in this study, the injured runners needed to record 10 minutes of running before the onset of any symptoms. This is an important distinction because the aim isn't to identify the change in mechanics while a runner is in pain. Instead, to identify a difference in mechanics comparing non injured runners and injured runners running symptom free. This study identified three significant differences between the two groups:

1. Contralateral hip drop: This determines how stable each side of the hips are during mid-stance. For example, when the right foot is planted directly under the hips, how far does the left hip travel towards the floor. This pattern seemed to be the most significant finding, and for every 1° increase in pelvic drop, there was an 80% increase in the odds of being classified as injured. A pelvic drop fits the findings from Eric Hegedus in Chapter three, who highlighted the importance of gluteus medius strength to reduce the likelihood of injury and can be the primary cause of a contralateral hip drop.

**Contralateral pelvic drop
and hip adduction**

Injured runner   Healthy runner

2. Forward trunk lean at midstance: A forward trunk lean may have a correlation with injury. This refers to the degree of flexion made at the hip and torso. Some health professionals and coaches cue their runners to run with a slight forward lean. This cue can help with reducing braking forces and maintaining forward momentum. If executed well, a very mild straight lean of the entire body is established, and the chest and head remain tall. While this cue may work for some, it may cause an exaggerated bend of the hips, resulting in the chest and head translating forward.

3. Greater knee extension and dorsiflexion: At initial contact, a straighter knee with higher pointed toes may be linked with higher injury rates. This particular running style may generate high braking forces and is typically found in runners who over-stride, which is described later in the chapter.

Forward trunk lean, knee flexion and ankle dorsiflexion

Injured runner   Healthy runner

I had the pleasure of interviewing Chris Bramah on episode 61 of the Run Smarter Podcast. The title was '*Running Technique Insight for Injury Prevention and Performance*', and below are some key comments he made when I asked what he looked for during a treadmill assessment [27]:

> "There are key things that we know from science that can impact upon performance and can influence injury. I always start looking around the pelvis and the spine to look for excessive pelvis rotation. This could show signs of excessive braking as the runner hits the ground".

> "If you have someone who leans really far forward, it can shift your mass too far in front of your body and a runner will compensate by reaching the leg forward and slamming on the brakes to catch themselves and stop them falling over. The reality is we want to run with a very slight forward lean, too upright and it can lead to an inability to activate certain

hip muscles to propel ourselves forward. It's all about finding the goldilocks zone of optimal trunk lean".

"The other obvious one is where the foot is landing in relation to their centre of mass. We know this overstride is linked to greater braking forces and the only way to compensate for these forces is to sink and excessively bend through the knee which would lead to the knee being overloaded".

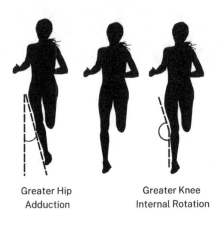

Greater Hip
Adduction

Greater Knee
Internal Rotation

It is also worth pointing out that none of these studies found a correlation between the type of foot contact and injury. So, despite the overwhelming information criticising heel striking, it seems a rearfoot initial contact seems safe provided they do not elicit any traits listed above.

Pronation

Another abnormality commonly believed to increase injury is the eversion mechanics of the foot and ankle, commonly known as pronation. The Ceyssens systematic review found conflicting evidence linking pronation to injury [25]. They stated:

> *"Current prospective evidence does not support a persistent and widespread belief that ankle and rearfoot eversion is related to an increased risk for running-related injuries. These findings are in line with retrospective evidence in patellofemoral pain, while contradictory findings have been reported in runners with iliotibial band syndrome".*

Ground Reaction Force

The ground reaction force is essentially how hard you hit the ground, and the sudden shock the ground returns onto the body. Ceyssens' systematic review suggests it could be possible that a higher vertical loading rate could elevate the risk of injury but would only apply to specific injuries. For example, work from Kristin Poppa and colleagues reveals females with a history of stress fractures hit the ground harder when running fatigued [28].

Another interesting paper by Zoe Chan and colleagues examined two groups of 320 novice runners on a specially designed treadmill [29]. Group one was the control group and attended regular treadmill running sessions without feedback. However, the second group had the luxury of a screen displaying their real-time ground reaction force in front of them.

Both groups attended eight treadmill sessions across two weeks, and only the second group received gait retraining feedback. The participants were asked to run softer to reduce the peak of vertical ground reaction force. Throughout the two week training period, the second group would gradually learn to diminish the initial ground reaction peak and adopt a more gradual load onto the foot.

Twelve months after the treadmill sessions, the researchers followed up with each group. They found a 62% reduction in injury rates in the intervention group compared to the control group. It is important to highlight that this is only one study, and when considering all other publications, a correlation is less clear. Given, however, that it had a large sample size and was the only study I could find that implemented real-time ground reaction force feedback, its findings should be taken into consideration.

Understanding Cadence

As mentioned above, your cadence or step rate measures the number of steps taken per minute. Visualise two identical runners side by side running at the same speed. On the left, a runner takes 150 steps per minute while the runner opposite takes 180 steps per minute. In this scenario, you would observe two main differences. Firstly, the runner on the left will bounce up and down at a larger amplitude because he is taking longer yet fewer steps. Not only would you observe the runner move up and down at a larger amplitude, but you may also hear them make a louder impact on the ground. Someone who runs with a larger vertical displacement is more likely to strike the ground at a greater velocity and hence, increase their ground reaction force.

The second common observation is an overstride running pattern. This trait is correlated with the extended knee mentioned by Chris Bramah earlier in the chapter. Overstriding may not appear in all runners with a low cadence but it is more common. When first making contact with the ground, the leg can over-extend and make an initial contact too far in front of the runner's centre of gravity.

No overstride pattern   Overstride pattern

This trait contributes to excessive braking forces, and I often recommend making adjustments in order to produce a more efficient stride. Running with large braking forces is like trying to drive down the highway with your handbrake on. If you exhibit this trait and also record a low cadence, elevating your cadence will improve running efficiency by reducing vertical displacement, improving hip muscle activation and eliminating an overstride pattern. With a higher cadence, the swinging leg doesn't have enough time to travel too far forward, so an overstride is commonly corrected without much thought.

Changes in cadence and other running mechanics are documented in a systematic review by Amy Schubert and colleagues [30]. After sifting through the available literature, the authors found:

> *"An increased stride rate appears to reduce the magnitude of several key biomechanical factors associated with running injuries".*

> *"Specifically, similarities are seen across all studies, with decreased center of mass, vertical excursion, ground reaction force, impact shock and attenuation, and energy*

> absorbed at the hip, knee, and ankle as step rate is increased
> or step length is decreased at a constant speed".

In other words, if your cadence is suboptimal, increasing your cadence will positively influence almost all the above traits that are suspected of playing a role in injury. Most of the included studies increased the running cadence by 10%. However, benefits are seen in as little as a 5% increase.

Calculating Your Cadence

Some wearable devices and apps can accurately measure your running cadence. If you wear a fitness tracker when you run, it will have a built-in accelerometer to measure your movements. Your arms swing at an identical rate to your legs, making it easy to calculate cadence. After a run, simply look up your average cadence or average step rate on your device. Keep in mind that if your exercise contains periods of walking, this will produce an inaccurate number. Continuous running is required.

If you do not use a fitness tracker, you can use simple metronome apps. During your run, open the application and tap the screen in sync with your step rate. This will calculate your cadence. You only need to tap the screen for 10 seconds to get an accurate measure.

Do You Need to Change Your Cadence?

One hundred and eighty steps per minute is a common misconception circulating the running community as the magic cadence number. I, too, was told this when I graduated. However, evidence has failed to recommend a universal number. Runners consist of different body shapes, so everyone will have a slightly different cadence for optimal performance. For example, a study conducted by Adam Tenforde and colleagues discovered that runners with longer legs operate more efficiently with a lower cadence than shorter runners [31].

There are general guidelines for runners which I consider as a running cadence safe zone. The debate continues, but most researchers and health professionals recommend a cadence between 165 and 185. Depending on your average cadence, you may or may not need to take action. Here are some recommendations:

> If your cadence is less than 160: You will likely benefit from an increased cadence if you measure below this average step rate. If you fit within this category, take your current cadence and increase it by 5–10%. For example, if your previous cadence was 158 and you increased it by 7.5%, then your new cadence is 170 steps per minute. Set a metronome to this new cadence and run at this tempo. It might feel weird at first, but eventually, you should find a rhythm. If you find this adjustment is too much, take a more conservative approach and increase by 5%.

> If your cadence is between 160–170: This range is in the lower quadrant within the safe zone and increasing your cadence is not necessary unless you are battling injuries or looking for ways to improve efficiency. For example, imagine a runner with knee pain struggling to return to pain free running. If we recorded their cadence and measured 165, they would most likely still benefit from a cadence increase. The runner's efficiency will most likely improve, and the cumulative loads through the knee joint will reduce [31]. You can make the same adjustment for other stubborn injuries such as ITB syndrome and shin splints.

If your cadence is >170: For most runners, a cadence between 170 and 185 is an ideal range. Therefore, the justification for changing running cadence is rare. Keep in mind that the benefits of increasing your cadence are not linear. In other words, if your cadence is already 180, and you increase by 10%, you will not reap the same benefit.

Does Cadence Change with Speed?

A common observation is a change in cadence when a runner manipulates their running speed. For example, a runner might hover their cadence in the 170s during a moderately challenging run but will observe a drop into the 160s when executing their slow, easy running. Research from Tim Dorn and colleagues suggests that changes in speed should have little to no effect on cadence unless operating at maximum sprints [32].

In fact, when operating at speeds between 10 kilometres per hour and 20 kilometres per hour (6 to 12 miles per hour), your cadence should only fluctuate by 5%. Dorn's work suggests that as running speed increases, cadence remains the same but steps become larger.

If your goal is to increase cadence, it is important that your natural, easy running speed is not affected. A common mistake runners make when increasing their cadence is to run faster. Remember, manipulating your cadence to a more optimal range is designed for your stride to become more efficient. However, some runners set their metronome to a new select cadence, and within minutes their heart rate increases and they start gasping for air. In cases like this, they are often increasing their running speed.

The idea is to travel at the same speed but take shorter steps. For this reason, it is often helpful to practice manipulating your cadence on a treadmill. The treadmill will ensure your running speed remains consistent while making the cadence adjustments.

As mentioned above, another mistake runners make is significantly lowering their cadence during a low intensity run. I have witnessed many runners operate within an accepted cadence range, but during their easy runs, it significantly drops into the low 160s. I believe this is happening because the runner is losing their efficient spring and may indicate that they are running lazy or sloppy, leading to inefficiencies in running stride.

Below is an example of one of my interval training sessions. I chose this because, within my four kilometre session, I manipulated my speed significantly. Here are my splits per kilometre.

Splits per km:
4 min 53 sec
3 min 47 sec
3 min 48 sec
5 min 03 sec

The graph below displays my variable speed during the workout alongside my real-time cadence. Notice with the change in speed, my cadence remains consistent. No matter the speed, endurance runners should remain within an ideal cadence range between 165 and 185. Drastic running speed changes should only manipulate your cadence by 5%. If you notice a significant drop, try working on your running efficiency and elevating the cadence back to healthy ranges.

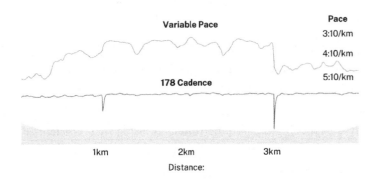

Increasing Cadence when Injured

If you face an injury and your cadence is lower than recommended, elevating to the acceptable range could make a profound difference. Firstly, in the paper mentioned above by Amy Schubert and colleagues, they also discovered a cadence increase improved energy absorption at the hip, knee and ankle joints.

A second study by John Willson and colleagues looked at the effects of running cadence in 10 female runners with, and 13 females without, kneecap pain [33]. This study analysed all participants running at their preferred cadence, 10% lower than their preferred cadence and 10% higher than their preferred cadence. At the end of the study, they discovered a 31% increase in stress around the kneecap joint with a lowered cadence and a 22% per cent decrease in stress when cadence increased.

The 22% decrease in load applies to the knee joint per step. However, if every step reduces the load on the joint by 22%, but more steps are taken, wouldn't the accumulation of load be similar? This study considered this question and calculated an overall reduction of 14% for every running mile. Put succinctly, increasing your cadence by

10% will reduce the overall load on your knee by 14%. That is a remarkable difference.

Increasing your cadence can also be effective for other running related injuries. I have seen success with ITB injuries, shin splints, plantar fasciitis, and other overuse injuries.

Case Study: Cadence Enhancing Rehabilitation

Sometimes, the Run Smarter Podcast releases Q&A episodes. I reach out to fellow listeners across social media and ask them to submit questions on various topics. One day I received a question from Terry, a loyal listener, about his current injury. Here was his message:

> *"Hi, Brodie. I have a marathon coming up and recently picked up shin splints as I moved back from regular trail runs to the road. My pain score when running can be anything from a zero to two out of ten and settles down to zero or one within 15 minutes after running".*

> *"Interestingly I've been reducing my running speed in an effort to keep my heart rate in zone two in preparation for the longer distance training. On occasion, this seems to tie in with the pain score moving up. My cadence is usually in the high 170s, since reducing the speed my cadence is in the mid to high 160s".*

Intrigued with Terry's symptom presentation, I asked if he could provide more detail. He sent me a screenshot of his workout along with his shin pain during the run:

Picture 1:
Duration: 30 minutes
Average pace: 10'56" per mile
Average cadence: 168
Pain: 2/10

Picture 2:
Duration: 40 minutes
Average pace: 10'04" per mile
Average cadence: 181
Pain: 0–1/10

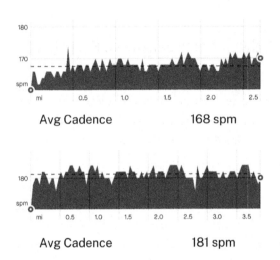

Avg Cadence   168 spm

Avg Cadence   181 spm

Suspecting that the reduced cadence was contributing to Terry's running inefficiency and therefore, generating higher loads on his shins, I asked if he could try managing a high cadence during his slow running. A few days later, I received another message from him:

"Very interesting results! Yesterday's 30 minute run had a shin pain score of around two out of ten with a cadence average of 168. Today's average cadence was 178 for the same 30 minutes, but the pain score on the shin was virtually zero".

"The other win in this is that, in order to keep cadence high, I'm really focusing on my form. I'm not saying that my running now feels effortless, but it certainly feels more like I'm

> *gliding along, resulting in fewer feelings of impact and still a very fresh pair of legs after the run. Thanks for a simple solution to what was becoming a frustrating problem".*

Running Technique Conclusion

Runners, running coaches and health professionals quickly identify minuscule errors during a running assessment. No one is perfect, and there will always be some minor inefficiencies. If injured, rather than quickly blaming running technique, posture or strength, attention should focus on training errors or inadequate recovery. Unless you possess an obvious flaw in your running, you should be fine, provided that training errors are absent.

Rather than blaming biomechanics, it is helpful to analyse and look at all aspects of your training with a broader scope. When I interviewed Chris Bramah on the podcast [27], he said:

> *"Running related injuries and running performances are influenced by a massive amount of factors, not just running biomechanics. I like to have an in-depth conversation about the runner's lifestyle to try and understand all the different contributors to their performance, so we can hopefully make more holistic advice".*

For the most part, recreational runners will display a wide range of running techniques. However, provided that training is sensible, the body will adapt to these small variations. Chris Napier wrote the book called '*Science of Running: Analyse Your Technique, Prevent Injury, Revolutionise Your Training*' [34] and summarised this concept beautifully:

> "Some anatomical 'abnormalities' such as flat feet or knock knees, are considered risk factors for running injuries, but this belief has not been backed up by research. Your body becomes accustomed to its own anatomy and will adapt to your training as long as you build up your training load gradually".

Considering this, some running traits may leave a runner more susceptible to injury when a training error is present. The major culprits are a cadence lower than 160 and an overstride pattern. Less of a concern, but still worth mentioning, include a narrow step width, contralateral hip drop, knee internal rotation, excessive dorsiflexion at initial contact and an excessive lean forward at the hips.

Chapter 6 Summary

1. Robust research returns inconclusive findings linking running technique and risk of injury.

2. One-off studies have found traits that may increase the likelihood of injury including a hip drop, forward trunk lean, excessive dorsiflexion and knee internal rotation.

3. A runner can survive and thrive with these traits provided their training is sensible.

4. Increasing your cadence towards an optimal range will help stride efficiency and can help with managing certain running related injuries.

Action Items

1. Identify your running cadence when running at different speeds.

2. If found to have a cadence below 165, try increasing your step rate by 5–10%.

3. If your cadence during a slow run compared to a faster effort has dropped by more than 5%, retrain yourself to run at a slower speed with more efficiency.

4. Practice running at an optimal cadence on a treadmill to keep running speed constant.

CHAPTER SIX

TRAINING BASICS FOR INJURY REDUCTION

Pete rested his achilles for the next two days as instructed by Daniel. Day three called for his rehabilitation exercises which were designed to raise the tendon's capacity to better prepare it for running loads. Pete opened up his phone to double check the instructions. He had practised these at the clinic but kept the instructions to ensure he used the correct technique.

Pete was instructed to do 12 repetitions, which made up one set. He was also instructed to wait two minutes before repeating a second and third set. The exercise didn't seem to bother the achilles. Throughout the final few repetitions, he could notice a mild burn in his calf and achilles, but it quickly dissipated. Afterwards, there was no limping nor any signs of irritation. He was also instructed to repeat his three sets later the same day. If there was no sign of irritation, then he could add five kilograms into a backpack and repeat the process.

The following morning Pete awoke to assess his symptoms. After two days of complete rest, his usual morning symptoms were two out of ten lasting five minutes. Today, after stepping on the floor, Pete experienced a similar level of pain but it only lasted three minutes. Since symptoms were not aggravated above his normal baseline, he would add weight to his rehabilitation exercises tomorrow. Today he was scheduled for a three kilometre run. Daniel mentioned that a walk-run strategy might be beneficial if continuous running irritated the tendon. Still, Pete was happy to try a continuous run today and reduce to a walk-run only if necessary. More importantly, today's run required Pete to run with a higher cadence than usual. Daniel calculated Pete's average cadence at 150 and advised Pete to raise this number to 165.

Before setting off on his run, Pete searched online for a metronome app and downloaded the first one that appeared. He set a beat to correspond with his cadence goal. After a brief warm-up, he set off at a slow jog. As usual, his attention was focused on the achilles symptoms. Surprisingly, the pain severity wasn't as bad as he had experienced in his previous run. Pete placed his level of discomfort at two out of ten for the first five minutes before it settled between zero and one out of ten.

Once Pete was warmed up, and into a steady stride, he reached into his pocket for his phone. He opened up the metronome app and ensured the beat per minute was correct. Once he pressed play, his phone started beeping at 165 beats per minute, and it was his goal to step in rhythm.

The task to step into rhythm was difficult at first. Pete's legs were not fast enough. Taking a more gradual approach, he lowered the metronome by five beats per minute. Allowing a few seconds to adjust, Pete found himself in rhythm. He landed his foot perfectly in sync with his phone. It felt strange. Taking shorter steps was unnatural, but he understood this is a skill to practice. After a few minutes, Pete's heart rate became elevated, and his breathing was laboured. He mixed up the remainder of his run with one minute of walking followed by one minute of running at his goal cadence and one minute of his natural cadence. He was ready to report back to Daniel tomorrow.

The next day Pete was keen to go back to the physiotherapy clinic. After yesterday's run, his symptoms had remained low. Before his consult, he repeated his rehabilitation exercises with the addition of five kilograms. While the exercise produced higher fatigue levels, it didn't spark any increase in symptoms. Pete updated Daniel on the past three days. When he detailed the increase in effort levels with the cadence change, Daniel asked if he recorded his activity on his phone. Pete handed his fitness tracker over to Daniel so he could analyse his activity. Daniel noticed that his running speed increased along with his cadence. This issue is common and requires some practice to overcome. Daniel suggested he practised maintaining a steady speed by using a treadmill.

He explained that a treadmill offered a perfect opportunity to adjust cadence. In this setting, the speed can remain constant as the belt travels at the same speed. Pete and Daniel spent the next 10 minutes adjusting Pete's cadence and practising small, quick steps at a slow speed. Daniel explained that this adjustment may take up to two weeks to feel natural. Once 160 became comfortable he could raise the cadence by another five steps and continue in this manner until his cadence reached his goal

After the treadmill session, Pete sat back down in Daniel's consult room. Daniel looked over Pete's current schedule and started thinking about the next steps. He wrote a running plan for the next four weeks. Providing his symptoms remained stable. In addition, he added progressions to the eccentric heel raise exercise along with instructions on whether to continue progressing or seek modifications.

	MON	TUE	WED	THU	FRI	SAT	SUN
WEEK 1	Rehab	3k	Rehab	3k	Rehab	5k	Rehab
WEEK 2	Rest	4k	Rehab	3k	Rehab	6k	Rehab
WEEK 3	Rest	4k	Rehab	5k	Rehab	6k	Rehab
WEEK 4	Rest	5k	Rehab	5k	Rehab	7k	Rehab

Physiotherapy Instructions:

Eccentric heel raise progressions:

- Phase 1: 3x12 with 5kgs
- Phase 2: 3x8 with 8kgs
- Phase 3: 3x12 with 8kgs
- Phase 4: 3x8 with 15kgs
- Phase 5: 3x12 with 15kgs

Continue to progress running program and rehabilitation exercises if:

- Pain is less than 4/10 during exercise
- Symptoms return to baseline within 24 hours
- Overall symptoms improved week by week

Daniel made sure Pete understood each element and was clear on the progression instructions. Lastly, Daniel wanted to discuss the training error that initially resulted in the achilles injury. He felt that a lot of his training methods were sound, particularly the high frequency and gradual weekly mileage which is a safe option. However, there were a few elements he may want to consider once he was back to pain free running.

Pete's ears pricked up, any additional tips that could potentially reduce his risk of injury would be extremely valuable. Daniel suggested that once he had built a substantial base without a return of his symptoms, it would be beneficial to introduce some faster running in small doses. These harder efforts could come in a variety of forms, including interval training, hill sprints, stride sessions or time-trial sessions, but needed to be implemented methodically to not overload the body. Pete was concerned that faster running would generate high loads on his body and wondered if it would be safer to keep all running at low intensity. Daniel reassured him that having your body adapt to higher speeds would build resiliency. In an ideal scenario, Pete needed to be strong and capable over a wide range of stimuli. Daniel told Pete that if he only adapted to slow speeds, he would be destined for injury whenever he decided to push the envelope with activities such as competing in an event.

Pete pictured this scenario. He imagined being strong and resilient in every training zone. The idea was daunting and overwhelming but with patience and careful planning maybe it was achievable. He decided to focus on the rehabilitation phase and then, all going well, slowly integrate a tailor made training schedule.

Run Smarter Lesson 6

This book has already covered some key components of a running routine. If certain elements are added with the right balance, it can enhance your ability to adapt and lower your risk of injury. Firstly, your training schedule should avoid any abrupt changes to the body. This includes weekly volume, session duration, speed, terrain and many other elements that change the demand on the body. Secondly, was the discussion of training frequency which includes optimising your running frequency to ensure you spend more time within your adaptation zone, triggering the exercise response and reaping the reward.

The remainder of this chapter will cover basic training principles to reduce the risk of injury. More complex training principles will be introduced in Chapter 12 to continue elevating your running performance.

The 10% Rule

One of the most recognised training rules, the 10% rule, signifies that overall training loads should not exceed this amount per week. In a way, this rule is in place to make abrupt changes extremely difficult and to train safely without injury. The 10% rule is a very general guideline to follow and has its limitations.

The first limitation is it only applies to weekly mileage and is one very small piece of the puzzle. For example, a runner could run 30 easy kilometres on week one but run 33 hard kilometres on week two and still fall within the guidelines. In addition to speed, the rule also doesn't account for elevation, recovery, stress and the other factors considered within the 'load versus capacity' relationship.

The 10% rule also becomes unreasonable when factoring in either beginner runners at low mileage or ultra runners at high mileage. If a beginner runner can only commit to three days of running per week, their progression will be too gradual if following the 10% rule. On the other hand, if an ultra runner could no longer spend time running during the week, their 10% rule for weekends may be too abrupt.

Example #1: Low Mileage Runner with the 10% Rule (too gradual)

	MON	TUE	WED	THU	FRI	SAT	SUN	TOT:
WEEK 1		3k			2k		4k	9k
WEEK 2		3k			3k		4k	10k
WEEK 3		3k			3k		5k	11k

Example #2: High Mileage Runner with the 10% Rule (too abrupt)

	MON	TUE	WED	THU	FRI	SAT	SUN	TOT:
WEEK 1		15k	10k		10k	20k	15k	70k
WEEK 2		15k	10k		10k	27k	15k	77k
WEEK 3		15k	10k		10k	27k	22k	84k

While general guidelines may point runners in the right direction, it should be made clear that there is no steadfast rule for safely progressing training loads. Chris Bramah is a chapter author in the book *'The Science and Practice of Middle and Long-distance Running'* and stated:

> *"Several studies have attempted to identify the relationship between weekly training volume increase and running-re-*

> *lated injury. Increases of greater than 30% have been reported to increase the risk of injury. However, no difference in injury rates has been identified when increasing weekly mileage by less than 10% or between 10 and 30%".* [36 37 38]

> *"Therefore, current scientific evidence is unable to identify a specific threshold for which a sudden increase in training volume can influence running injury risk".*

If you are training for a race and looking to build your weekly mileage slowly, I advise runners to start between 10 and 15%. However, this increase should be absent from abrupt speed, terrain, and intensity changes. From this point, you can choose to increase or decrease the percentage based on your body's response. For example, if you are a low mileage runner and decide to train for a marathon, you might choose to increase your mileage by 15% each week. After two weeks, if your body is responding well, you may choose to increase another 5 or 10%. However, by week five, if continuing at this rate produces muscle soreness, fatigue or early signs of injury, it would be wise to reduce the percentage between 5 or 10%.

With this approach, you start conservatively and make additional modifications by listening to your body. In this way, you can pay attention to Eric Hegedus' early signs of injury explained in Chapter three. These elements include fatigue, muscle soreness, stress and poor sleep. If you're ranking poorly across all four domains, an injury may be around the corner, and immediate adjustments should be made. Remember, weekly mileage is only one piece of the puzzle and introducing any other element should be done gradually.

The 80/20 Rule

The 80/20 rule applies to intensity distribution spread across any given week of training. Generally speaking, 80% of your overall weekly mileage should be dedicated to low intensity, leaving 20% of your mileage to more strenuous efforts. To help assign the appropriate intensity levels, my preference is to incorporate an RPE or rate of perceived exertion chart. Even though intensity can be calculated with running speed, heart rate or power, these may be misleading as they lack the internal perception of effort which can indicate a lack of recovery, stress and other hidden elements.

When applying the RPE to the 80/20 rule, I advise that 80% of the weekly training volume be spent below a five out of ten. This is the threshold between comfortable and uncomfortable when training endurance. When running with a four out of ten RPE, your breath rate should be under control, your legs should feel strong, and you should have the sensation that you can maintain this intensity for up to sixty minutes. Considering this, an intensity below four out of ten should feel like the intensity can be maintained beyond one hour and is where I like my training to be the majority of the time.

RATE OF PERCEIVED EXERTION (RPE) SCALE	80/20 DISTRIBUTION
10 Max Effort: Almost impossible to maintain, unable to talk	
9 Very hard: Can barely breathe, can only speak a few words	20% of your training load should be >5/10
7–8 Vigorous: Borderline uncomfortable, can speak a sentence	
4–6 Moderate: Somewhat comfortable, becoming more challenging	
2–3 Light: Feels like you can maintain for hours	80% of your training should be <5/10
1 Very light: Hardly any exertion, but more than complete rest	

On the Run Smarter Podcast, I had the pleasure of speaking to Matt Fitzgerald, author of '*80/20 Running: Run Stronger and Race Faster By Training Slower*'. Matt clearly explained why training below this threshold is so important for recovery and performance [39]. He said:

"In the last 15 to 20 years there has been an emerging consensus that the proper boundary between low and moderate-intensity aligns with the first ventilatory threshold, which falls between 77% and 81% of the maximum heart rate for a typical runner. Most runners would know experientially that this heart rate zone is not very hard. In terms of RPE, it aligns perfectly with a four out of ten".

"This is critical because if you are training just above this threshold, then it is much more stressful to your autonomic nervous system and it takes longer to recover. If you are

> *training just below it, you recover much more quickly and it is much less stressful on your autonomic nervous system".*
>
> *"If you are above that threshold when you intend to be at a low intensity just one time, no big deal. But if you do that habitually, which most recreational endurance athletes do, then it creates this chronic burden of unresolved fatigue".*

So, the 80/20 rule dictates that 80% of your running is spent at or below four out of ten. Personally, I like to perform most of my running intensity at three on the RPE scale. Low intensity running can be a game changer for runners because it allows you to build a large running volume in the safest way possible. If you are struggling to maintain a low intensity with continuous running, you can include walking intervals. If you dedicate a training session to an intensity below a four on the RPE scale, you should complete the run feeling fresh and composed. Feeling fresh after a run can be a foreign experience for some people but is a deliberate intention to reduce injury risk.

This training principle aims to foster the correct balance between adaptation and recovery. If the training intensities are far removed from this guideline, the risk of overuse elevates. For example, commonly beginner runners perceive every running session as an intense workout. Perhaps it is impatience, inexperience or a misunderstanding of expectations but each running effort is an attempt to break their personal best. If this habit continues, the likelihood of exceeding the body's adaptation zone is high. Instead, if running intensities were lower, this would lower the demand placed on the body and mileage could progress safely.

However, the majority of runners want to run fast. Whether it is a race to compete, or setting a personal best, making goals and breaking records is a part of the fun. Unless the envelope is pushed and capabilities are challenged, these goals won't be achieved. It is all about finding the optimal balance between high and low intensity which is key for optimal performance and reducing injury risk.

The Skill of Slow Running

Many beginner runners commit most of their running to high intensity. I believe this is one of the primary reasons someone might start running and quit after a few weeks. If hard running is your intent, it is hard to find love for the sport. If every session consists of burning legs, laboured breathing, and profuse sweating, it is physically and mentally tough to endure. It isn't until running becomes easier through adaptation, or the runner learns to run slower, that the love for running blooms.

I didn't possess a love for running straight away. Initially, my running had been fueled by half marathon ambitions, and since my sister was also training for the event, accountability played a role. Walking breaks were necessary for the first three weeks of training as my body screamed at me to stop. Even when I built enough fitness for continuous running, I still encountered muscle stiffness, general fatigue and cardiovascular strain. These effects lasted about six weeks, and the enjoyment of running was low. I wasn't looking forward to my scheduled runs, and when I convinced myself to head out the door, I would constantly count down the minutes to when I could stop.

After the six week mark, however, two major things changed that served to enhance my enjoyment of running. First was building up enough fitness to achieve running at a steady state. When you're running at a steady state, your heart rate, respiratory rate, and perceived effort don't gradually climb and instead, hover at a comfortable level without internal alarm bells or signs of distress. The second factor was my ability to run slow. For some reason, I had in my head that I needed to run at a certain speed to class myself as a runner. It seems silly now, but once I learnt to run slow, not only did I enjoy running, but I could do it more often. I no longer had to wait three days for my body to recover. Instead, I was running on consecutive days and bouncing back quickly.

I still remember the first time I stepped out my front door and was excited to go for a run. It was a crisp morning, with hardly any wind and the birds were chirping. It was coming out of summer, and the trees were showing their first autumn colours. Living with my parents at the time, my running track consisted of creek trails and bushland paths that offered tonnes of Australian wildlife. I had an eight kilometre run scheduled and I was going to take my time completing it. With the sun rising, I took in a deep breath of fresh air and felt a genuine sense of appreciation. A switch flicked in my brain, and it was the first time I was excited to run. That moment was when I caught the running bug, and it launched me into a passionate career both professionally and recreationally.

I consider slow running a skill. Some runners learn this skill quicker than others, and the benefits are profound once they do. I cannot think of a more fitting example than my sister, Zoe. For years, she ran recreationally with the occasional 10 kilometre, and half marathon events. She would run consistently throughout the week, especially when training. However, she would be frustrated with her lack of progress. When she asked me for help, I advised her on the 80/20 intensity distribution. I explained that 80% of her weekly mileage should be low intensity. However, after trying to follow my advice, her progress remained hindered.

This problem continued for years until we both realised the underlying issue. I asked Zoe how her body felt during her scheduled slow run. She listed several descriptions, including an elevated heart rate, burning lungs and heavy legs. When I reminded her to stay at a low intensity she replied by saying her running speed is slow enough as it is.

It turns out Zoe was comparing her slow run pace to other runners. Even though she was running at a pace she considered slow, her body was telling her otherwise. While she believed she was keeping to the 80/20 rule, it turned out that none of her training sessions were low intensity. She then reduced her running speed significantly, even implementing walking intervals during warm weather to maintain a low intensity. After implementing this strategy, several revolutionary changes happened. First, her legs and lungs stayed under control throughout the entire run. Secondly, she found new enjoyment in running.

No longer was every run a battle. Zoe looked forward to putting on her shoes and heading out the door for the first time in years. Her transformation was so compelling that I asked her to share it on my podcast. We recorded episode 144 titled *Are You Really Running Slow Enough?* [40], which received ten times the amount of positive feedback I regularly get from listeners.

Do Not Just Train Smart, Train Hard

While developing the skill to run slow has its advantages, athletes also need to consider pushing harder occasionally, to offer the body variety. When appreciating and respecting the accumulation of training load, a reasonable reaction would be to train conservatively.

However, while the goal is to avoid abrupt changes, constantly training at a conservative slow speed can have its disadvantages. As mentioned earlier, most runners want to better themselves, compete in races and challenge their own capabilities. To achieve this, you will have to add high quality, fast sessions into your routine. Following the intensity distribution rule, this can be close to 20% but may require tailored adjustments.

Not only are speed sessions required for physical development, but it is also necessary for reducing your risk of injury. Runners should not assume that high training loads cause injury. If you progress your training with patience and build a large foundation mixed with different speeds and terrain, this can actually be protective against injury.

This concept is illustrated in Tim Gabbett's paper titled '*The Training-injury Prevention Paradox: Should Athletes be Training Smarter and Harder?* [41] In this paper, Tim concluded:

> *"While there is a relationship between high training loads and injury, this paper demonstrates that the problem is not with training per se, but more likely the inappropriate training that is being prescribed. Excessive and rapid increases in training loads are likely responsible for a large proportion of non-contact, soft-tissue injuries. However, physically hard (and appropriate) training develops physical qualities, which in turn protects against injuries".*

This theory supports our current understanding. Successfully building a large training volume comprising of various training demands helps raise the overall capacity and athletic development. So, while abrupt changes of any sort should be approached with caution, the goal to progress all qualities in running should be encouraged. This approach requires patience but will play a pivotal role in preventing future injury.

Performing strides at the end of your easy running session once a week is a good starting point. Strides involve gradual accelerations that reach close to maximal speed in a short period of time. Find a flat section where you can allow a straight 30 second run. Start with a slow jog and add a slow acceleration for 15 seconds. After this acceleration period, you should be reaching 90% of your maximal sprint or, if injured, as fast as the injury dictates. Hold this top desired speed for 8 to 10 seconds before allowing a 5 second deceleration. For beginners, repeat the sequence up to four times, or up to eight times for those with more experience. Allow one to two minutes in between each repeat for recovery. Strides will help your body adapt to very fast speeds over very short distances and strengthen another chink in your armour.

Stride Phases

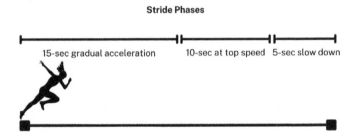

15-sec gradual acceleration   10-sec at top speed   5-sec slow down

Other examples of quality workouts include interval running, fartlek workouts and tempo sessions. Each has endless combinations of intensities under different durations but can serve as a great tool for athletic development. An interval session might include a ten minute warm-up, followed by one minute intervals alternating between easy jogging and fast running for ten rounds. Strides require a large amount of force from the muscles and tendons but are not taxing on the heart and lungs. Alternatively, longer interval sessions will demand a lot from the cardiovascular and musculoskeletal systems.

Each quality speed session should fall within the runner's capabilities and abrupt demands that exceed capacity should be avoided. If executed correctly, adapting to these high quality speed sessions should build overall resiliency and aid future performance.

Avoid the Running Intensity Grey Zone

Abiding by the 80/20 rule isn't just about building a bigger base safely. It also assists in polarising your training. Polarisation refers to a greater disparity in training intensities such as training really easy, then really hard. This concept is important because, without focus or a schedule to follow, runners can easily fall into a grey zone of intensity.

The grey zone of intensity refers to runners training too hard on their easy days, leaving them unable to fully recover and therefore, unable to push out maximum efforts on their fast days. Illustrating this concept on the Run Smarter Podcast was professor Shona Halson. Shona is a world renowned physiologist on recovery and during our conversation, she highlighted:

> *"Easy days are supposed to be easy. If you are waking up the next day feeling flat or sore, then perhaps you have done too much".*
>
> *"Studies have shown when people plan their hard days, they don't go as hard as they should. On easy days, they never train as easy as they should".*

Imagine scheduling a 30 minute easy run and planning to conduct the session at an RPE of three. Throughout the run, the legs feel fresh and the run feels too easy, so you pick up the pace. With 10 minutes to go, you check your average pace on your watch and it displays 5 minutes and 30 seconds per kilometre. You then have a hit of motivation to finish with an average pace of under five minutes. The final two minutes contain an uphill street back to your house and you decide on a final push.

Looking back on your run, the three RPE may have been closer to five. This trend continues on the next two easy runs before the high quality interval workout later in the week. By this stage, your legs feel fresh, but halfway through your first interval, your legs quickly burn up and start getting heavy. When the grey zone of intensity creeps in, you will be too depleted to reach your max efforts because you are not taking it easy when you should.

Each training session should have a focus, and sometimes the focus is to remain fresh throughout the entire run. This suggestion can often meet resistance because some runners have an inbuilt philosophy that running hard will create better results. In their eyes, an easy running session that doesn't offer a cardiovascular challenge, is a waste of time, or counterproductive. However, if the polarised training is executed with the correct balance, a runner can push out harder efforts during dedicated speed sessions and get better results in the process.

There have been countless times when a runner has given me pushback or arguments when I advised they are not going slow enough during their easy runs. Eventually, runners will concede when they give it a go and start witnessing the outcome as a result. Within as short as a few weeks, runners start impressing themselves with the time trial splits they are able to achieve and the race time they accomplish. Since they are getting faster, they begin to embrace slow running which becomes a permanent part of their training philosophy.

The same effect surprised my sister when she finally started slow running. As I mentioned above, Zoe thought she was running slow but was comparing her speed to everyone else. When she decided to interpret her own effort levels instead of the running pace, her legs began to feel fresh and her love for running reignited. One revolution I didn't mention earlier was the improvement in her running speed. Because she was spending 80% of her week maintaining a fresh, calm composure, the dedicated speed sessions were met with a newfound burst of energy. During this moment in Zoe's life, our online group family chats regularly featured screenshots of her workouts highlighting a new personal best.

Waves Arriving at an 80/20 Distribution

By now, you should have an accurate measure of the waves that are arriving and colliding with your iceberg. The precise height and speed of the incoming waves should be dialled in to suit the intention. In addition, you should also have a deep understanding of your iceberg's ability to tolerate the incoming wave. Both of these measurements represent the workout load and the capacity to tolerate the workout.

However, larger waves should arrive occasionally and deliberately to suit a different purpose that cannot be achieved by smaller, more conservative waves. For instance, higher waves can reach a greater surface area. Spreading nourishing water to parts of the iceberg inaccessible by smaller waves.

This scenario would reap a lot of benefits and your iceberg would expand and grow a lot quicker if large waves were a part of your toolkit. Growing your iceberg quicker would result in greater resilience and better performance. Caution should be taken with large waves, but if executed properly, the reward is worth it.

The balance between too hard, and too conservative needs to play out carefully. Each extreme has its advantages and disadvantages. If the goal is to build a larger iceberg, playing it safe too often may hinder this process. This delicate balance is a part of the game and gives you a good opportunity to learn more about your limits and capabilities.

Chapter 6 Summary

1. Increasing your mileage by 10% per week is a good guideline but has its limitations.

2. Increasing mileage by 10–15% is a good starting point but requires constant monitoring and necessary adjustments while listening to your body.

3. In a general sense, 80% of your training should be spent at a low intensity, leaving 20% dedicated to harder efforts.

4. Challenging your body with progressive loads across different intensities is key for a robust body with a high capacity, but requires patience.

Action Items

1. Learn to run slow and avoid training too hard on your easy days.

2. Finish your easy runs feeling fresh and composed.

3. If not already doing so, accompany your easy running with harder workouts once per week. Ensure the introduction is gradual and that it progresses sensibly.

CHAPTER SEVEN

THE HIDDEN DANGERS THAT CAUSE INJURY

Within four weeks, Pete made significant progress. The combination of strength training and decreased mileage gradually reduced symptoms. He worked closely with Daniel to slowly reintroduce mileage and progress the strength exercises. To date, Pete had increased his weekend run to seven kilometres, and his single leg heel raises built up to three sets of eight repetitions with a 15 kilogram dumbbell. Since the rehabilitation exercises were getting tougher, Daniel advised Pete to reduce the frequency to twice a week. This adjustment also opened up a fourth day for running. Daniel also added future weeks to Pete's training sessions to ensure no abrupt changes were present.

Pete's Running Schedule

WEEK	MON	TUE	WED	THU	FRI	SAT	SUN	TOT
5	Rest	5k	Rehab	6k	Rest	8k	Rehab	17
6	3k	4k	Rehab	5k	Rest	8k	Rehab	20

| 7 | 4k | 4k | Rehab | 5k | Rest | 9k | Rehab | 22 |
| 8 | 5k | 4k | Rehab | 6k | Rest | 10k | Rehab | 25 |

After completing his eighth week, Pete was feeling strong. His symptoms were barely noticeable throughout the week. However, the buildup in mileage seemed pointless. He noticed his complacency and realised he was more motivated when he had a goal. One day, during his lunch break, he opened up his browser to search for upcoming races. After a few minutes of scanning, Pete landed on the perfect race. A marathon around his local parklands. It involved eight laps around a flat bike path terrain. The race was six months away, which seemed like ample time. It also had a half marathon option which could be his safety net if he encountered setbacks. This new goal daunted Pete but reignited his motivation.

Three months went by, and Pete continued to follow a thorough running plan organised by Daniel. Based on his past training errors, he made a conscious effort to slowly introduce new variables such as hills and speed intervals. Occasionally, his achilles symptoms would surface, but symptoms only lasted a few days because the training dosages increased gradually. In moments of a flareup, he would still run but made a conscious effort to avoid uphill running, running on consecutive days and speedwork. Once symptoms had settled, he was back to uninterrupted marathon training.

With three months until race day, Pete continued to observe tremendous gains. His long weekend run was climbing north of 20 kilometres. Under Daniel's instruction, he carefully implemented interval sessions ranging from 500 metre repeats to five kilometre time trials. Additionally, Friday's run would finish with stride repeats. Pete was happy to see his weekly mileage pick up and remain successful at different running speeds. The bulk of his running was at an easy intensity, but the remainder included a wide array of intensities. At times, he was committing to short sprints as fast as possible. Other times, he was trying to maintain hard, uncomfortable efforts for longer than five minutes. This range of intensities helped him feel prepared for any challenge and he welcomed the variety.

WEEK	MON	TUE	WED	THU	FRI	SAT	SUN	TOT
20	Rest	8k easy	5k +intervals	Rest	10k easy +strides	20k	Rehab	43ks

Shortly after, Pete's boss offered him a new job opportunity that would involve working with a high profile company for the next two months. The additional pay was handsome but would involve a lot of pressure, longer working hours and working most weekends. After some deliberation, he accepted the offer. The stress loomed over him, but he reminded himself that it was only for two months. After accepting the offer, the paperwork instantly mounted. His lunch breaks consisted of phone calls, and he was inundated with emails. Even though the stress was rising, he still found time to switch off from work and complete his nighttime run.

It was two weeks into Pete's new work routine, and it was already taking a toll. Sometimes, he'd lie awake in bed for hours thinking about work. Luckily, he still had his running and it was the only time he'd forget about work. The only hurdle he encountered was the available time for a long run on weekends. He needed to squeeze in a 20 kilometre run before clocking into work at 9:00 am. He made this work by waking up earlier. Since he had been running pain free for months, he wanted to continue making progress and sticking to Daniel's running plan.

The alarm clock woke Pete up the following Saturday morning. Without opening his eyes, he reached out of bed and hit stop. He forced his eyes open to view the clock which displayed 5:45am. Today's run called for 22 kilometres. While it was a struggle to get out of bed, Pete knew he would get a surge of energy and positivity once his feet hit the pavement. As he slipped on his shoes and headed out the door, the time was 6:00am. His mind immediately started calculating. If he averaged six minutes per kilometre, he would finish at 8:15am and leave 45 minutes to shower and prepare for his online meeting. As predicted, he felt great once he reached a casual steady state. Taking in the cool morning air rejuvenated his entire body and allowed him to switch his mind off

For the first 10 kilometres, he felt fresh and effortless. Everything seemed to be moving in sync, both physically and mentally. Suddenly, Pete's meditative trance was interrupted by the beeping of his watch, notifying the 15 kilometre mark. Looking at his split of 6 minutes and 20 seconds, he was surprised as he thought he was travelling faster. He wasn't too worried, there would still be plenty of time to shower and get ready for work. As the remaining kilometres ticked over though he noticed his legs felt heavier than his previous long run. His breathing also seemed heavier, and his stride more sluggish. Putting it down to the lack of sleep he battled through the final kilometres.

At the 20 kilometre mark, Pete noticed a weird strain developing around his kneecap. It wasn't painful, more an awkward sensation. Like something was out of place. Since there was no pain, he pushed through the final two kilometres. He didn't have time to troubleshoot these unusual symptoms as he needed to get ready for his meeting.

Pausing his watch at exactly 22 kilometres, Pete finished on his doorstep. He took off his shoes and crept into the bathroom. After stepping into the shower, Pete experienced a sharp, fleeting pain underneath his kneecap. Now he knew this was serious. He gingerly nursed his knee while getting ready for his meeting. While attending the two hour call, he noticed a dull throb residing at the front of the knee. The new knee symptoms were puzzling. He had been progressing his training plan gradually, exactly as set down by Daniel. He couldn't understand why another injury would occur. He felt very despondent and was sure he was the only runner to be injury prone.

Run Smarter Lesson 7

Previous chapters have extensively covered the load versus capacity relationship. To date, the focus has been on the external load and avoiding abrupt changes to these elements. This chapter narrows the focus on capacity. In particular, hidden elements in everyday life that positively or negatively influence your capacity to tolerate load. Let's look back at a paragraph from Chapter two:

> *"There is a large distinction between applied load and tissue capacity that athletes of any ability need to understand to lower injury risk. The first element to consider is a load which can be defined as a stimulus applied directly to the body".*

> *"The next variable to consider is the body's capacity to handle the applied load. In a sense, each ligament, muscle, tendon and bone within the body holds a level of capacity. In other words, they will reach a limit before the likelihood of injury increases. For decades, it has been suggested that the balance between external load and tissue capacity plays a significant causative role in injury amongst athletes".*

On occasion, I will consult a runner with an overuse injury. They would be puzzled by their seemingly unprovoked symptoms because an abrupt change was absent in their training. Once I dive deeper into their training volumes and agree with them that no external load was present, I often turn my attention to lifestyle changes. Through extensive questioning, I can often identify stressful scenarios, work and family drama, and other lifestyle situations that may present as a likely cause.

When unexplained symptoms or signs of early injury occur, it is valuable to focus on the broader picture. But when you readjust your focus, it is important to know what you're looking for and how to interpret certain psycho-social scenarios accurately. Considering all elements within and outside of training can add another tool to your injury prevention tool box.

Everyday Wellbeing on Injury Prevention

Scientific papers have recognised the relationship between the health and wellbeing of the athlete and the likelihood of injury for several years. These daily stressors extend beyond the emotions of competition and into everyday life such as work, family and other relationships.

Torbjorn Soligard and colleagues published an Olympic committee consensus paper focussing on load management and injury [42]. The paper recognised the role of poor load management as a major risk factor for injury. However, they also acknowledged the role of psychological wellbeing. They stated:

> "A key concept to appreciate for those responsible for managing load is that maladaptations are triggered not only by poor management of training and competition loads but

> *also by interaction with psychological non-sport stressors, such as negative life-event stress and daily hassles".*

Andreas Ivarsson and colleagues also investigated the correlation between psychosocial factors and injury [43]. They conducted a meta-analysis to see if these variables could predict injury and if interventions to help negative lifestyle factors could prevent injury. The first step was to examine the relationship between psychosocial factors and injury. Here is what they found:

> *"High levels of negative life-event stress and strong stress responsivity were the two variables in the model of stress and athletic injury that had the strongest associations with injury risk".*

Ivarsson's paper includes a path diagram explaining this correlation and several variables making up the stress versus injury relationship. The authors suggested that the response to stress will depend on the athlete's cognitive appraisal of the situation, which is influenced by personality factors, history of stressors, and coping resources.

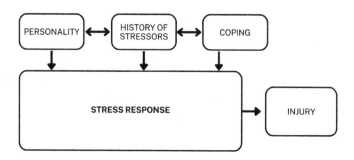

We have all witnessed people react differently to stressful situations, which is why personality plays an important role. If high pressure competition doesn't affect you too much, the stress response will be less severe. On the other hand, a history of stressors may influence your future response and even your personality traits in certain situations. A teenager who hasn't been exposed to many life stressors will create a different stress response to a runner who has experienced life tragedies, the stress of competition, episodes of injury, and other lifestyle hassles. Lastly, a factor that may help or hinder the stress response is your particular coping strategies, discussed later in the chapter.

Similar statements were made in a consensus review by Wiese-Bjornstal [44], who stated:

> "With respect to specific psychosocial vulnerabilities to sports injury, one of the most consistent findings in the pre-injury literature surrounds life event stress".

> "Major life event stress (defined as the perceived strain associated with major life event stressors such as starting at a new school or death of a family member), and in particular negative life event stress, in most studies to date is predictive of sports injury occurrence".

> "This seems particularly apparent among those high major life event stress athletes who simultaneously self-report few coping skills or social resources to deal with the stress. Minor life event stress, studied under constructs such as daily hassles and everyday problems, has also been implicated in the relationship between accumulative small stressors and sports injury incidence, although it has received lesser research attention".

Why is There a Link Between Stress and Injury?

During your life, you encounter different types of stress. Firstly, you have the benefits of physical stress in the form of exercise. When participating in physical activity, your body is automatically triggered into a 'fight or flight' response, releasing certain stress hormones to help you perform. Let's consider cortisol, for example. If you need to run from danger, higher cortisol levels are released to increase your heart rate and blood pressure. Another fight or flight hormone is noradrenaline. Like cortisol, it helps increase heart rate and helps mobilise the brain and body for action by increasing alertness and vigilance.

While hormones such as cortisol and noradrenaline circulate through our bloodstream, our body is primed for exercise. Once you stop exercising, the mind and body calm themselves, and these hormone levels settle. By lowering these hormone levels, your body can easily enter recovery mode. Lowering these stress hormones is vital for recovery and injury prevention, otherwise you won't get stronger and adapt during a workout. Instead, the adaptation phase occurs after the workout during relaxation.

Imagine your body holds an important stress cup. When you exercise, the level of physical stress begins to fill the cup. If the cup starts overflowing with contents, the body can easily malfunction, becoming overloaded and increasing the likelihood of injury. However, when the body enters a relaxed state, it can begin processing the activity and slowly drain the contents within the stress cup.

While the impact of physical stress is easy to comprehend, a runner also needs to consider the impact of psychological stress. In circumstances where psychological stress is present, identical hormones are triggered. When you are angry, frustrated or stressed, your heart rate elevates, your blood pressure increases, and you develop a surge of energy ready for action. Daily stress also prevents your body from entering the crucial recovery mode.

For example, if you run in the morning for 45 minutes, your stress cup begins to fill. If the rest of your day is complete with work stress, family drama and a restless night's sleep, you haven't provided your body with the right conditions to empty your stress cup. If tomorrow involves more physical activity, the stress cup continues to fill, threatening the possibility of overflow and increasing the likelihood of injury. In other words, your body simply cannot recognise the difference between physical stress and mental stress. The same hormones are triggered, and both situations prevent the body from entering recovery mode.

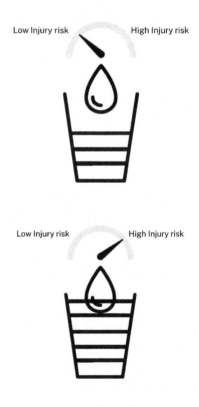

What can often present as a problem are runners who run to relieve stress. If faced with stressful situations, and other burdens, some runners may use running as a solution to their current state. This particular balance needs to be negotiated carefully. If running significantly reduces mental stress, which fosters a calm state for a prolonged period, it can be a useful strategy. Although, if running doesn't relieve the mental stress, or the stress returns rather quickly, then you could be filling your cup with two independent jugs of water and putting yourself in danger.

Think back to Pete's situation. Even though he continued to progress through his training plan carefully, he was taking on additional psychological stress and failed to recognise the early signs of under-recovery. Not only was his additional emotional stress adding water to the stress cup, but his lack of sleep created an inability to remove the contents within the stress cup. As a result, he experienced a lack of energy and fatigue during his run, ignoring it until an injury surfaced.

Let's look at the graph during Pete's recent lifestyle change to illustrate his knee pain. If he knew of these hidden dangers or recognised the signs of under-recovery, he may have played it safe and reduced his running volume during this stressful period.

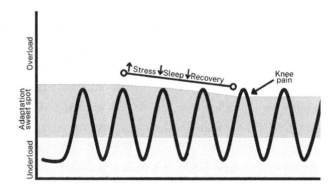

Sleep Deprivation and Injury

Sleep deprivation is one of the top modifiable risk factors for human health, but research shows that nearly 50% of us fail to get the recommended duration of seven to nine hours [45]. As previously explained, sleep is a vital part of the recovery process. During sleep, the body will process, absorb and adapt to the physical and psychological stressors that have occurred throughout the day. Good quality sleep reduces the contents of your stress cup so you are able to bounce back the following day. Depriving yourself of this essential recovery tool will leave you in strife and significantly heighten your risk of injury.

In addition, those who are sleep deprived have been shown to have a reduced aerobic capacity, lower muscle strength, and decreased power output. They exhibit increased perceived exercise intensity, fatigue, altered mood status, and reduced cognitive function [46]. Each affected component plays a role in reducing a runner's capacity to tolerate load and severe training considerations should be made if sleep is lacking.

A 2012 study investigated sleep deprivation and injury within the adolescent population. Conducted by Matthew Milewski and colleagues, these researchers designed an online survey for the participants to complete and asked various questions about their chosen sport, sleep habits and training habits [47].

The survey was completed by 112 adolescents over 21 months. After this data collection phase, the researchers could cross-reference their results with the injury log from the school's athletic training room. Surprisingly, the study found athletes who slept on average less than eight hours per night were 70% more likely to have had an injury than athletes who slept for longer than eight hours. The authors recorded:

"*Our study shows that the amount of sleep per night is associated with the risk of injuries in adolescent athletes. This association was observed even after accounting for other factors that might affect injury rates such as grade in school or amount of time spent participating in sports*".

"*This finding is not surprising in view of previous research that shows that even modest sleep loss is associated with impairment of psychomotor performance. Sleep deprivation can affect motor function, mood, and cognitive functions, all of which could affect a young student athlete's performance and injury risk*".

More recently, in 2020, a study conducted by Richard Johnston and colleagues focused their attention on 95 endurance sporting athletes [48]. These athletes were recruited from running, triathlon, swimming, cycling and rowing disciplines. They were required to submit weekly training data, subjective health complaints, sleep quality and injury reports. Over the 52 week study period, the researchers discovered those who reported a psychological or lifestyle health complaint had a 32% increased risk of an injury the following week.

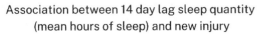

Additionally, researchers found a significant increase in injury risk if an athlete had a 14 day lag of fewer than seven hours of sleep per night. Conversely, a 14 day lag of more than seven hours of sleep significantly reduced the risk of injury.

It is clear that good quality sleep will help assist your running endeavours. If you are training for an event, raising your training volumes, and lacking sleep, I strongly recommend developing strategies to assist. More information and useful strategies will be available in Chapter 18.

Stress Management for Injury Prevention

When Ivarsson's meta-analysis [43] discovered that psychological stressors were linked to injury risk, their next step was to investigate stress management strategies. More specifically, can we use stress management interventions to prevent sports injuries. After all, coping strategies seemed to play a factor in their stress model. They concluded:

> *"All psychosocially-based interventions included in the review showed fewer injuries in the intervention groups in comparison to the control groups. Psychosocially-based interventions should be considered when designing injury prevention programs".*

Below is a shortlist of psychosocially based interventions that are considered to reduce stress levels. These suggestions may not work for everyone, so it is recommended that you investigate and practise a strategy that you personally find useful.

- Psychological skills training: This method refers to the systematic and consistent practice of mental or psychological skills to enhance performance, increase enjoyment, or achieve greater sport and physical activity self satisfaction [49]. For example, if you are stressed about competition or elements of performance, then mentally rehearsing the task using visualisation strategies, imagery or attentional focus may be useful.

- Cognitive behavioural therapy: This method is based on the premise that how you think and act affects how you feel. For example, you may have a particular distortion in thinking that isn't serving you. Perhaps you are fearful of reinjury, or social situations trigger anxiety. These thoughts can manifest unnecessary and unhelpful levels of stress, which in turn affects how you feel. Cognitive behavioural therapy aims to identify these patterns, shift your narrative in thinking and develop a greater sense of confidence.

- Mindfulness: Mindfulness is about being present in your body without interpretation or judgement. Practising mindfulness involves breathing methods, guided imagery, and other practices to relax the body and mind and help reduce stress.

It is unrealistic for the average runner to avoid stress completely. While it is healthy to change your response to stressful situations if necessary, the truth is, sometimes there are moments when stress overrides your daily life. Like Pete, it is not uncommon for people to have stressful periods at work. Your career, family dramas, sickness, a death in the family, moving house, having a newborn baby and countless other scenarios can create an unusually high amount of stress.

It is important to implement the above interventions when dealing with moments like these. Equally as important, is making the necessary adjustments in your training. Looking at my own lifestyle, I tend to lose quality sleep when I have exciting business ideas. Starting the Run Smarter Podcast is a prime example. As soon as I had the podcast name, I would lay in bed thinking about episode ideas, the podcast mission, the artwork and guests. My creativity took over and my ideas would swim around in my head. It was the perfect fit to accompany my online physiotherapy business, and its potential to be a success got me really excited.

Unfortunately, while I love moments like these, they do negatively impact my sleep patterns. I find myself constantly waking up in the middle of the night, coming up with a new idea that fires up my nervous system. During these moments, I implement different strategies to help my sleep. I go to bed earlier, write my ideas on paper and listen to audio guided meditations to help calm my mind. If my quality of sleep still suffers, I make a proactive decision to reduce my training load. I recognise that my stress cup isn't emptying at the same rate, and I don't risk overloading myself.

If I decide to reduce my training load, I also let my body dictate my training. Constantly checking in with my body for unusual signs of fatigue, muscle soreness, and tiredness is a useful tool to help guide my training. If I feel particularly fresh and excited to train, I will increase my workload and vice versa.

In these examples, after a few weeks, when my sleep quality had improved, I built my mileage and intensity back up. Pete could have taken a similar approach. He could have increased his sleep by going to bed earlier and finding other avenues to enhance the recovery process. Equally as important, he could have recognised his lack of recovery and adjusted his training before his injury surfaced.

Conclusion

Rarely is the correlation of daily stress investigated when dealing with an injury. If you are injured, fostering the environment for your body to heal is essential, particularly if stress and sleep are not well managed. If reducing your risk of injury is high on your list, recognise this lesson and have enough foresight to mitigate the risk of injury. You can do this by changing your response to stressful situations, implementing strategies to reduce your stressful state, enhancing the quality of your sleep, and making adjustments in your training if required.

By making these adjustments, you reduce the risk of your stress cup overflowing and allow your body to recover and tolerate higher training loads. Not only does this concept apply to rehabilitation and injury prevention, but also with increasing running performance. We will discuss this further in Chapter 18.

Your Iceberg's Hidden Dangers

Chapter seven focuses on the body's ability to handle the training load. The internal strength of the muscles, tendons, ligaments and bones and their level of adequate recovery. When applying this to your iceberg, this represents the internal structure of the ice. In particular, the quality and density of the ice to tolerate incoming waves. There may be hidden dangers that go unnoticed if you're not observant of your entire surroundings.

For example, your iceberg could be subject to a harsher sun over different periods of the year. If it was floating in a calm ocean, you might visibly notice signs of distress like subtle melting on the surface. However, these signs may go undetected if you aren't looking for them and are too busy with regular waves to take notice. If a harsh sun takes its toll, then the robust internal structure of the ice could be compromised and can slowly morph into something more fragile.

In this case, if the harsh sun is negatively impacting the internal structure, it would be wise to reduce the ferocity of the incoming waves. Don't stop the waves coming in altogether. After all, you don't want your iceberg to melt. Instead, pick the right moments to nurture your iceberg and wait for parts of the day and parts of the year when the sun isn't compromising your iceberg to bring on challenging waves.

The key here is not to narrow your focus. Focus on the bigger picture. Inspect the waves, reassess your iceberg and look around at other potential factors. In this instance, look up.

Chapter 7 Summary

1. Identical stress hormones are released during physical activity and daily psychological stress that inhibits the body from entering recovery mode.

2. While physical and mental stress fills up your stress cup, adequate recovery, such as sleep, assists in emptying your stress cup.

Action Items

1. If you are unsure and concerned about sleep levels, start to measure sleep with a suitable wearable device.

2. If stress is an ongoing issue, implement interventions such as meditation, breathing exercises and mindfulness.

3. If interventions are still causing sub-par recovery, alter your training accordingly.

CHAPTER EIGHT

WHEN TO REST AND WHEN TO RUN

Pete was in panic mode with his new knee symptoms. As the weekend went by, the pain in his knee worsened. Walking seemed fine, but anytime he stepped awkwardly, walked upstairs or stood up from a chair, he'd experience a sharp pain around the border of his kneecap. Symptoms didn't improve as the work week started. Monday's meeting involved 60 minutes of sitting and he couldn't help but fixate on the deep throb. Another injury was the last thing he needed. Running was his only outlet to destress from the increase in work demands.

The marathon was nine weeks away and the training plan scheduled a 25 kilometre run next weekend. Doing the calculations in his head, he decided to have an entire week off running. After a week without running, the symptoms should settle and the training could resume. He would then make subtle adjustments to every weekend run and gradually catch up on the lost mileage. If the gradual catch up was successful, he would be back on track in three weeks.

WEEK	SAT	
21	~~25km~~ 22km	Rest
22	~~27km~~ 25km	Modify
23	~~28km~~ 27km	Modify
24	29km	Resume

Not running drove Pete crazy. He felt lazy but recognised it needed to be done. With work stress building, he kept his sanity by walking for 40 minutes daily. As the days rolled by, symptoms continued to improve. Sitting was symptom free, and the sharp pain when walking upstairs was reduced to a two out of ten. After a long week, he was ready to start his weekend run. By Saturday, his symptoms had subsided completely, but he still wanted to be cautious. He decided to repeat the 22 kilometre run from last weekend.

After his routine stretches and warm-up, Pete set out for his run. In the beginning, everything felt strong. With the decision to run slowly, he used the time outdoors as an opportunity to be grateful for his surroundings. He was blessed to have the ability to run. He appreciated the smell of the freshly cut grass and listened to the sound of calm flowing rivers. Suddenly, his flow state was interrupted with a familiar sharp kneecap sensation. He looked down at his watch. He had completed 7.5 kilometres and the pain was already surfacing. Assessing the symptoms further, he continued running but pulled the pin at 12 kilometres and walked home. The long walk gave him plenty of time to think about a plan B.

High levels of frustration and worry surfaced during Pete's long walk home. But thinking about his next proactive plan kept him occupied. By the time he stepped into his house, he had it all planned out. After a quick shower and work meetings, he wrote his new plan down on paper. In his mind, the knee required more healing time. So, he decided to rest for another four days. Come Wednesday, he would go for a casual five kilometre run after work. If all went well, he would run seven kilometres on Friday and 14 kilometres on Sunday. If success continued, he would modify the remainder of his training plan to achieve 35 kilometres before race day. While he was still frustrated about another setback, he was optimistic about this new plan.

WEEK	MON	TUE	WED	THU	FRI	SAT	SUN
21	Rest					Pain at 11km	
22	Rest	Rest	5k	Rest	7k	Rest	14km
23	Rest	8k easy	5k +intervals	Rest	10k easy +strides	20k	Rest

Wednesday rolled around, and Pete's plan B was in full swing. His knee symptoms had dissipated, and he felt tonight's five kilometre run should be a walk in the park. After a quick jog on the spot, he started his watch and worked into his fluent stride. Initially, he was apprehensive, but the more steps he took, the more he became reassured. There was no pain. After a few minutes, his cautious trot turned into strong and confident steps. Keeping to the streets, he decided to repeat short loops around the house. He didn't want a long, frustrating walk of shame like last week's run if symptoms occurred.

Pete's watch beeped, signalling his latest kilometre split and notifying him of the three kilometre mark. He wasn't too worried about the speed, though. He was grateful to be out running pain free and was surprised at the level of ease. His breath was under control, his splits were under a good time and his legs felt fresh. This was reassuring because he had been worried about losing his fitness level throughout the recent rest period. He had worked so hard to build up his aerobic fitness and he didn't want to start from scratch.

Running across the empty street, Pete stepped onto the sidewalk and felt a familiar, sharp pain from his kneecap. Trying to forget about it, he continued a cautious jog for another 30 seconds. There was no denying it. The pain had returned only four kilometres into the run. Pete was perplexed. It was only two weeks ago that he ran 20 kilometres without pain. Frustration turned to panic. The goal to complete a marathon seemed impossible now. He looked down at his watch and saw it was approaching 8:00pm. Daniel's physiotherapy clinic was open for another 10 minutes. He immediately called the clinic and booked an appointment for the next day.

Run Smarter Lesson 8

When a structure in the body becomes overloaded, it will often produce pain and irritation. In its current irritated state, the injury could not tolerate training loads that were successful beforehand. Pete's knee became overloaded and remained painful for a few days before showing signs of improvement. Initial symptoms would elevate when squatting, climbing stairs and standing from a chair. His body and brain send signals to remind him to be careful and not do too much.

The job of injured athletes in this scenario is to find the injury's new adaptation zone. For most running related overuse injuries, guidelines can be followed to indicate the correct adaptation zone. Remember, every injury is different, and you should consider a health professional for tailored guidance if not seeing improvement. However, let's recap these generic instructions from Chapter three:

Finding the adaptation zone of an injured site:

1. Pain should remain below a four out of ten during activity.
2. Pain should settle after activity and return to baseline in less than 24 hours.
3. There should be a marked improvement in symptoms week by week.

When is Rest Indicated?

Very rarely is complete rest the answer; certain medical conditions such as bone stress reactions and stress fractures are the exception to the rule. Even if running fails to pass the acceptable pain guidelines listed above, there may still be an exercise alternative to promote fitness and maintain strength. Exceptions aside, it is important to note that an injury still has an adaptation zone. It may be sensitive and sore during particular activities, but rehabilitation becomes easier once you find this new adaptation zone.

Health professionals are increasingly accepting these active recovery principles and shying away from complete rest as a recovery plan. Before becoming a physiotherapist, I worked as a sports trainer and first aid officer. I'd constantly treat traumatic sports injuries and regularly attend first aid courses on up to date injury management. While the management principles slowly evolved, the fundamentals revolved around the R.I.C.E. principle.

R.I.C.E. : Acronym for Injury management

R = Rest:
Avoiding activity that causes pain. This could be as simple as avoiding sport or painful tasks but could also involve immobilisation with a cast or offloading with crutches.

I = Ice:

Apply ice for 15 to 20 minutes, three times a day for 48 hours, limiting inflammation and promoting healing.

C = Compress:

Apply compression bandages or compression tubing around the injured site to reduce inflammation.

E = Elevate:

Keep the injured area above the level of your heart as often as possible for the next 48 hours and allow gravity to remove the swelling.

In 2020, an editorial was published in the British Journal of Sports Medicine. Authors Blaise Dubois and Jean-Francois Esculier discussed the need to replace the outdated R.I.C.E. acronym for injury management [50]. One of its significant limitations is the application for only acute based injuries such as rolled ankles, muscle tears, and traumatic ligament injuries. Acute, trauma based injuries are rare in the running population, and most injuries typically involve chronic overuse. Additionally, this outdated method doesn't include the psychosocial factors to enhance recovery.

This paper proposes the acronym P.E.A.C.E. and L.O.V.E. for injury management as a way to solve these limitations. P.E.A.C.E. refers to the acute management of trauma based injuries, much of which isn't related to running related overuse injuries.

P.E.A.C.E. and L.O.V.E. : Acronym for Injury Management

P = Protect:

Unload or restrict movement for one to three days to reduce the risk of aggravating the injury. Hence offering protection from progressing the injury to anything more sinister. Rest should be minimised as prolonged rest can compromise tissue strength and quality. Pain and symptoms should be used as a guide to judge the level of protection and when protection is no longer required.

E = Elevate:
Promote the movement of fluid by elevating the injured limb higher than the heart as often as possible. Despite weak evidence supporting its use, it is still recommended when considering its potential benefit against the low risks associated with implementation.

A = Avoid anti-inflammatories:
Inflammation aids various phases of the healing process. Therefore, medications that inhibit the inflammatory process may negatively affect long term tissue healing. This paper also questions the use of icing as there is an absence of high quality evidence on its effectiveness for treating soft tissue injuries. Both medication and ice may help at reducing symptoms, but it primarily inhibits pain signals rather than assists the healing process.

C = Compression:
Despite conflicting studies, compression after an ankle sprain seems to reduce swelling and improve quality of life [51]. Providing external pressure with tape or bandages may help the healing process in the short term.

E = Education:
Runners should be educated on the best management for their injury. In particular, empowering treatment options such as active rehabilitation rather than passive, hands-on therapies. Or at least a combination of the two.

As mentioned above, the start of this acronym is reserved for acute, traumatic injuries and should only be followed for a few days before progressing forward. However, it can be argued that most running related injuries do not require this phase and instead should skip straight to the L.O.V.E. component.

L = Load:
An active approach to movement and exercise benefits most patients with musculoskeletal disorders. Optimal loading with strengthening exercises without exacerbating symptoms promotes repair and builds tissue tolerance. This fits our pain principles from Chapter three as we let symptoms guide our management while staying as proactive as possible.

O = Optimism:
Psychological influences play a crucial role in the recovery process. If a runner has optimistic expectations about recovery, they are associated with better outcomes. Conversely, catastrophisation, depression and fear can represent barriers to recovery.

V = Vascularisation:
Cardiovascular activity represents a cornerstone in the management of musculoskeletal injuries. For example, cross training that remains within acceptable pain levels will promote blood flow, boost motivation and help return physical function. As a bonus to the circulating blood delivering vital components to aid the healing process, athletes can maintain their cardiovascular fitness.

E = Exercise:
Some runners may be apprehensive about their return to running or exercise when faced with an injury; often they have reduced confidence and increased injury hypervigilance. However, with the right medical advice and correct interpretation of symptoms, a return to exercise should be encouraged as soon as possible.

Each element of this injury management acronym helps promote a proactive, empowering solution and if followed correctly, will aid healing in the fastest way possible. Rarely is complete rest indicated for overuse injuries, and in rare cases when rest is indicated, mechanical loading should resume as soon as possible.

Avoiding the Pain, Rest, Weakness Downward Spiral

One concept I constantly mention with my clients is the pain, rest, weakness downward spiral. As discussed earlier, when in a painful state, an injury cannot tolerate training loads that were successful pre-injury. In other words, the sensitivity creates a momentary weakness that the athlete has to negotiate or risk further irritation.

If this irritable state is followed by prolonged rest, it can perpetuate weakness and lower injury adaptation zones. After Pete's initial run that triggered knee pain, the knee could not tolerate stair climbing, deep squatting and high mileage running. This was only a short term reduction in capacity, and most activities quickly returned to normal pain limits. His decision to take seven days of rest, however, offered an environment that promoted further weakening. If a return to exercise overshoots your injury's adaptation zone, this will spark further irritation and allow the downward spiral to continue. Like Pete, most runners interpret a flareup of symptoms as meaning the injury requires more time to heal and self prescribe more rest. Be careful with your decision to completely rest an injury as you promote greater weakness and increase your likelihood of another flare-up upon return to exercise.

In Pete's situation, symptoms first surfaced after running 20 kilometres. Treatment involved seven days of complete rest even though the irritated area's adaptation zone had the potential for exercise and strength. After spiralling downward for one week, symptoms produced a lot earlier than expected.

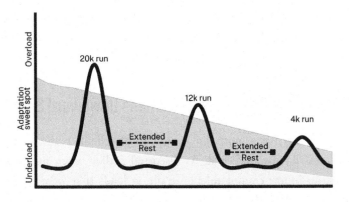

To be clear, Pete's sudden downward trajectory is primarily caused by injury irritation, not weakness. You cannot spiral down to one fifth of your running strength in only three weeks, but as irritation further restricts exercise limits, weakness slowly follows. Pain and weakness will be discussed later in the chapter.

I have witnessed this downward spiral trajectory slowly over several months and sometimes over years. Depending on the injury and the management choices, it could be so gradual that it goes by undetected. One condition that often sends runners into this downward spiral is proximal hamstring tendinopathy. Often, this condition is caused by an abrupt change in training load, particularly involving speedwork when running or cycling. Proximal hamstring tendinopathy affects the tendon that attaches to the sit bone and, once irritated, can make bending, sitting and squatting painful. This downward spiral is so prevalent and severe within this condition because of the high likelihood of becoming problematic outside of training and in everyday life.

In episode 89 of the Run Smarter Podcast, I interviewed Michelle to share her proximal hamstring tendinopathy rehabilitation success story [52]. It was one of my first ever success stories on the podcast and became so popular that the success story format became a permanent feature of the show. She shared her story and the progression of the pathology, which followed the pain, rest, weakness downward spiral. In 2019, while training for the Melbourne marathon, she first encountered soreness around her glutes and sitting bone area. For several weeks, she ignored the symptoms and continued to train, which slowly perpetuated symptoms. It wasn't until speedwork, and long running sessions caused significant discomfort that she went to a physiotherapist for help.

Unfortunately, her physiotherapist advised that she decrease her running volume, and as symptoms persisted, the guidance quickly changed to avoid running. In the meantime, Michelle was instructed to perform double leg bridges, which weren't enough to challenge the tendon to get stronger. Over the next four months, she continued to avoid running, but symptoms persisted and even became more irritated. She continued gym classes to maintain strength and fitness, but over several months, more exercises would create a flare-up and be quickly removed or modified. On the podcast, she explained that lunges and high step-ups were particularly problematic.

The downward spiral continued and affected Michelle's life outside of exercise. The pathology started to affect her sitting and she would notice that over time, she could tolerate less and less. This sitting tolerance became so bad that it resulted in her constantly standing during her working hours. Any short drive to fulfil family duties left her in pain. This created extreme frustration, depression and debilitation. Running was her main outlet for stress relief, and she didn't feel anyone around her recognised the suffering she was dealing with.

Unfortunately, this trend developed because health professionals told Michelle to avoid loading her proximal hamstring tendon. Based on this information, she developed the belief and fear that loading or stretching the tendon created further damage to the tendon, and therefore, should be avoided. In other words, the complete opposite of the guidelines in the P.E.A.C.E. and L.O.V.E. injury management philosophy. Following this advice created a perfect environment for the pain, rest, weakness downward spiral to manifest in Michelle's condition.

It wasn't until Michelle started learning about the above load management principles that her rehabilitation turned a corner. Her beliefs moved away from a fear of loading as she learnt that not only was loading okay, it was actually encouraged. She began implementing deadlifts and single leg deadlifts into her rehabilitation, provided that pain levels were low and the tendon showed no irritation the following day. I asked her on the podcast when her rehabilitation started to have a positive effect. She answered:

> *"Probably when I started to introduce more loading exercises, it started to bring back some of my confidence. There may have been some pain but it was tolerable. Once I started introducing loaded exercises I then started the walk-run program".*

> *"Even though it was slow, just being able to do more was giving me more confidence. Just doing the bridges felt like I wasn't getting anywhere. Once more exercises were introduced and I could provide more loading to the tendon, it was giving me more confidence than what I had previously".*

By the time Michelle returned to short running intervals, her body was so deconditioned that muscle soreness developed around her legs and hips. Running again felt awkward, and the walk intervals were greatly welcomed as her cardiovascular system struggled. Over time, as her running became more frequent and her loading progressed, she started to make significant gains in both her fitness and her pain levels.

At the time of recording, Michelle had been progressing her rehabilitation for three months. On the podcast, she shared that she was back to running four days per week, including a 70 minute long run mixed with cross training and strength training. She continued to load the tendon with low pain levels, provided there was no irritation the following day. It had been 12 months in total from the onset of symptoms until the podcast recording. This is a prime example of the downward spiral slowly taking effect, and the further down the spiral you find yourself, the more difficult it becomes to climb up.

Proactive Measures to Avoid the Downward Spiral

The pain, rest, weakness downward spiral applies to most overuse injuries. Runners must identify this downward trend and start taking proactive measures to counteract its trajectory. When injured, measures should be taken to identify the painful structure's new adaptation zone and training should remain within this sweet spot. If done correctly, you will start to observe a reduction in symptoms along with a successful increase in training loads.

The decision to continue running, reduce running or cease running will be guided by pain and symptoms, therefore accurate interpretation is required. Remember, most injuries will respond well if pain during exercises remains below a four out of ten and symptoms return to baseline within 24 hours. In addition, your injury should see meaningful improvement week by week.

If symptoms are still unacceptable with minimal running dosages, you may need to cease running. To still avoid the downward spiral, you will need to substitute your loading with strength training, cross training and rehabilitation exercises. This is where a proficient health professional can facilitate the rehabilitation process. While following the same pain guidelines, the focus should be on restoring the capacity of the injured area to tolerate low loads of running. Once you have bridged the gap between your current capacity and running demands, a progressive running program can start alongside a progressive rehabilitation program.

The idea is to be creative and resourceful when managing an injury to avoid the pain, rest, weakness downward spiral. There will always be a creative solution that provides the sweet spot between overload and underload. If you are struggling to find a solution or unsure how to progress your way back up the spiral, enlist the help of a health professional.

Pain Does Not Equal Weakness

When managing an injury, an increase in symptoms or a flareup can easily be misinterpreted as a sign of weakness. For example, if Pete managed to run 20 kilometres one week before the knee pain and subsequent runs were unsuccessful at 12 and then four kilometres, it would be easy for him to conclude that he is losing strength.

A similar conclusion is made when injured runners negotiate several weeks of progressive rehabilitation, only to encounter a severe flareup. When this happens, runners think all their progress is undone, and they must revert back to phase one of their rehabilitation. Say a runner manages persistent shin splints and has spent the last four weeks building up their running tolerance. Following the acceptable pain guidelines, they increase their running by one minute every run and eventually reach 15 minutes successfully.

Encountering a flareup, perhaps with a change in terrain or footwear, can increase irritability levels and negatively impact tolerable running dosages. If pain then occurs at the two minute mark, the runner might think that all their hard work is undone, and now the structure is back to its previously weakened state.

This is where the distinction is important. In this example, the injury has not become weaker, rather it is irritable and needs to settle. Once again, it is the job of the runner to find the new adaptation zone and build it back up. Since strength is still preserved, building back to 15 minutes of running is a lot quicker, sometimes as soon as a few days. Such a swift return is further proof that one is dealing with the symptoms of irritability and not weakness.

In reality, it takes several weeks of underloading to see signs of weakness. This is why the pain, rest, weakness downward spiral manifests over several weeks and months. Do not be discouraged if you face a temporary flareup. Do not think you have to revert back to phase one and repeat the same slow process over again. Trust the rehabilitation process, and accept that flareups are a part of the rehabilitation journey. Simply refocus and continue proactively progressing on your rehabilitation plan.

Running is Rehab, Not the End Result

If you are injured and you have to take an extended time off running, it's highly unlikely your injury will recover enough to immediately tolerate pre-injury levels of running. Some runners believe if they take the necessary time off and do their rehabilitation exercises, they'll hit a moment when they can suddenly run pain free. In this scenario, it is important to address that running is now part of the rehabilitation process, not the end result. The runner needs to slowly integrate the skill of running into the rehabilitation plan, progressing the dosage the same way progression in a strengthening exercise would be prescribed.

Once running is implemented in dosages that the injury can tolerate, it can then begin adapting and rebuilding to this specific task. This topic was discussed on episode 137 of the Run Smarter Podcast when I interviewed Greg Lehman. The title was '*Running is Rehab: When Doing is the Fixing*' [53]. Greg explained:

> "The best thing to prepare you for running, is running. If you have a good coach or you are good at managing your volume, recovery and speed workouts, then that is the best way to prepare yourself for running".
>
> "It also holds true for rehab. If you're injured, running has to be a part of your rehab. That is the way you apply stressors to the body and the person adapts. There is a role for other things, but running should be the primary part of getting back to running".

Let's imagine a gym-goer develops knee pain after increasing their squat from 50 kilograms to 60 kilograms. In the knee's current, irritable state they determine their knee can only tolerate squats with 10 kilograms while keeping symptoms within acceptable boundaries. After three sets of 10 repetitions with this weight, the gym-goer's knee symptoms remain mild and absent of irritation afterwards.

In this case, 10 kilograms would be the rehabilitation starting point and would involve a slow and careful process of squatting heavier weights once the knee recovers and can tolerate higher dosages. It would be naive for this gym-goer to expect to return to pre-injury squatting after a period of rest. Additionally, it would be unreasonable to hope for a successful return to pre-injury squatting if the time off was spent doing different exercises like heel raises or chest presses. The best way to recover and get back to squatting is by incorporating squatting into your rehabilitation. The same process should be considered with running injuries. The best way to recover and get back to running is by incorporating running into your rehabilitation.

Conclusion

When it comes to running related injuries, rest is not always best. If experiencing severe discomfort and irritation, allow symptoms to settle with a few days of rest. After this period, be as proactive as possible and let symptoms guide your management. It is important to recognise and avoid the pain, rest, weakness downward spiral trend. The goal is to remain proactive and resourceful in the presence of an injury. With the help of a health professional, you can find current running dosages, strengthening exercises and cross training exercises that fall nicely into your new adaptation zone.

Resting your Iceberg

Imagine your iceberg was subjected to a barrage of waves which inevitably resulted in damage. Small pieces of your iceberg have detached, and cracks have formed around the impact site. You must immediately repair the vulnerable area to restore it back to its original state.

In this scenario, complete rest sounds like a ridiculous, counterproductive option. Ceasing all waves and allowing your iceberg to float in a vulnerable state without intervention will not solve anything. Remember, water is still required to rebuild its size and integrity. If you leave your damaged, vulnerable iceberg floating in the ocean without any nourishing water, the damaged site remains untreated. Even worse, a complete absence of waves would lead to melting, slowly decreasing the size of the iceberg and weakening not only for the impacted site but for the entire iceberg.

In these circumstances, you can be more proactive than you realise. You could apply very gentle waves just to the damaged area. You could also apply bigger, more challenging waves to areas of your iceberg away from the damaged site. When applied to a runner, depending on the injury, you remain running while changing the terrain, shoe type, running speed, running cadence and many other variables.

There is still one powerful tool at your disposal for situations like this. One that will increase your level of resourcefulness and is a crucial component if you find yourself deep in a downward spiral. This powerful tool will be covered in the next chapter.

Chapter 8 Summary

1. When injured, it is best to avoid complete rest, ice and other passive anti-inflammatory methods.

2. Instead, encourage optimism, exercise and loading within acceptable limits.

3. After this brief phase, it's time to train within your new adaptation zone and progressively rebuild.

4. If capacity rapidly reduces during a flareup, be reassured that it is only temporary irritation and that you have not lost strength.

Action Items

1. In the face of an injury, be creative and resourceful with exercise alternatives and running modifications to remain as active as possible while following acceptable pain guidelines.

2. If an injury is extremely irritating, you may require two to three days of relative rest.

3. Work with your rehabilitation team to incorporate running into your rehabilitation as soon as symptoms allow.

CHAPTER NINE

STRENGTH TRAINING AND CROSS TRAINING

The following day Pete was back in Daniel's clinic. His knee had been achy overnight, but this morning he noticed an improvement. Daniel was keen to hear about his marathon training. Sadly, Pete updated him on the recent knee pain and the slim likelihood of the marathon going ahead.

Pete outlined his frustration. He had been following the program diligently, yet an injury still occurred. Daniel suggested, given his recent work commitments, that it was most likely that his body was under-recovering which would explain why his running was feeling more laboured than usual and why the knee couldn't tolerate the 20 kilometre run. In addition, his increased psychological stress and lack of sleep also hindered recovery, which led to the eventual overload.

After his examination, Daniel explained that Pete had developed patellofemoral pain which is an overload of the kneecap joint. Like any other joint in your body, it has a certain capacity which is challenged when running, squatting and climbing stairs. He explained that while he isn't exactly sure where the new adaptation zone is, he can make an educated guess based on Pete's current training regime. Once a stable exercise dosage is found, rehabilitation can build from there.

Firstly, Daniel instructed Pete to hold a wall sit for 20 seconds. When Pete mentioned that it didn't cause any pain he progressed the exercise to a single leg wall squat. After 15 seconds of holding, a two out of ten ache emerged. With no irritation persisting once the exercise stopped, Daniel added this exercise into Pete's program.

Next, Daniel moved a 12 inch high box into the middle of the room and instructed Pete to step up and down, reporting symptoms throughout. Daniel repeated the step up 10 times and described an awareness around the knee but no pain. To progress, Pete was instructed to hold two dumbbells weighing five kilograms each. This time, he reported mild pain, which he placed as one or two by the end of the set. Daniel was happy with this response and added weighted step-ups to the program.

Lastly, Daniel handed Pete two 10 kilogram dumbbells and asked him to hold the weights at shoulder height and move from a sitting position to a standing position. Once again, Pete followed Daniel's instructions, but this exercise was more challenging. By the 5th repetition, he experienced pain close to four out of ten. Daniel immediately stopped the exercise and swapped the 10 kilogram weights for seven kilograms. Repeating the exercise with this weight kept the pain at an acceptable limit and was added to the program.

Daniel wrote up each exercise along with progression phases. Pete was instructed to progress each phase if symptoms allowed. For example, if a phase one exercise became too easy or if symptoms were close to pain free, then trial phase two. If phase two produced mild levels of discomfort but didn't elevate pain afterwards, then phase two would be repeated until phase three became appropriate. Each exercise was to be done once a day on non-running days.

Rehabilitation List

PHASE	12 INCH STEP-UPS	DL SIT TO STAND	SL WALL SIT
1	3x8 with 5kg DBs	3x12 with 7kg DBs	5x20 sec holds
2	3x8 with 7kg DBs	3x12 with 9kg DBs	5x40 sec holds
3	3x8 with 9kg DBs	3x12 with 11kg DBs	5x60 sec holds

In relation to running, Daniel advised that Pete could run every second day, but needed to start conservatively. He created a walk-run program to follow, provided symptoms remained under control. The running dosages were not enough to maintain Pete's overall fitness levels, so Daniel also recommended swimming or intervals with a skipping rope as a cross training alternative. These alternatives offered a relatively low load to Pete's knees and shouldn't pose a threat.

Daniel completed the walk-run program and skipping rope intervals and handed the sheet to Pete. The first phase required eight rounds of running for two minutes and walking for two minutes. The marathon was slipping further from reality, but at least he had a plan to get back on track.

MON	TUE	WED	THU	FRI	SAT	SUN
Rehab +20min swim	Run	Rehab +skip rope	Run	Rehab +20min swim	Run	Rehab +skip rope

PHASE	WALK-RUN SCHEDULE	SKIPPING ROPE SCHEDULE
1	8x (2'R, 2'W)	5 rounds (30-sec jump, 60-sec rest)
2	12x (2'R, 2'W)	8 rounds (30-sec jump, 60-sec rest)
3	8x (3'R, 1'W)	5 rounds (45-sec jump, 60-sec rest)
4	12x (3'R, 1'W)	5 rounds (60-sec jump, 60-sec rest)
5	8x (5'R, 1'W)	8 rounds (60-sec jump, 40-sec rest)
6	12x (5'R, 1'W)	10 rounds (60-sec jump, 40-sec rest)

Run Smarter Lesson 9

Cross training is a fitness alternative that engages your cardiovascular system, activates different energy systems and loads the body in a variety of ways. Cardiovascular cross training options include cycling, swimming, group fitness classes, the elliptical trainer, rowing machine and other similar forms of exercise. Strength training should not be considered cross training. Some benefits may overlap, but strength training allows you to develop other areas of strength, balance, proprioception and coordination. In the presence of an injury, strength training can be primarily utilised to restore strength and capacity, while cross training is primarily used to preserve endurance and cardiovascular fitness.

Does Strength Training Reduce the Risk of Injury?

Following the load versus capacity relationship, one might conclude that strong runners are more resilient than weaker runners. After all, strength training will help raise the capacity of tissues that will allow for higher training loads without breaking down.

Lauersen and colleagues conducted a large systematic review in 2013 to investigate a correlation between strength training and all sports injuries [54]. After gathering data that included over 26,000 participants, they discovered:

> *"Strength training reduced sports injuries to less than one-third and overuse injuries could be almost halved".*

While these findings are extremely positive in favour of strength training, this large study failed to include any study involving the running population, with most studies including basketball, soccer and football. When focusing purely on the running population, there is a lack of publications with large sample sizes. The available evidence also fails to identify a correlation between lower limb strength and running related injuries.

Stephen Messier and colleagues followed 300 recreational runners over two years, intending to identify baseline characteristics linked to injury [55]. Messier also failed to find a relationship. The authors commented:

> *"Lack of muscular strength is an often-cited risk factor for running-related injuries, attributed in part to the reduced ability of the surrounding muscles to absorb shock. Surprisingly, we found no significant differences in strength between the injured and uninjured groups. The trend was for greater strength in the uninjured group".*

> *"Proportionally more women were in the injured group, and they had significantly less lower extremity strength than the men. Controlling for sex, however, did not alter the statistical results. Strength was not predictive of injury".*

> *"Perhaps enhanced neuromuscular control that improves the runner's ability to utilise muscular strength effectively is more important than strength alone in preventing injury".*

Important to keep in mind with the Messier publication is the study design of assessing baseline characteristics. For example, within a given population, weak runners were injured at the same rate compared to strong runners. A more interesting—but difficult—design would be to follow the same group of runners one year after their baseline measurements were taken, increase their strength with a training program and observe any difference in injury rates before and after.

The bigger question is, why has Messier failed to identify a link with strength training in recreational runners when other sports shown in the Lauersen paper have reported overuse injuries halved due to strength training? I believe one factor has to do with running as a sport compared to team sports such as basketball, soccer and football. Recreational running has an open-ended ceiling of limitations in which the participant can continue pushing themselves as far as they desire. The majority of runners want to continue pushing their capabilities, either striving for longer distances or faster times. This results in a runner constantly flirting with the boundaries of their training load and their maximum capacity.

While athletes competing in a team sport may constantly strive to better themselves, their drive to greatness involves an extremely different path. If a soccer player competes for 90 minutes during a game, they wouldn't aim to get better by playing harder soccer games for two hours and eventually progress to four hours. This is how a runner treats this situation, continuously pushing the envelope. In contrast, athletes competing in team sports focus on sprinting faster, jumping higher and participating in skill based drills to get the upper edge.

Applying this to strength training, most athletes involved in team sports have a reasonably capped training load that strength training can help tolerate. Whereas a strong recreational runner can just as easily overload themselves compared to a weak runner by mismanaging their training loads. This, in theory, is a potential reason for witnessing strength training reducing the likelihood of overuse injuries in team sports compared to recreational runners.

It is also worth considering research that focuses on injury specific risk factors. Hip weakness has been an associated risk factor for patellofemoral pain syndrome, shin splints, ITB syndrome and achilles tendinopathy [56][57][58][59]. However, we need to interpret these findings with caution, as some studies conducted strength tests during the injury, which begs the question, are they injured because they are weak, or are they weak because of the injury?

While it is important to be specific in your training, it is also important to challenge the bones, muscles and tendons, exposing them to different stimuli. Strength training offers slow, heavy loading with a longer time under tension that running alone cannot offer. As a result, it allows your muscles and tendons to develop different qualities. This can assist in greater bone density, stronger tendons and greater fatigue resistance without the added risk of more mileage. For example, a knee extension exercise consisting of 10 sets of 10 repetitions at 70% of a one repetition maximum offers the same tendon stimulus to the tendons of the knee compared to a 36 kilometre run [60].

Until more robust, well designed studies are released that help answer the questions associated with strength, we are left with theoretical hypotheses and guidance of expert opinion. Here are some quotes from world leading researchers on this topic from the book 'The Science and Practice of Middle and Long-distance Running':

Chris Bramah:

> "An inability to repeatedly generate and absorb these forces is likely to lead to earlier muscular fatigue, an inability to maintain appropriate biomechanics, reduced force absorption and increased strain placed upon tendons and bones. As such, it seems probable that a minimum strength requirement is necessary in order to protect the musculo-skeletal system from injury development". [61]

Richard Blagrove and David Hooper:

> "One logical way of lowering injury risk is to increase tissue capacity, so it can withstand higher volumes of loading. Gradual increases in running volume will progressively expose tissues to more load, and therefore cause the tissue to adapt. However, strength training exercises may provide a more potent stimulus to build structural resilience". [62]

Strength training also assists in an athlete becoming diverse and developing several strength and fitness qualities, resulting in a well rounded performer. Research published by Richard Blagrove, and many other studies, has shown that runners who participate in heavy strength training improve long distance running times. While the evidence for injury prevention is flimsy, it is copious and robust for increasing running performance which will be discussed in Chapter 13.

Cross Training for Injury Prevention

Chapter two highlights the high levels of strain placed on the body when running. To recap, Dorn's paper reveals that the ground reaction force during each step while running is more than 2.5 times your body weight. The situation becomes even more impressive when considering individual structures of the body such as your calf complex, which produces a force over 6.5 times your body weight. While this is measured per step, the overall ground reaction force quickly accumulates throughout each run and again when considering each run throughout the week.

Now consider the reason behind most running related injuries. In particular, an overload to the structure by exceeding the internal capacity. On one side, it is important to run frequently, which will ensure your body adapts to the specific loads. On the other hand, if you run six or seven times a week and encounter a handful of overuse injuries in any given year, it is worth considering more rest or a cardiovascular alternative.

In addition to building your cardiovascular fitness, cross training has the added benefit of distributing load to different areas of your body. Running requires a great demand on your plantar fascia, achilles tendon and calf muscles, for example, and running hills and increasing speed further increase the demand on these structures. However, cycling or spin classes have significantly lower demand in these areas while still offering a challenging workout for the knees, hips and cardiovascular system. Therefore, if a runner had a long history of achilles tendinopathy, plantar fasciitis or calf strains, it may be justified to shift the load distribution throughout the week by implementing healthy cross training alternatives.

There are plenty of reasons to clinically justify cross training to reduce your risk of injury, but they are based on individual circumstances such as current running history, training philosophy, injury history and intensity distribution. Some runners may have profound benefits when cross training, while it may be less necessary in others.

Strength Training and Cross Training for Rehabilitation

Being injured is never fun. Physically, it can halt your fitness and mentally, it can drive you crazy, but acceptable and stable pain levels during running, strength training and cross training can provide tremendous benefits. Finding some form of exercise that increases blood flow while maintaining aerobic fitness should always be in a runner's toolkit. While maintaining cardiovascular fitness is front of mind for most injured runners, they also need to consider utilising strength training and cross training to rebuild the strength and capacity of the injured area and surrounding structures.

To illustrate this point is a study by Bruno Saragiotto and colleagues [63]. In 2014, they conducted a systematic review and pooled 4,500 participants across 60 different potential injury risk factors. In their analysis, the authors of this paper found the strongest link for a future injury was the presence of another injury in the past 12 months. These findings can be interpreted in many ways. Still, a likely cause for this finding is the inadequate rehabilitation process that eventually leads to a previous injury resurfacing or another area being overloaded by a compensatory movement pattern.

In other words, runners should prioritise strengthening the joints, tendons and muscles of the injured structure and address any movement limitations. Completing rehabilitation in this fashion will reduce the likelihood of an injury resurfacing or load being unnecessarily transferred elsewhere.

Strength training and cross training also assist runners in avoiding the pain, rest, weakness downward spiral discussed in Chapter eight. Firstly, pain is controlled within acceptable boundaries, whether running, strength training or cross training. Next, rest is kept to a minimum as there are a plethora of options one has access to based on the injury and severity. Lastly, in the spiral is weakness. While a return to pre-injury running dosage may take time, these exercise alternatives ensure cardiovascular fitness and strength are preserved within the injured site and the rest of the body.

While it is important to consider the tissue capacity and to rebuild the strength in the rehabilitation process, it is additionally important to discuss the mental wellbeing aspect of exercise. As a physiotherapist, I have seen the common boom-bust injury cycle for runners who struggle to find a cross training option when injured. This limitation can hinder the physical and psychological recovery plan. Suppose a recreational runner runs four times per week and loves running for the physical and mental benefits. In that case, a halt in their running due to injury will deeply impact their wellbeing. This runner would likely continue running on their injury, potentially creating further damage, or return to pre-injury running too quickly at the first sign of improvement. The latter scenario follows a classic boom-bust injury cycle and usually leads to a build up of frustration when an individual is unable to run or makes an overzealous return.

I have seen this pattern more common in athletes that are strictly runners, and therefore will not consider alternatives in their recovery plan. Remember, the rehabilitation process is about being proactive and resourceful. Trying a new cross training alternative when injured can be a proactive way out of the boom-bust cycle while receiving physical and mental benefits from exercise. Prescribing the correct alternative is an art as well as a science. There is a fine line between exercise productivity and injury irritability, and if prescribed in the correct balance, it will aid rehabilitation.

It requires not only the right exercise selection but also an allocation of the correct dosage. For instance, Pete's weighted step-ups could be productive when set at three sets of eight repetitions on each side and with five kilogram dumbbells. However, this same exercise could also irritate the knee and be counterproductive if the dosage or weight were inappropriate.

Cross Training Alternatives when Injured

After I completed my first marathon in 2015, I turned my attention to sprint distance triathlons. While I hated swimming initially, I eventually learned to tolerate it. The love for cycling came quickly. After pushing through the first few months of mediocre fitness, I enjoyed the fitness gains both to my legs and cardiovascular system. For decades prior, I had also enjoyed gym workouts primarily within my home set-up. Being a physiotherapist, I understood strength training, technique, and appropriate progression.

I am blessed to have these exercise options at my disposal and am prepared with this arsenal in case of future injury. For example, I casually dial back my running dosage while dialling up my cycling workouts in moments of plantar fascia pain. In addition, I'll add in plantar fascia strengthening exercises until I am back to full fitness. These dials only require slight adjustments if an injury is caught early enough, but cross training and strength training options will still be available even in severe cases.

While the most effective rehabilitation plan requires a tailored approach suited to the type of athlete, injury, and severity, there are some general guidelines to follow. As discussed earlier, plantar fasciitis is better managed with cycling as opposed to running. Certain cross training alternatives demand different loads in the body and are discussed below:

> Injuries to the foot, calf, achilles and shins: Swimming is a perfect example of non-weight bearing activities for severe symptoms below the knee and will still challenge your cardiovascular system. For mild cases of irritability, rowing and cycling can be integrated. If your injury can tolerate walking but still isn't tolerating adequate levels of running, integrate hiking, elliptical training and stair climbing.

> Injuries around the knee: For moderate to severe irritability, cross training options such as the elliptical trainer, swimming and double leg jump rope can offer cardiovascular benefits. If the injury improves to a mild state of irritability, cycling, squats, and lunges can be prescribed with caution. Allow symptoms to guide the exercise prescription and dosage while working alongside a trained health professional.

> High hamstring and gluteal injuries: Cross training options like double leg jump rope, star jumps, elliptical trainer and swimming can offer the hamstring and gluteal muscles some relative relief while still building upon your fitness. Cycling may provide less demand than running but should be prescribed with caution.

Introducing a New Water Delivery System

When first introducing the iceberg concept, one of the only environmental factors under your control was the speed, height and frequency of incoming waves. However, these waves are related only to aerobic activities such as running. When it comes to strength training, the water delivery method completely changes.

What if you had the power to carefully direct small amounts of water to anywhere on your iceberg? Instead of a wave, this time, you can fill up buckets of seawater, walk around your iceberg and gently pour the nourishing water over vulnerable sections. If you had this power, you might choose to focus on the microscopic cracks. You might also notice areas of your iceberg that are hit harder by incoming waves than others. In this case, you might want to carefully pour water into this area and fortify the contact point.

This bucket delivery system represents the true power of strength training. Imagine your achilles tendon is particularly susceptible to high loads during running. Perhaps you prefer speed work, running uphill or running in zero drop shoes. They would naturally adopt a lot of strength if your training fostered the correct environment. However, if you were to have a training error or encounter a hidden danger discussed in Chapter seven, the achilles tendon would have a high chance of developing symptoms compared to other areas in the body. It would then be imperative to spend time pouring water over this area, fortifying its foundation. You could implement high resistance heel raises in the gym or plyometric drills with a jump rope in this example.

Apply this same scenario to recurring running injuries. If you regularly pay attention to sections of your iceberg prone to cracking, you give yourself a greater probability of future success. Identify weak links in your own body and pay close attention to them during your strength sessions. If you are prone to knee injuries, then build up the strength, capacity and function of the hip and knee.

If the level of damage to your iceberg is significant, representing a severe injury, you might feel comfortable gently pouring water over the vulnerable area. This gentle pouring can be done several times a day as it doesn't require the recovery time that a wave creates. As the crack in the ice improves and your confidence in this vulnerable area grows, you might progress beyond a gentle pour. In fact, towards the end stage of your injury rehabilitation, you might choose to aggressively throw buckets of water at a section you have been nursing.

As you progress to more forceful throws of water, it gradually mimics the high forces produced by the waves. It is this gradual progression that represents the correct execution of rehabilitation. First, you build up the foundational strength. Next, you progressively increase the demands to mimic the requirements of your chosen sport. Later, you may choose to challenge the body beyond the capacity of your sport, reducing the risk of future overload. Once you are set into a nice routine with the bucket delivery system, you can implement it a few times per week in conjunction with your sensible wave prescription.

Chapter 9 Summary

1. Strength training and cross training gives your muscles and tendons an opportunity to develop different qualities.

2. Cross training and strength training is suited to preventing the pain, rest, weakness, downward spiral.

3. When injured, strength training and cross training can be designed to bridge the gap and eventually exceed the capacity of the load required for running.

Action Items

1. If you are an injury prone athlete who exclusively runs, consider integrating other exercise alternatives to redistribute weekly loads placed on the body.

2. When injured, implement alternative forms of exercise and strength training to maintain fitness and build upon the strength and capacity of vulnerable areas.

3. You may require professional advice for exercise selection and dosage.

CHAPTER TEN

PERSONALITY TRAITS AND INJURY RISK

P ete was happy to have a new plan. As always, he would follow Daniel's instructions carefully, but he was disappointed to revert to a walk-run program. The first few running sessions were symptom free, which was a relief even though the running dosages were minimal. The strength exercises were a good distraction and offered an additional rehabilitation goal during this period of minimal running.

By this stage, Pete's work demands had eased which allowed him to destress and sleep easier. After three slow weeks of rehabilitation, he had completed the last phase of his walk-run program. It involved five minutes of running followed by one minute of walking for 12 rounds which accumulated to 60 minutes of running. Concurrently, his rehabilitation exercises progressed through each phase, and his knee and lower leg strength continued to improve.

While Pete was happy with the progress, a thick cloud of defeat lingered. The 42 kilometre marathon seemed like an impossible task at this point. After visiting Daniel for one last session and reporting his progress, they decided the marathon was too risky. Instead, Daniel got to work formulating a four week training plan to prepare him for the upcoming half marathon. The plan included more running days but still had the occasional rehabilitation and cross training sessions. The four week plan still had its risks, but Daniel and Pete were happy to take them on if the preparation phase was successful.

Each subsequent weekend increased by two kilometres which meant a 16 kilometre run was scheduled the week before the event. To Pete's surprise, the knee felt stronger than ever, and symptoms remained non-existent.

Pete's 4 Week Half Marathon Plan:

WEEK	MON	TUE	WED	THU	FRI	SAT	SUN
0	Rehab +20min swim	8x (5'R, 1'W)	Rehab	8x (5'R, 1'W)	Rehab	12x (5'R, 1'W)	Rehab +skip rope
1	5k run	Rehab +cross train	6k run +strides	Rest	5k run +intervals	12km	Rehab
2	5k run	Rehab +cross train	6k run +strides	Rest	6k run +intervals	14km	Rehab
3	5k run	Rehab +cross train	7k run +strides	Rest	6k run +intervals	16km	Rehab
4	5k run	Rehab	5k run +strides	Rest	Rest	Half marathon 21.1km	

As event day rolled around, Pete was determined to make the best of the day. Based on his interrupted training, he knew today's race wouldn't be a stellar performance. Instead, he decided the primary focus was to have fun and enjoy the day. After all, he loved drawing off the energy of a crowd and embracing the running community.

The marathon runners had to complete eight laps of the local parklands, and since Pete changed his entry to a half marathon, he needed to complete four laps. Approaching the event centre, he found the registration tent and received his race number.

Pete checked his watch, it was less than five minutes until the run was scheduled to start. Looking around, he estimated 200 runners for the event. He began his usual warm-up routine and happily placed himself at the back of the pack waiting at the starting line. Suddenly, the crowd started counting down from ten and his nerves unexpectedly surfaced. The last time he ran this distance was over two months ago, resulting in knee pain. He started to second guess himself but now wasn't the time to back out. He was determined to enjoy the day and deal with whatever came later.

The countdown reached zero and the pack of runners started slowly finding their own running space and getting into their stride. Pete planned to take an easy, even pace around the entire course. For the first 30 minutes, his stride was fluent, his effort levels were low and he was pleased with his position in the race. He guessed he was roughly in the middle third of the half marathon group. After completing his first lap he hadn't felt any trouble in his knee.

Pete approached the halfway mark of his third lap without drama. He looked down at his watch to check his most recent kilometre split. His watch displayed 5 minutes and 45 seconds. This pace was similar to his recent weekend runs and he knew it was safe for his knee. However, after completing his third lap, the spectators at the event centre began to morph into a roaring crowd. They started cheering and shouting as he ran past, which gave him an energy boost. He picked up the pace and started slowly passing people. He liked running past people so deep into the race, that he felt another surge of motivation and kept running at a faster pace.

Pete's watch alerted him to his recent kilometre split. Looking down, his watch displayed 5 minutes and 10 seconds. It also displayed the total running distance of 18 kilometres. With the finish line in sight, he tried to harness his last remaining energy. Although he was starting to fatigue, he was happy to dig deep into his reserves with the finish line so close.

Suddenly, Pete felt a familiar sensation in his knee. A shock of pain that almost buckled his leg. He winced and started limping while assessing the situation. The initial sharp pain peaked at seven out of ten, but now an ache remained at a two. He was quick to blame himself. His plan to take an easy, even paced race had gone out the window, and now he was suffering the consequences. The ache began to worsen, which forced him to slow down even more. He cursed himself. All the runners he had passed minutes before were gradually overtaking him, which only worsened his mood. Looking down at his watch, he saw he needed to hold on for only another 500 metres.

Pete's symptoms continued to increase, but he put on a brave face and tried not to limp as he approached the finish line. After crossing it, he slowed down to a walk and his limp became more severe. He looked down at his watch. He completed the half marathon in 2 hours and 3 minutes. He was happy with the time, but the pain in his knee overshadowed his success.

While the positive energy of race day excited Pete, he couldn't escape the reality that today was meant to be his marathon day. Yet again, an injury had forced him to abandon a goal he had worked hard on. To make matters worse, he hadn't even been able to complete a half marathon without breaking down. Looking back on the past 12 months of his running career, he was happy that he found the sport of running. This has been the most active year in Pete's memory, and he knew deep down that running would be a part of his life. However, with this setback, doubts set in and he questioned whether he would ever complete a marathon and wondered if he was destined to always end up with an injury.

Pete sat under a tree and watched those who entered the full marathon cross the finish line. He tried to think of reasons why they possessed the ability to complete a marathon while he was left in pain. While he enjoyed the rest of the race day festivities, he couldn't help but feel frustrated and resentful.

Run Smarter Lesson 10

Throughout my career, I have witnessed an array of personality traits that help or hinder one's progress. Commonly, runners are self driven, highly motivated and goal oriented. These traits contribute to consistency, self improvement and performance outcomes. Unless a recreational runner has a training coach, there is a low level of accountability, and therefore, self motivation is required to reach success in their running goals. Runners hold themselves to a high standard. They will get out of bed on a cold winter morning because they have committed to a long weekend run, and will often end up pushing themselves to go greater distances and race faster times.

These same traits however, may also bring runners undone in certain circumstances. For instance, facing early signs of an injury or struggling to return to pain free running. This chapter dives into a runner's mindset and the likelihood of injury and the battles they face when injured.

Personality Trait 1: The Self Sabotaging Runner

While Type A personality traits such as competitiveness and being highly focussed have their advantages in the running world, they can also be problematic and self destructive in the face of injury. For example, high levels of self drive can also increase the likelihood of over-training. Similarly, traits of perfectionism can quickly turn into stubbornness during the early stages of injury.

Being injured is a frustrating phase for any athlete. But it is common to see runners self sabotage and create their own worst scenarios based on their personality impulses, habits, and drive. This is more common in runners who highly prioritise performance, are compelled to run every day, or have a poor training philosophy, believing pain and stiffness are part of the sport. These runners work hard, train hard and often burn the candle at both ends until their body shows signs of overload. More often than not, they continue to run through early signs of injury, making the injured area more severe. Next, the injury becomes so bad that the runner must cease running. Even though their decision making leads to this situation, they curse themselves with frustration and anger.

We, as runners, are often very hard on ourselves, which is part of the self sabotage process. Alongside the frustration of injury, guilt often arises for letting this injury escalate to the point of needing to cease running. These negative emotions are disastrous for the recovery process and, if accompanied by stress, can hinder recovery times. Negative states also narrow your focus and limit your ability to be resourceful and develop the necessary steps back to pain free running. Instead, self criticism and blame override any proactivity.

Pain is closely associated with misery. No one likes to be in pain. But runners also face a loss of identity when an injury has forced them to cease running. This cognitive dissonance can almost be as frustrating as the injury itself. Some runners are so passionate and love being identified as a runner so much that an injury forcing them out of this identity causes an emotional dilemma. Whether this identity crisis is on a conscious or unconscious level, it is likely to have the runner returning to running too quickly, flaring up symptoms, and repeating the same vicious cycle.

Riding this emotional roller coaster can also be fear and worry. Fear about reinjury can cripple confidence levels and leave runners paralysed in a state of frustration. In addition, worry about needing to abort upcoming races, letting down teammates and losing fitness levels only creates more tension.

Desperately holding onto an upcoming race is a scenario I often encounter with my clients. These are tricky waters to navigate. When an upcoming race is dangling in front of a runner, they constantly have a reference point of where they think they should be in preparation for race day. For example, if someone is preparing for a marathon that is 10 weeks away, their long run should be 25 kilometres and their weekly mileage around 40 kilometres. If an injury halts their progress for two weeks, the point of reference ticks in their subconscious. Each week that passes, widens the gap between their current capacity and where they should be.

I say these are tricky waters to navigate because when this hypothetical runner shows the first, early signs of improvement, they are likely to hit the accelerator and try to catch up to their reference point. This is a dangerous scenario because the acceleration may overload their injury, causing another flareup, further setbacks, and risk to their race participation.

Commonly, when I treat an injured runner, I ask them what their goals are. In the case of a runner who has been unable to run for several months, they will often reply with their goal just to run pain free. I will then elaborate on what running pain free means to them. They might say it involves a five kilometre trail run three times a week. If they can reach this milestone, they will be happy and content. Time and time again, I witness runners achieve their running goal, and without even appreciating and celebrating their achievement, they have already moved the goal line. Suddenly, with only two weeks of steady progress, they have set their sights on a marathon race that is way too ambitious. The self sabotage traits creep in once again.

As a physiotherapist and running coach, my aim for some runners is to push them outside of their comfort zone. If an injured runner is fearful of reinjury and nervous about mild pain levels, my approach requires education about pain and pathology, reassurance, and slow integration into exercise as confidence builds. On the other hand, sometimes, my role is to pull the reins back on training plans and intensity. These runners are the opposite and will run as far and fast as possible if given permission. Based on these extreme personality traits, each presents its barriers. Too cautious creates inaction and slow progression while too much willingness leads to injury flareups. The behaviour patterns should be identified, and rules should be assigned to help guide proper action.

On the extreme side of self sabotage are those who are addicted to exercise. You can take something really good for you, and can transform it into something bad for you when taken too far. In episode 81 of the Run Smarter Podcast, I interviewed Dr Heather Hausenblas on exercise addiction [64]. Heather started by reassuring listeners that exercise addiction is rare and is only classified as an addiction in extreme circumstances. Here is a quote from Dr Hausenblas:

> *"Just because somebody does marathons, ultramarathons, ironmans or goes hiking all day long, doesn't mean this individual is addicted to exercise. Instead, it is the ability to stop, the ability to take time off and the ability to have a balance is where it is really key".*

While I believe that true exercise addiction is rare in the running population, I believe it commonly appears in mild forms. For example, Heather mentions some key signs of exercise addiction, including withdrawal effects and the inability to stop exercising even though it is detrimental to the individual. I have witnessed subtle withdrawal effects such as emotional irritability, frustration, and even depression when people cannot run. In addition, I have seen an unwillingness to take rest days or take a reduction in mileage even when managing injury. Here is a list of personality traits that runners can review to self-reflect without judgement and decide if they possess certain traits, whether they have helped or hindered their progress.

Self-sabotage Patterns:

When injury free and feeling good:

- Exercise addiction
- Perfectionism
- Obsession
- Overly competitive

Mild symptoms/niggles:

- Overtraining
- Poor load management
- Stubbornness

Injury restricting running limiting progress:

- Poor load management continued
- Frustration
- Worry

Unable to run due to injury:

- Catastrophisation
- Self blame
- Anger
- Guilt
- Fear of reinjury

We all love running. Sometimes though, we get in our own way of success and hinder our own potential with the personality traits we possess. However, you may have more control than you think. The first step is recognising these traits and whether they are truly helping or hindering your athletic endeavours. If you are displaying behaviour patterns of self sabotage, break the cycle and thought patterns. Whether it is for injury prevention or overcoming a current injury, recognise that sometimes mental toughness means pulling back rather than pushing forward. If you are facing an injury, your response to the injury determines your overall experience. It is up to you to decide whether you have a miserable experience or see it as a challenging but ultimately rewarding journey.

Personality Trait 2: Striving for Perfection (or injury)

This book has extensively covered the role of abrupt changes in load leading to a likelihood of injury. But what personality traits compel a runner to subject themselves to these abrupt changes? Research published by Wiese-Bjornstal identifies certain psychological risk factors as a cause of injury [65]. Mood state is one example, with evidence relating pre-injury negative mood to increased injury incidence, particularly with respect to high fatigue or lack of vigour. Other personality traits, risk behaviours and excessive training behaviours are also shown to increase injury risk.

In 2018, a paper was published by Daniel Madigana and colleagues to investigate the risks associated with perfectionism [66]. With a sample of 80 junior athletes, this cohort completed questionnaires with a physiotherapist onsite to document the occurrence of injuries. These athletes competed in soccer, basketball, athletics, and rugby and trained 10 hours per week on average.

The questionnaire contained a seven item subscale capturing personal standards. For example, statements like, *'I have extremely high goals for myself in my sport'*. The questionnaire also included a five item subscale capturing striving for perfection. For example, *'I strive to be as perfect as possible'*. Lastly, the authors found it essential to measure perfectionistic concerns. They did this by correlating the incidence of injury with the athlete marking highly on concerning statements. These are statements such as, *'People will probably think less of me if I make mistakes in competition'* and, *'I feel extremely stressed if everything does not go perfectly'*.

The results showed perfectionism positively predicted injury, but only perfectionistic concerns emerged as a significant positive predictor. Perfectionistic concerns showed a significant positive correlation with an injury that approached medium size, but perfectionistic strivings did not. Once they applied these findings to a model to predict future injuries, they found:

> *"The analysis suggested that the likelihood of sustaining an injury was increased by over two times for each one standard deviation increase in perfectionistic concerns".*

> *"If we were to compare any two athletes from the present sample, the athlete with higher perfectionistic concerns would show a higher risk of injury than the athlete with lower perfectionistic concerns. Moreover, if we were to compare two athletes who had the same level of perfectionistic strivings, the athlete with higher perfectionistic*

concerns would still show a higher risk of injury than the athlete with lower perfectionistic concerns".

The authors of this paper suggest two hypothetical pathways for why perfectionistic concerns may cause injury. First is the stress-injury model. Previous research has associated perfectionism with chronic stress, and this stress, in turn, may provide a mechanism for increased injury risk. This stress-injury model matches the details in Chapter seven. Psychological stressors release hormones throughout the body that inhibit the body from entering recovery mode. Therefore, personality traits such as perfectionism may be associated with high or chronic levels of psychological stress, increasing the likelihood of injury.

The second pathway offers a closer association between the load versus capacity relationship. This paper proposes that those with greater perfectionism concerns may also encounter high training stress. In other words, training harder and for longer than non-perfectionistic athletes. This will, in theory, lead personality traits such as perfectionism to push beyond their capacity until they develop an overuse injury. Madigana's two pathway models are illustrated below, which draws similarities to Ivarsson's work in Chapter seven, explaining that personality, history of stressors and coping strategies play an important role in injury development.

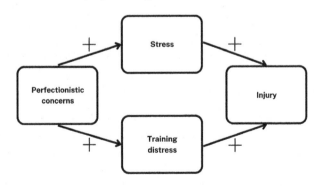

Personality Trait 3: An Optimistic Outlook on Recovery

One of the initial steps to forming a more positive outlook is dispelling any unhelpful myths of mechanical abnormalities. When injured, runners feel like their body has let them down. To make matters worse, they may see a health professional or coach that identifies an abnormality as the potential cause. Here are a few common statements:

- Your ITB is tight and pulling your leg out of alignment
- Your feet are collapsing and causing your knees to buckle
- You have one leg longer than the other which puts strain on your spine
- One side of your pelvis is rotated, potentially due to muscle weakness

As you can imagine, this language coming from a health professional escalates the level of threat and confirms the belief that your body is faulty. For some, these are the initial steps that contribute to fear of movement and anxiety. When returning to running, the fear of reinjury is heightened. After all, running on a faulty body seems like a high risk. Unfortunately, despite how common these statements are, they are most often unlikely, unnecessary and in my opinion, should be removed from the clinician's vocabulary. Kevin Maggs illustrated this point concisely on the British Journal of Sports Medicine YouTube channel [67].

> *"Most injuries can be attributed to this load, capacity relationship. Unfortunately, many people are told that their pain is due to biomechanical abnormalities, such as asymmetries in their anatomy or that they move wrong. Examples of this can include a short leg, flat feet, their glutes not activating, their sacrum is out of place or other things".*

> "These factors have been researched and the conclusions are that many simply don't even exist. Of those that do exist, they may very well lead to higher stressors on certain tissues. But even then, they play a small, if any, role in pain and injury. The fact is, if you give the body enough time to adapt, injury and pain are unlikely, even if we aren't built perfectly or we don't move perfectly".

> "Try not to get down on yourself in thinking you're defective in some way and don't be over analytical about how you move. Just think back about when you changed something too rapidly in your sport, your running, or your daily life".

Reassurance and confidence are often restored when the right information is delivered to injured runners. If the injury is severe or the runner has a particularly anxious personality, it is helpful to recognise the role of the emotional state during recovery. As authors Carrie Cheadle and Cindy Kuzma mentioned [68], in order to rebound from injury, you must:

- Understand that injury is mental and physical
- Believe that your mindset affects your recovery
- Embrace the power to positively influence your trajectory

Part of an optimistic, positive outlook requires a structured recovery plan. One that contains small milestones and guidelines back to pain free running. However, it isn't all up to the therapist. Take personal responsibility for your recovery and put yourself in the driver's seat. Your rehabilitation team can give you the roadmap, but you need to take control of the wheel.

Emotional States that Hinder Recovery

Chapter seven discusses the role of chronic stress in inhibiting the body from entering recovery mode. While this is a crucial insight to reduce your risk of injury, it can be just as important in the rehabilitation process. As mentioned in the book *'Rebound: Train Your Mind to Bounce Back Stronger from Sports Injuries'*, stress slows down the rate of tissue repair, creates dysfunction in the immune system, disrupts sleep and increases the risk of reinjury [68].

When faced with an injury, the injury itself now becomes another stressor in the athlete's life, leading to detrimental thoughts, feelings, and actions. In a similar fashion to the pain, rest, weakness downward spiral, a runner can often perpetuate a negative mindset, causing further worry, stress, and anxiety. As a result, pain heightens which prolongs recovery, creating further stress, and the cycle repeats.

As established by researcher Wiese-Bjornstal, self appraisal qualities such as a sense of self, identity, loss, optimism, challenge, or burnout in addition to psychological responses of emotion and behaviour, all influence physical recovery [65]. For example, pain catastrophisation is related to greater fear and anxiety, which can hinder effective mental and physical recoveries. Julio Domenech and colleagues also demonstrated this with a particular focus on catastrophisation and kinesiophobia [69]. Pain catastrophisation tends to describe a painful experience in more exaggerated terms, while kinesiophobia is the fear of pain due to movement. To be clear, this isn't the severity of pain that movement causes, but instead, the fear of potential pain.

Domenech studied 47 participants with chronic knee pain. Through pain and disability questionnaires before and after treatment, found anxiety, depression, catastrophisation, and kinesiophobia correlated with residual ongoing pain and disability. Even if two people received identical treatment, the one who rated higher on these subscales would have a worse outcome. In fact, they calculated that 48% of pain was correlated with a change in catastrophisation. They concluded [69]:

> *"What has been found suggests that clinical improvement in pain and disability is associated with a reduction in catastrophising and kinesiophobia. Therefore, co-interventions to reduce catastrophising thinking and kinesiophobia may enhance the results".*

This relates to the P.E.A.C.E. and L.O.V.E. acronym for injury management. In particular, education and optimism. If the education is delivered in the right way, it can significantly reduce the high levels of anxiety, depression, catastrophisation, and kinesiophobia. Education should focus on management principles, the anatomy and physiology of the condition, acceptable levels of pain, likely prognosis, and it should dispel any unhelpful myths. Here is a statement from that paper [69]:

> *"Optimistic patient expectations are associated with better outcomes and prognosis. Psychological factors such as catastrophisation, depression and fear can represent barriers to recovery. Beliefs and emotions are thought to explain more of the variation in symptoms following an ankle sprain than the degree of pathophysiology".*

You are Not a Runner, But an Athlete

As mentioned earlier, the loss of identity when unable to run is a frustrating disconnect. Runners love talking about running, training for races and socialising at events. When an injury takes most of these away, the struggle can sometimes be worse mentally than physically. With a growing body of evidence suggesting that the patient's thoughts and behaviours affect the speed of recovery, it is worth shifting the narrative to mitigate this mental battle and set the runner on the path to positivity.

Carla Wakefield released a paper titled '*Patient as Athlete: A Metaphor for Injury Rehabilitation*' and discussed the concept of viewing the injured participant as more than just a runner [70]. As the title suggests, this involves shifting the narrative away from a sport specific focus and encompassing all the elements of an all around athlete. Wakefield mentions:

> "The goal of this paper is to present a psychology of injury rehabilitation that is based on the metaphor of "patient as athlete". "Thus, guiding the patient in thinking and acting like an athlete becomes a central goal of rehabilitation".

> "As a general rule, to the extent that patients are athletes, their skills need to be transferred to the rehabilitation setting".

> "Superficially, an association with athleticism casts rehabilitation in a positive and upbeat light. Rehabilitation is thus defined as the challenge to body and mind that it truly is, by reference to the work ethic of athleticism: personal dedication, goal orientation, challenging practice regimens, pain tolerance, and striving to move to a higher level of performance. This comparison helps normalise the sometimes bewildering struggle in which patients find themselves embroiled. It legitimises their suffering".

As Carrie Cheadle described in episode 41 of the Run Smarter Podcast, '*Rehabilitation is now your sport*'. Not only can you broaden your scope by focusing on the rehabilitation process in a proactive manner, but you can use the Type A personality traits to positively impact your recovery process. This might involve developing rehabilitation milestones, organising each step systematically, or approaching each goal with enthusiasm. It could also involve building upon other skills that will transfer over into running at a later date, such as lower limb strength, balance and coordination. After all, you are not just a runner, you are an adaptable athlete.

Coping Strategies

Developing the correct coping skills is fundamental to physical and mental recovery. Below is my list of techniques and tips to boost your rehabilitation journey.

1. Positive thought and optimism: This is difficult when injured. Luckily however, positive thinking (like running) is a skill that can be developed and used to your advantage. Think about the opportunities your rehabilitation can open up, such as a chance to develop strength or learn how to squat. Be grateful for the things you *can* do rather than the things you cannot. For instance, running may not be an option right now, but cross training and upper body workouts may still offer cardiovascular benefits.

2. Understand your negative thought patterns: While positive thought patterns can be a learned skill, so too can negative loops. If the negative thought patterns are reinforced with repetition, you suddenly start seeing the downside to every opportunity instead of the upside. Recognise that negative

thoughts are okay sometimes, but break the reinforced habit and search for the positive instead.

3. Build a plan forward: When I started working with runners, one thing that surprised me was the relief clients would report once a plan was in place. During any given consult, I would lay out their exercise and rehabilitation each day, along with the dosages for each and the symptom guidelines to follow. The plan cleared out the guesswork, confusion and frustrations, which reduced stress and assisted the recovery.

4. Cross training alternatives: As mentioned earlier, runners who only run and refuse to partake in other forms of exercise are severely limited in their rehabilitation. The overall rehabilitation experience is poor and filled with a lot of frustration. You may not like cross training straight away. Many times I have seen a rigid runner open up to other alternatives and end up enjoying the benefit.

5. Goal setting: Laying out tangible mini goals throughout the rehabilitation process can assist in focus and motivation. For instance, your first goal may be to learn a deadlift action. Next might be to achieve three sets of deadlifts at 30 kilograms. On the running side of things, jump rope or jogging on the spot for 60 seconds could be the first step. Next, single leg hopping for 30 seconds. After that, a walk-run interval plan can be set. In addition, every mini goal accomplished should be celebrated. Give yourself a pat on the back, or assign yourself a small reward for each milestone.

6. Supportive social connections: Low levels of social support are related to poor injury outcomes [71]. Take a look at your social circle and identify key relationships that can help you through the rehabilitation process. If you are a part of a running club

and unable to run, do not stay home. Instead, help out the club in the best way you can, socialise with each member, crew at running races, and keep your love of running alive.

7. Build the right rehabilitation team: This chapter has already covered the importance of receiving the right information about your condition and selecting appropriate management. In order to receive the right education, you need the right rehabilitation team members. Find members who encourage an active approach to recovery with a focus on long term solutions. It is also important that you participate in decision making and not be a passive bystander.

8. Developing a flareup plan: Flareups are a part of the rehabilitation process. They help us learn your current limitations and identify mistakes in your current management plan. However, few runners ask their rehabilitation team for a guide on when things may go wrong. Talk with your medical team and put together a proactive contingency plan to help the process.

9. Establish what is within and out of your control: During your rehabilitation, it is helpful to identify what factors are within and out of your control. For instance, if you are unable to run due to a stress fracture, healing times and upcoming race dates are out of your control. Because they are out of your control, it is not worth your time dwelling on them. Therefore, it is healthier to focus on the elements that are within your control such as better nutrition, improved sleep, strengthening other muscle groups and finding a fitness solution.

Conclusion

The fact is, injuries are a part of running. There will always be another race. The trick is to stay optimistic in the most challenging circumstances. Not only does optimism help the body heal, but it helps with mental clarity. When your mind is clear, you can be more creative, and resourceful and become a better problem solver. Accept that injuries are just another chapter in your running journey. Each injury can be considered a part of the game, full of fluctuating emotions. In fact, dealing with injuries is just another opportunity to build on your running insight, develop more running tools and test out your true character.

For Pete, every time he faced an injury, he learned more information and developed critical tools to reduce the risk of future injury. His frustration is understandable given the circumstances, but in reality, this is his first year of running, and expectations shouldn't be set too high. I always mention that runners are too harsh on themselves, especially when injured. Reframing your circumstances to something more positive is a skill and requires practice. It is a habit that can solidify over years of repetition.

This habit is particularly hard in the face of a painful injury. It is hard to be optimistic when you are in pain. Your natural default emotion is despair, misery and helplessness. Learn to break this pattern and be kinder to yourself.

Managing Your Emotional Iceberg

So far, this book has explained each principle to better understand how to reduce your risk of injury and improve the outcome of a current injury. The iceberg analogy is useful in illustrating each part of this process. Firstly, the intention is set to grow your iceberg as large as possible. This represents resilience amongst the harsh ocean conditions. Next is controlling the volume, speed and frequency of each incoming wave. Each impact represents an opportunity to grow your iceberg or threaten its integrity. In addition to incoming waves are your strength training buckets of water that can be strategically placed in areas that are vulnerable, or that need reinforcing.

This final chapter has a particular focus on the personality traits and the emotional state of a runner. In the case of an iceberg, your emotional state represents the ocean conditions and water surrounding your iceberg. While you have complete control over the waves, you have a limited capacity to control which ocean your iceberg drifts into. There may be oceans with warmer waters, harsh currents, or sharp coral reefs putting your iceberg in danger.

You may have the best intentions to push your iceberg into ideal waters, but it is very hard to stop once your iceberg drifts in a certain direction with enough momentum. Like your emotional state, sometimes you have little control over the final decision. It is challenging to switch to an optimistic demeanour when frustrated or in pain.

It may seem obvious, but you wouldn't subject your iceberg to waves if the ocean was warm. In contrast to a runner, exercising when stressed, angry, tired and irritable is much the same. You can make smarter decisions by waiting until more favourable conditions before subjecting your body to more strenuous efforts.

By building upon your emotional intelligence, you can strengthen your ability to understand, use, and manage emotions. Building emotional intelligence is a practice that develops over time but it starts with a strong awareness of your feelings and why certain emotions are surfacing. More control and understanding over your emotions will enable you to control the slow drift of your iceberg and guide it toward safer, healthier waters.

Chapter 10 Summary

1. The same type A personality traits that help a runner succeed can also be detrimental when taken to extremes.

2. Perfectionism, obsession and competitiveness increase the likelihood of overtraining and therefore, injury.

3. When injured, personality and emotional states may help or hinder the recovery process.

4. Remaining optimistic when injured clears your mind to become more creative, resourceful and a better problem solver.

5. Remember you are not a runner, but an adaptable athlete who is now focussing on rehabilitation as your sport.

Action Items

1. Write down your main personality traits and behaviours. Next, think back to when these traits may have helped, or hindered your running career. Use this exercise for future decision making.

2. Identify elements that are out of your control and do not give them any attention. Focus on the elements within your control.

3. When injured, write a list of five things you are still grateful for. Each week add five more items to the list.

4. Build upon and utilise your social support system. You will need them, and they will need you, throughout many athletic challenges.

5. If struggling with rehabilitation, find the right team, and build a suitable plan mixed with mini goals and a proactive flareup plan.

CONCLUSION

After completing his half marathon, Pete diligently followed a revised training plan and continued with his knee and achilles exercises. Six weeks later, after he was running consistently without hassle, he set his sights back on marathon training. He jumped straight into his previous marathon training plan and carefully built up the mileage. His training moved from strength to strength and it only took three months of training before Pete could call himself a marathon finisher. While it was the hardest task he had ever done, he loved every moment. He stumbled over the finish line in 4 hours and 22 minutes.

He had continued the knee and achilles rehabilitation exercises twice a week throughout the entire training cycle. While his knee occasionally flared up, he could quickly settle symptoms by dialling back his training intensity and momentarily upping the frequency of his rehabilitation exercises.

Based on all the lessons he learned in his first year of running, he made an effort to sleep better and train smarter. Two weeks after his first marathon, he booked in for a check up with his doctor who was stunned at the rapid improvement in his health. He had lost eight kilograms, and all his health tests showed marked improvement. Pete was no longer worried about keeping up with his family during their weekly physical activities. In fact, he could not remember the last time he had this much energy. Regularly, the family would attend Parkrun, and a love for recreational running was starting to permeate into every family member. This only provided more fuel for Pete to seek greater running challenges.

Revisiting the frustrating moments in his training gave him a new perspective. In the heat of the moment, the injuries that sidelined his running felt disastrous. Now, he recognised that there would always be another race and reminded himself to take a step back and detach from the typical setbacks many runners experienced. His family and work colleagues mentioned that he seemed more optimistic than usual and Pete noticed it too. Work stress was no longer affecting him as it had in the past. Not only was running helping his physical health but also his mental resilience.

Part 1 Final Summary

1. Most running related injuries stem from the load/capacity relationship.

2. The body will adapt to almost anything with enough time and correct dosage.

3. You cannot get your injury risk to zero. The goal should be to identify early signs, make adjustments and abolish symptoms without losing fitness.

Action Items

1. Learn to run slow, and dedicate most of your running to low intensity.

2. Find an ideal running cadence for you and keep close to this value in both hard and easy workouts.

3. Monitor your training loads closely and avoid abrupt changes in running mileage, speed and terrain.

4. When injured, be kind to yourself. Be proactive, creative and resourceful with the right rehabilitation team.

PART TWO

INCREASING
PERFORMANCE

CHAPTER ELEVEN

THE POWER OF GOAL SETTING

After the success of his first marathon, Pete maintained 30 kilometres per week. His baseline mileage would pick up respectively when training for a race. Six months following the marathon, he entered a trail marathon. The race required him to incorporate hilly runs into his week as the course description highlighted over 2,000 feet of elevation.

The following year Pete and his family took a trip to Italy which would include his next running challenge. Looking ahead in his racing calendar, he saw his trip would coincide with the Rome marathon. While his training wasn't optimal, and jet lag would play a crucial role in his performance, he was happy to add another marathon to his list of achievements while concurrently sightseeing through the beautiful city. While his second and third marathons offered a challenging distance and variety, he played it safe and raced within his means.

Now, over 12 months since Pete's last marathon, a comfortable and complacent routine had seeped in. He needed more excitement in his life and running career. His overall health was good, but his life lacked passion. One morning, after completing his regular 10 kilometre weekend jog, an idea struck him and he decided to strive for a marathon personal best. He knew he was on the right track because of the excitement that had begun to course through his body. A list of questions quickly built up in his head.

"How much time should I give myself to prepare?"
"What terrain should I pick?"
"What time should I aim for?"

Pete's mind then halted when he remembered the confusion and misery when he set his sights on a challenging goal of this magnitude. His second and third marathons were taken lightly without any stretch to perform, but this next goal would challenge his capabilities similar to his first year of running. Memories of his stubborn achilles pain flooded in along with the wrong decisions he made following it, and the final decision to change his entry to a half marathon. He wanted to make sure that history didn't repeat itself. He was determined to train smarter.

Step one was to lay out a plan and write down specific goals. He decided to write down his goals on paper, which would allow him to look at them everyday to generate motivation and keep him on track. The first thing he wrote down was his current weekly mileage. Next, he wrote down his longest run in the past month and a five kilometre best in the past three months.

Pete's Current Fitness Benchmark

Current running mileage: 30 kilometres
Longest run in four weeks: 10 kilometres
Recent five kilometre time trial: 23 mins 45 sec (4'45 pace)

After looking over these numbers, Pete reverse engineered the time it would take to build back up to 42 kilometres. He calculated 16 weeks and added an extra three weeks for wiggle-room if he encountered unexpected setbacks.

Pete's Marathon Timeline

- At week 1: 10km long run
- By week 10: 22km long run
- By week 16: 35km long run
- (Add a 3 week buffer)
- Marathon preparation time: 19 weeks

Perfect! Pete's eyes lit up when he found a marathon that was 20 weeks away. He read the description as *'one of the most prestigious marathons in the world with a flat, fast and scenic course.'* The stars were aligning, and excitement was building, but there was one more vital piece to write down. A marathon completion time.

Pete wrote down on paper his previous best along with his other two past marathon times. His goal was to achieve his fastest ever marathon time, but surely he could strive for something a bit more ambitious. Then a lightbulb went off in his head to write down an 'A' goal, a 'B' goal and a 'C' goal. The lustrous goal of a sub four hour marathon appeared as the obvious 'A' goal. Not only was it a popular benchmark, but it would set a substantial challenge. Pete's 'C' goal was also apparent. He wrote down a time that was one second faster than his previous best. That only left 4 hours and 10 minutes—that was an even split between the others.

Marathon Completion Time

- Previous best: 4 hours 21 minutes and 59 seconds
- Trail marathon: 4 hours 40 minutes 23 seconds
- Rome marathon: 4 hours 28 minutes and 10 seconds

- A goal: 3 hours 59 minutes and 59 seconds
- B goal: 4 hours 10 minutes
- C goal: 4 hours 21 minutes and 58 seconds

Pete also realised that he needed the help of a professional to increase his likelihood of success. Someone who could write out a tailored running program and offer insight when unforeseeable hurdles presented themselves. The following day, he called up his physiotherapist and running coach Daniel for an assessment.

Run Smarter Lesson 11

We cannot discuss the topic of running performance without first covering goal setting. In fact, you may not even register an improvement without assigning goals in your training. Having running goals assists in directing attention, maintaining motivation, mobilising effort and strategy implementation for success. This chapter helps explain the reason behind goal setting and useful principles to consider.

Think it, then Ink it

Goal setting may seem straightforward, but few runners put this into practice and even fewer commit to writing them down. Once it is down on paper, the goal challenge becomes real, and the level of commitment heightens. The hesitancy to write down goals may come from the fear of failure. If you keep them in your head and fail, the accountability and price for failure is lower. But, in the same way, not writing them down gives you an easy out. Writing them down leads to greater commitment and, therefore, success.

In addition, writing down your goals and subsequent strategic planning lays out a visual roadmap. If the steps to achieving your goals are on paper, you can identify any missing gaps. Like Pete, laying out the number of weeks until race day and backtracking the necessary mileage would be difficult or inaccurate when picturing it in your head. This way, each week can be thought out, and the goal parameters clearly defined. This process also lowers the risk of overtraining and overuse injuries. You are more likely to commit to benchmarks that are written down instead of overreaching when things are feeling good.

When you are in the process of writing down your goals on paper, take some time to think about the reason why you are striving toward them. Dig deep to find the powerful, fundamental drive behind your endeavours. Once you find your reason, add it to the goals you have written down. This idea came from running coach Jake Lowe, who discussed it on episode 74 of the Run Smarter Podcast. The episode was titled '*Goal Setting and Getting Results*' and Jake mentioned:

> "Getting a goal out of your head and down on paper is very important. I believe that writing down your 'why' is also important because your why is not always in the forefront of your mind". [77]

Recreational runners are self-motivated and leap from goal to goal, race to race on their own accord, but how often do we self-reflect and analyse the deep seated reason behind testing our limitations? If you dig deep enough and uncover why you do these challenges, then keep it at the forefront of your mind and use it to drive you forward.

Not only should your goals and your reason why be written down, but they also should be kept in a place where they can be seen easily and regularly. A simple post-it note on a computer screen, fridge, or phone background screen will keep the journey top of mind.

Benefits of Having Goals

While most of us love running and will continue running even without an assigned goal or race, goal setting should be top of mind if your aim is to perform at your best. For instance, I still love to run five days per week when I don't have any races coming up. I will occasionally add speed sessions and longer runs purely for the love of running and the joy I experience after exercise. However, when a race is in front of me, continuing to run faster and further without any assigned goal will hinder my potential.

As mentioned earlier, goals help direct attention in your training. If my goal were to average a four minute pace for my upcoming race, I would be forced to adjust my training accordingly and keep my attention on this benchmark to give me the best chance of success. Exercising without a goal also fosters complacency. I constantly see this in runners with their strength training. They are happy to share their strength routine to aid their running performance, but when I ask them about the details of their training, they have committed to the same exercises with the same weight, repetitions and sets over the past six months. This would be a different workout if goals were in place to help maintain focus and build motivation.

Goal setting also eliminates some confusion and guesswork within your training. If your goal is to run a sub four hour marathon in two months, then you have an indication of the journey and how you should be tracking each subsequent week. The vaguer the goal, the more guesswork in your training. For instance, if you didn't have a time in mind for your upcoming marathon, you know the distance you need to cover and the number of weeks to train, but the speed and time trial sessions will lack direction.

Five Goal Setting Principles

Locke and Latham's goal setting theory details five key principles that support the creation of effective and motivating goals [78]. While these principles are originally intended for individual and team based goals in the workplace, carry over has been shown in sports performance [79].

1. Clarity: When your goals are clear, you can lay down an effective strategy. In addition, you can track your progress with more accuracy. A clear running goal would be to run five kilometres in under 21 minutes, on flat terrain, in eight weeks. With this goal set, you can assign a realistic journey and accurately measure your progress. Conversely, if your goal was to run 10 kilometres, there are many unanswered questions. Does it also include walk breaks? Is the completion time important? Does it matter when the goal is achieved?

Such ill-defined goals can lead to confusion and wiggle-room for laziness once the task becomes too hard. Perhaps reaching eight kilometres becomes too uncomfortable, and the runner chooses to maintain this distance for several weeks. Or maybe the final 10 kilometre effort is mixed with a lot of walking because the effort levels were too high. This is a prime example of poor focus, low accountability and wiggle-room for laziness because the goal wasn't clear.

It is important to know all the race variables in relation to assigning a running race goal. Aside from race distance, factors such as weather, terrain and elevation should be considered. This insight will help assign a clear purpose and assist in formulating a plan to get there.

2. Challenge: Setting goals is meant to spark motivation. Assigning the right level of difficulty or challenge to your goals is essential, and if a goal isn't set within the challenge sweet spot, it could lead to poor passion and a high likelihood of abandonment.

Take Pete and his marathon completion time, his previous best was just under 4 hours and 22 minutes which only required adequate training. If his next goal was to improve this time and his training produce immediate results, complacency would begin to sink into the routine. In this scenario, the level of challenge is low. Conversely, if his goal was to complete the marathon in 3 hours and 22 minutes, a full 60 minutes faster than previously, he might either get injured or fall off track. In either case, motivation levels would plummet.

Runners can also consider readjusting goals throughout the journey to keep the level of challenge within their sweet spot. If you recall from the first chapter, I began my running journey because my sister was training for a half marathon and asked if I wanted to join. It was tough adjusting to long distance running, but my body slowly adapted. Within a few months, I had already increased my distance beyond 15 kilometres. With the half marathon still several months away, I had to readjust my goals to keep my motivation levels high. Luckily, this particular race had a full marathon option, so I switched to the longer distance and set my sights on a bigger challenge.

When you assign a goal, pay close attention to how you feel. Are you scared, excited, overwhelmed or indifferent? Reevaluating your drive and excitement levels can be a good indication of the level of challenge you have set for yourself. The tricky part is that for most running related goals, a difficult challenge will often include a ramp-up of the training load. If the challenge is too difficult, it can dramatically increase the likelihood of injury. Even a goal that hits a sweet spot of difficulty will have associated risks and is a tough scenario to navigate.

When a runner asks me how they can prepare for a race without getting injured, I am quick to remind them that all running endeavours have risks. There are plenty of systems to put in place to reduce the risk of injury, but unfortunately, someone can make all the right moves and still develop an injury if their goal is to improve. As I have mentioned in the book, you cannot get your risk of injury to zero, but you can make smart decisions to get close to zero. When symptoms do arise, it is about making sensible decisions to quickly negotiate injury without losing fitness.

3. Commitment: The likelihood of achieving your set goals ties closely with your level of commitment. Everything we have already discussed will play a role. If you write down your goals, your commitment is likely to increase. The same holds true if those goals have clarity and hit a challenging sweet spot. Tapping into your emotions will also raise the level of commitment. When it comes to goal setting, motives matter, and if a goal builds enjoyment throughout the journey, you are setting yourself up for success.

I brought up the topic of goal setting with running coach Tyson Popplestone. When appearing on episode 27 of the Run Smarter Podcast, Tyson raised an interesting point about motivation and enjoyment during the goal setting process. When the journey has a high enjoyment factor, achieving the goal becomes more likely. Here is what he said:

> *"The idea of training for a big event like a marathon is great, but setting the goal in a short period seems to put a lot of pressure onto runners and ruins the enjoyment of the sport".*
>
> *"I always encourage athletes to think about it from a longevity point of view. When you expand the time frame and focus on the little breakthroughs in your performance, it becomes much more enjoyable".* [80]

We are all motivated in different ways, and elements of enjoyment will vary from runner to runner. When planning your goals and your deep seated reason behind accomplishing the goal, it is important to self-reflect and dive deeply into what makes you tick. Ask yourself what motivates you, what excites you, and what fosters complacency, and then construct your plan.

In my case, I have found that a varied training plan was more exciting. This is why after completing my first marathon, I switched things up and moved into sprint distance triathlons. I thoroughly enjoy the combination of disciplines and intensities on any given training day. I also enjoy nature, fresh air and flowing water. This means that during the triathlon off-season, I actively seek out trail events, which combine all of these things I love, along with an encouraging, supportive running community. Whenever I train for a trail event, I rarely encounter a dip in commitment, and it all started with an honest self-reflection.

List of Potential Motivators

- Travelling for events
- Trophies and race medals

- Running in nature
- Running with friends, family, a community, or your dog
- Running fast
- Running on challenging terrain
- Being an active role model
- Challenging yourself to greater distances

4. Feedback: Feedback is required to know if you are on track to meet your goal by the assigned deadline. If systems are in place to monitor your progress, you can make necessary adjustments if required, and increase your likelihood of success. Creating feedback markers should be brainstormed in the initial goal setting process. For instance, if your goal is to complete a sub 20 minute five kilometre run in eight weeks, you can calculate the average pace required and assign feedback sessions.

To be more specific, a sub 20 minute five kilometre effort requires a running pace under four minutes per kilometre. Given that, in week three, a three kilometre run under this pace will provide good feedback. Subsequently, a four kilometre run under this pace can be scheduled for week five. If these test runs go well, you will have a good sense of direction and see if you're on track to meet your goal. Here are a few more examples:

- Goal: Get more than eight hours of sleep on average for the next two weeks
- Feedback: Sleep data tracking with wearable devices
- Goal: Complete a half marathon with continuous running and no walk breaks in 10 weeks
- Feedback: Continuous running of 10 kilometres at week five and 15 kilometres at week eight

5. Complexity: If a goal is too complex, it can become overwhelming. Remember, your goals should create excitement and high motivation levels with a clear plan forward. While assigning a running goal that is too complex is uncommon, it can be true for inexperienced runners throwing themselves in the deep end. A beginner runner may attempt to follow goals set by more experienced peers, such as completing a race in a certain time. If this new runner is only starting on a walk-run program, having a race goal with a time in mind may present several challenges and too much pressure. In this instance, it is helpful to either reconsider the goal or break it into smaller subgoals. Below are four examples:

1. Complete 5K walk-run program in four weeks.
2. Maintain four runs per week, reaching 25 kilometres per week.
3. Increase a weekend long run to 10 kilometres in four weeks.
4. Complete 10k race in under 60 minutes.

Breaking complex goals into smaller subgoals will prevent the feeling of being overwhelmed and increase clarity. In addition, it will formulate sensible stepping stones to reduce the likelihood of overtraining when the path becomes complicated.

Goal Setting Mistakes

Goal Setting Mistake 1: Low Accountability

While writing down your goals makes the journey more real, implementing additional strategies to make yourself accountable will also increase the likelihood of success. Following are four tiers of accountability which you can explore if you want to boost motivation and success.

Accountability Tier One: Writing Down your Goals

As described above, if goals stay in your head, they become hard to track, and it is easy to back out when the journey becomes difficult. Committing your goals to paper raises your accountability and, therefore, is the first tier.

Accountability Tier Two: Sharing with Other People

Once you have written down your goals, it can still be easy to back out if no one else knows. Sharing your goals with your family members and running friends creates the next tier of accountability. Make sure you share the entire goal with them, including the allocated time to completion. In addition, create a goal that involves you and a close friend or family member. That way, you become accountable to each other and make the level of commitment greater.

Accountability Tier Three: Recruiting a Team and Resources

If your goal requires it, going one step further and enlisting help can generate the next level of accountability. If you have a team working with you to complete your goals, you now have people to share in your victories and setbacks. You could hire a coach, health professional, personal trainer, dietician or any other professional to increase your odds of success. To a lesser extent, allocating time, money and resources in other ways will raise your level of investment and, therefore, accountability. For example, if your goal involves building strength, then investing in a gym membership raises the stakes and the available resources.

Accountability Tier Four: Extend Beyond Personal Endeavours

Particularly for those who have made commitments in the past and haven't stuck to them, it might be time to strive for a goal beyond personal endeavours, such as setting a goal to raise awareness or money for a charity you care about. Taking on such a task requires more people to know about it and will increase the level of passion. A strategy like this is also important if you cannot think of a strong enough reason for committing to a goal.

In other words, if you wanted to complete a marathon and your deep seated 'why' wasn't enough to generate passion, excitement and commitment, raise the stakes and find a purpose bigger than yourself.

Goal Setting Mistake 2: Assigning "Do Your Best" Goals

Research has shown that in 90% of the studies, specific and challenging goals led to higher performance than easy goals, "do your best" goals or no goals [78]. Since we have already discussed the benefits of goal setting and assigning a goal with the right difficulty level, it is important to discuss "do your best" goals.

Firstly, these types of goals lack clarity and direction. In addition, it is more difficult to monitor your path with feedback. Instead of preparing goals such as "I want to complete a marathon in the fastest time possible", try to assign a specific completion time.

Goal Setting Mistake 3: Not Celebrating the Small Wins

As mentioned in Chapter 10, runners are often harsh on themselves. We hold ourselves to incredibly high standards and continue pushing the envelope to higher feats. To make matters worse, when our milestones, goals, and races are completed and even exceed our expectations, we quickly move on to the next goal without much thought or celebration. I believe taking the time to appreciate and celebrate needs to become a conscious effort and a habit to enhance the experience. After all, these goals are meant to be motivating and fun.

When writing down your goals, also lay down mini goals throughout the journey. Once these are written down, add a small reward or a celebration for yourself whenever a mini goal is completed. Be sure to find a compelling reward that will help with your motivation to complete the task.

Goal Setting Mistake 4: Incorrect Time Allocation

I have seen too many impatient runners leap from race to race without enough recovery time. As well as this, they often juggle multiple injuries along their journey. Running is a sport with a high incidence of injury. Therefore, it may be hard to assign a challenging goal that won't dramatically increase the likelihood of injury, especially if the goal is time sensitive. For example, the goal to run five kilometres without stopping is a healthy goal for a beginner runner, but it might be too easy if the time allocated is three months. Conversely, if the time allocated is three weeks, it may be too challenging with the risk of injury too high.

Race preparations are the most common time sensitive goals that runners struggle with. It is a delicate balance and if the runner is not experienced, it can be hard to judge how much time should be taken. If time is on your hands, it is safer and more sensible to take your time. Chapter six introduced the 10% rule to help guide training progressions. While the chapter discussed its limitations, it can also be used as a rough guideline. When applying this principle to training and injuries, researchers found that:

> *Increases of greater than 30% have been reported to increase the risk of injury. However, no difference in injury rates has been identified when increasing weekly mileage by less than 10% or between 10 and 30%".* [81,82,83]

Progressing your weekly mileage between 10 and 20% is typically safe for most runners. So, reverse engineering this guideline can help with calculating timeframes. If your goals are ambitious and require a long time, implementing mini goals can help. If you want to compete in an ultra marathon or ironman event, this could take two to three years. Some mini goals can include shorter races that increase distance throughout that time. The purpose is to bridge the gap between current and required fitness levels to achieve your goal.

With ambitious, long term goals that stretch beyond 12 months, mini goals can be used to differentiate between realistic and unrealistic expectations. For instance, it is hard to tell if you will have the required fitness levels for an ironman in two years, but bridging the gap with goals every three to six months can offer less complication. It may also help to assign some non-running goals that still aid in the final objective to keep things fun and varied. Below is a list of mini goals and non running goals that can help serve the bigger picture:

Marathon Training Mini Goals:

- Improve 1k time trial
- Improve 5k time trial
- Improve 10k time trial
- Establish an 80/20 intensity distribution
- Get 8+ hours of sleep five days per week
- Reach 45 kilometres per week in 10 weeks
- Identify optimal fueling strategy for longer runs
- PB a hilly segment close to home

- Reach half marathon distance in 12 weeks
- Improve squat weight by 20 kgs
- Drink more than 2 litres of water per day
- Cook a healthy dinner six days per week

Specifically for racing goals, it is useful to allocate a few buffer weeks for wiggle-room in case of unexpected circumstances. Many runners find a 16 week marathon training program and start week one 16 weeks before race day. This timeframe seems sensible, but it leaves no wiggle-room when life throws you a curveball. Consider the possibility of injury, illness, travel and unforeseen life commitments.

For example, if a runner is in week 10 of their program and encounters knee pain, this injury forces them to take one week off. Naturally, this follows two weeks of a slow integration back to pre-injury mileage. A runner will lose three weeks of progression in this scenario of only minor consequences. After halting their program for three weeks, this runner is faced with the dilemma of resuming their running. They could resume at the same pre-injury week and modify the subsequent weeks to catch up. Another option is to jump ahead, pass the weeks spent injured and hope for the best. Both options are associated with a high risk of reinjury, and in the end, may lead to being unable to complete the race at all.

When working with runners, I commonly see individuals who have left no wiggle-room in their program during the planning phase. Then, when faced with an injury, they return with a dosage that exceeds their limits, resulting in another flareup. This cycle continues as every attempt to keep up with their program becomes more desperate. Eventually, symptoms force the runner into three options.

1. Abandon the race altogether and live to fight another day.
2. Settle for a reduced race distance.

3. Take on the risk, stubbornly enter the race, and face the consequences.

A runner lowers the risk of facing this dilemma if they assign some wiggle-room. Like Pete, calculate the sensible number of weeks to prepare for the race. Next, add on two or three buffer weeks for unexpected circumstances. If these unexpected moments don't arise, great. Just repeat the previous weeks closer to race day to maintain fitness and peak at the right time.

When calculating and deciding upon the weeks required to complete the task, runners must weigh up the risk versus the reward of the goal they created. As mentioned earlier, it is important to find a challenging goal. Every performance goal has some associated risk, but laying down the risks and expectations will help the journey if injuries ensue. When a runner that I work with returns to pain free running, they are quick to ask when they can get back to entering races. It is best to discuss the risks and rewards in these scenarios because there is often no right or wrong, only greater and fewer risks.

It is important to have a candid discussion about possible risks versus the benefits and rewards if achieved. No matter the outcome, you should accept the associated risks and have contingencies in place if an injury occurs.

Running Performance on a Tightrope

Part one of the book contained my iceberg analogy to help understand the principles of injury prevention. Now, part two of the book will frequently visit my tightrope walking analogy, focusing on running performance. The goal of a tightrope walker is to make it to the other end without falling off. To help them with their task, they need equipment such as tightrope shoes, a balance bar and a trustworthy tightrope.

Throughout the journey across the rope, gusts of wind may disrupt their walk and potentially send them falling. For a runner, the wind element represents changes in training loads, and falling represents an injury. Several chapters in part two focus on different elements of the tightrope walker's journey and relate it to the goal of enhancing running performance safely.

Tightrope walking is a risky hobby. So if becoming a better performer is the goal, it is important to plan out performance based goals carefully. During the goal setting process, it is important to choose something challenging. That way, it ensures a high level of excitement and offers an opportunity to learn, grow and build confidence for future endeavours.

On the other hand, because the risks are high, it needs to be carefully balanced with realistic expectations. Tightrope walkers should select a goal that has an element of excitement but one that is within their capabilities. Imagine you are a tightrope walker who only practises on a five metre indoor tightrope that is twelve inches off the ground. You wouldn't set your next sights on an outdoor tightrope stretching around a mountainous gorge. While that may be your goal eventually, there are several more logical steps to complete first.

While crossing longer and higher tightropes are always top of mind, there are plenty of mini goals or other tangible goals that can assist. For instance, working on balancing exercises, core strength and precise foot placement drills. These goals can keep the journey fun and exciting while a more patient approach is taken for the bigger milestones.

Chapter 11 Summary

1. Clear, specific and challenging goals lead to better performance than easy goals, "do your best" goals, and no goals.

2. When goal setting, consider clarity, challenge, commitment, feedback and task complexity.

3. If preparing for a race, reverse engineer the time required to train with two to three buffer weeks for unexpected setbacks.

Action Items

1. Assign yourself three goals that help you become a well rounded athlete.

2. Raise your accountability by writing down goals, your reason why and sharing them with someone close to you.

3. Set and celebrate your mini goals, milestones and benchmarks. Enjoy the entire journey.

CHAPTER TWELVE

RUNNING PROGRAM CONSTRUCTION

O nce again, Pete found himself sitting in the waiting room of Daniel's physiotherapy clinic, but this time he wasn't injured. Instead, he was excited and ready to start his next running chapter. He updated Daniel on his new running ambitions. Not only was he entering another marathon, but he wanted to complete it in under four hours.

Daniel was impressed at Pete's sensible forward thinking and agreed that a tailored training plan was wise. He explained that most generic online training programs miss key information that may hinder running goals and that he should not only consider weekly mileage but also pace, effort levels and recovery. All of these elements would give Pete the best chance for success. Since Daniel hadn't seen Pete in quite some time, he asked some questions about his recent training history to help paint a better picture:

"Have there been any recent injuries or niggles in your training?"
"What is your current running mileage and what types of workouts are you doing?"

"Have you been doing strength training at all?"
"Are you feeling recovered, fresh and enthusiastic to train?"
"Any other concerns about your general health?"

Daniel carefully planned a two week training schedule and mentioned that it might not look like much, but wanted to see how Pete responded over the next few weeks before writing out a complete program.

Pete's Two Week Program

WEEK	MON	TUE	WED	THU	FRI	SAT	SUN
1	5k RPE 5 +strides		5k RPE 3	4k Intervals RPE 5		10k RPE3	
2	6k RPE 5 +strides		5k RPE 3	4k Intervals RPE 7		11k RPE3	

Program instructions:

Strides = 5 repeats of 100 metres. Top speed =
85% max sprint
Intervals = 8 rounds of 500 metres fast, 500
metres jog

Pete was already familiar with strides and interval sessions from his previous marathon program but there was confusion about the RPE number assigned to each session. Daniel explained that the RPE is your rate of perceived exertion. It represents how intensive an exercise is perceived out of 10 where 10 is maximal intensity.

Pete had never considered interpreting his workout intensity before but was happy to make a start. It may require practice, but he was committed to building this skill to become a better runner. If the next two weeks of training were successful, he was to return to see Daniel and receive a longer training plan. In addition, he was instructed to wear some exercise clothing to the next appointment. While Daniel didn't explain why, he did mention that there was still a missing piece if his goal was a marathon PB.

Run Smarter Lesson 12

Building a training plan is essential to enhance running performance. Not only will it lay a foundation and provide structure in order to avoid abrupt changes in training loads, but it will also serve as a monitor to your progress. Most generic training plans only cover basic information which can have severe limitations. Commonly, most marathon training plans are 12 to 20 weeks long, detailing the days of running and what distance. As the weeks progress closer to race day, the overall weekly mileage and fitness level build to the necessary level to hopefully cross the finish line.

Generic Running Program

WEEK	MON	TUE	WED	THU	FRI	SAT	SUN
1	Rest	5km run	6km run	4km run	Rest	10km run	1-hr x-train
......							
5	Rest	5km run	11km run	7km run	Rest	16km run	1-hr x-train

This simplistic design can be beneficial but lacks fundamental components such as training intensity. This is why components such as speed, power zones, heart-rate zones and perceived effort levels are the next essential piece to the puzzle.

Calculating Your Training Impulse

To recap from Chapter two, your rate of perceived exertion can be ranked from zero to ten and can be used to calculate a perceived overall workout intensity score, also known as your training impulse or "TRIMP".

For example, if your traditional running program told you to run five kilometres, it begs the question of how intense the session should be. If guesswork is required, it can lead to confusion and the possibility of overtraining even though the running distance is added sensibly. Completing a five kilometre run in 22 minutes requires more strain than 35 minutes. It is, therefore, necessary to factor in training intensity if you want to lower the risk of injury while committing to a greater performance goal.

Speed, power zones and monitoring your heart rate can be great tools for measuring your intensity. But there is still one more layer of complexity—your recovery. During your training, you may experience fluctuations in recovery. After all, you do have a life outside of running. Family commitments, work stressors, illness, sleep disruptions and nutritional changes can all impact how you feel and respond during a training session. In other words, a 25 minute five kilometre run may feel effortless during a training week where recovery is optimal. Conversely, experiencing illness, fatigue, muscle soreness, or low mood could be a sign of poor recovery and an identical 25 minute five kilometre run will elicit elevated effort levels.

While you might assume that an identical run exhibits the same external load through your body, your recovery status will influence your body's internal capacity to tolerate the load. In addition, higher levels of effort may lead to a longer time spent running in a fatigued state. Running fatigued can alter your running efficiency, foot strike and body mechanics, which can spike external and internal loads. These signs will not show up on power meters or heart rate data, so calculating your RPE and TRIMP scores are important.

Chapter Two Recap

RPE = Average perceived intensity for a particular training session

TRIMP = RPE x minutes of workout

> "Calculating your TRIMP score over a certain workload or over a long period of time factors in your body's response to exercise and can increase the accuracy of the load versus capacity relationship. For instance, if you are not sleeping well and getting adequate rest, your workouts will be perceived as harder. This will raise your effort levels and spike your TRIMP score. Below is an example of the difference when factoring in internal training loads". [Chapter 2]

Workout: 10K Run at 5 minute Per Kilometre Pace

When well recovered:

- RPE = 5
- Minutes = 60
- Total TRIMP = 300

During poor sleep/recovery:

- RPE = 8

- Minutes = 65
- Total TRIMP = 520

Back to Basics

Chapter six covers the training basics to reduce your risk of injury. Since increasing training loads safely is a crucial factor in running performance, it is worth recapping these principles:

The 10% rule signifies that overall training loads should not exceed 10% per week. While this is overly simplistic and is perhaps too conservative for most athletes, it acts as a loose guideline. More realistic measurements fluctuate between 10 and 15% based on the individual. This can be applied to overall weekly mileage, a weekly long run or overall weekly TRIMP scores.

The 80/20 rule applies to the distribution of your intensity levels across your weekly routine. Generally speaking, 80% of your overall weekly mileage should be dedicated to low intensity, leaving 20% to your more strenuous efforts.

RATE OF PERCEIVED EXERTION (RPE) SCALE	80/20 DISTRIBUTION
10 Max Effort: Almost impossible to maintain, unable to talk	20% of your training load should be >5/10
9 Very hard: Can barely breathe, can only speak a few words	
7–8 Vigorous: Borderline uncomfortable, can speak a sentence	
4–6 Moderate: Somewhat comfortable, becoming more challenging	
2–3 Light: Feels like you can maintain for hours	80% of your training should be <5/10
1 Very light: Hardly any exertion, but more than complete rest	

The skill of running slow was another concept introduced in Part one. If your goal is to run faster and outperform your previous self, your natural urge is to commit more time to running faster. The same goes for shifting the intensity distribution to containing a higher percentage of harder efforts. However, it is imperative that the basic principles remain. If the balance is off, you risk falling into the grey zone of intensity described in Chapter six. While your harder efforts should be challenging and your overall mileage will gradually increase, the idea should still be to maintain fresh legs during those harder training sessions. This can only be achieved if you commit to slow running during your easy sessions.

Assigning and calculating workouts around RPE can be a handy skill when preparing for a race or looking to enhance performance. However, I have witnessed two common mistakes when athletes try this out.

RPE Error #1: RPE is a Feeling, Not a Pace

Runners often ask what pace they should be running to for each designated RPE scale. As mentioned above, several internal and external factors can fluctuate your effort levels without changing your running speed. Here are some of these factors:

- Changes in temperature
- Hydration status
- Boredom levels
- Terrain gradients
- Over training
- Under recovery
- Nutritional intake

While it is helpful to use pace as a reference point for RPE, it is subject to change throughout the run itself. For myself, if I aim to reach an RPE of five over five kilometres, I would start at five minutes per kilometre. I decide on this pace based on my past experiences at this pace and find it matches the required RPE. If I maintain this steady pace but my effort levels rise above five, I will need to adjust my pace by slowing down to reach the allocated RPE. This mismatch could result from under recovery or one of the other influences listed above. Conversely, if holding a five minute pace maintains effort levels lower than five, picking up the pace is necessary.

RPE Error #2: RPE is an Average, Not the Final Effort

An error I often see is runners assigning an RPE to a workout based on how they feel in the final moments of the workout. For example, during a marathon race, you could push yourself to your physical limit and empty your tank in the last kilometre of the race. Upon crossing the finish line, you collapse under sheer exhaustion. In the moment, a runner might assign an eight or nine RPE on their program. The RPE, however, is the average of the entire workout. The effort level may have reached nine at the end, but it is unlikely and near impossible to have maintained it for so long.

In this instance, you will need to estimate the average RPE throughout the entire race. If you find it difficult to guess an average RPE during a certain workout, then breaking the workout into smaller sections will make it easier. This is particularly useful if the race is across a long duration, or if it contains several different effort levels, such as an escalating interval session.

Segmenting RPE and TRIMP across a marathon race:

Kilometre 0–10
60 mins RPE 3
TRIMP: 180

Kilometre 11–20
55 mins RPE 4
TRIMP: 220

Kilometre 21–30
65 mins RPE 6
TRIMP: 390

Kilometre 31–42.2
68 mins RPE 7
TRIMP: 476

Total marathon training impulse: 1,266

Whether you are retrospectively calculating your TRIMP score, or aiming to maintain an RPE throughout your workout, remember it is based on the average. If your weekend long run involves a challenging distance and has an assigned RPE of four, you will need to start the session at an easier effort level if you anticipate fatigue and soreness towards the end. That way, if the final kilometres peak your effort levels at five or six, then the average will still reach four. This might take practice initially but becomes a lot easier with repetition and learning to tune in with your body.

Building a Comprehensive Schedule

With all these principles in mind, you can start formulating your own running program and bringing all the pieces together. This particular format has proved successful with runners looking to return from injury and those injury-free runners looking to build upon their performance.

Training Schedule with Weekly TRIMP Calculation

WEEK	MON	TUE	WED	THU	FRI	SAT	SUN	TOT
1	Rest	20 min RPE 4 +strides	15 min RPE 3	20min +intervals RPE 7	Rest	60 min RPE 4	Cross-train	21kms
TRIMP		80	45	140		240		505
				....				
5	Rest	40 min RPE 4 +strides	15 min RPE 3	30min +intervals RPE 7	Rest	90 min RPE 4	Cross-train	34kms
TRIMP		160	45	210		360		775

In early 2022, I jumped on a free injury chat with a 42-year-old recreational runner named Chad. During our conversation, Chad highlighted his continuous string of injuries as he strived to run faster and further. Injuries kept hindering his progress, including achilles, knee and plantar fascia pain. When I asked him a few questions about his training methods, I instantly recognised that most of his training consisted of high intensity sessions. Coming from a background in short distance sprinting, Chad believed that slow running was counterproductive.

The majority of our conversation followed the aforementioned training philosophies, including running slow, calculating his TRIMP score and training the majority of the time at a low intensity. I shared my own running program with Chad, and he aimed to replicate the same philosophy. Six weeks later, I received this message in my inbox:

> "Hi brodie. I wanted to send a huge thank you for our web-chat a month or so ago. I've been using the excel log chart and my running has massively improved. I am injury and niggle-free and for the first time since I started running in 2018. I raced 10 kilometres last week and came within eight seconds of a PR without planning it and having more in the tank. I'm only halfway through my training block with this approach but it's really been a game-changer. At 42 years old I am achieving a lot more than I did in my peak years".

With such a profound change in a short period, I asked Chad if he would be interested in coming onto the podcast to talk about his transformation. Episode 228 was titled '*Chad Miller's Training Plan Success Story*' [84] which explored his previous mindset to running, implementing his new program and the tangible benefits to his performance and injury status.

It is important to note, however, that a training schedule is not set in stone. Life is unpredictable, and you have permission to adjust the program due to unforeseen circumstances. As a podcast host, I have had the opportunity to interview many running coaches, and one guest that highlighted the principle of adaptability was running coach Jake Lowe. We discussed the concept of goal setting, and this was Jake's advice:

> *"Firstly, you need to understand the magnitude of your running goal and have the awareness to adapt to your plan. Something will always get in the way whether it's a lack of motivation, injury, social engagements, work or bad weather. You've got to be adaptable and shift the plan depending on the obstacle in front of you".* [85]

I often think of a program as a template. You assign a well balanced plan with the right ingredients, but each week is subject to change based on unforeseen circumstances. Outside of being a runner, you have a life and commitments and sometimes, reshuffling days or modifying dosages and intensities is required. Consider adjusting the template as a part of the game and consider adaptability as a skill.

Training Program Errors

In June 2020, I also interviewed the running coach and Strength Running Podcast host Jason Fitzgerald. Throughout the episode, *'How Can I Boost my Running Program'* [86], Jason shared three common mistakes runners make when building a running schedule.

The first mistake Jason mentioned was that runners simply aren't running enough. He mentioned:

> *"I think if you want to improve and get better, the number one way to do that is to simply run more. Build up your running to 60, 70, 80 kilometres per week. Once you are running this amount, that's what I'd consider a pretty high, competitive running mileage level. The mistake is that many runners stick to low mileage levels for years, and then they wonder why they don't improve".*

Many recreational runners fail to recognise the time and patience required to successfully build a robust training base. Every case is unique, but it will often take over 12 months of consistent running to safely build a weekly mileage above 50 kilometres. Those resilient runners who are successfully operating at a higher mileage would have dedicated several years to achieve this base without developing an injury. In addition, most of these runners are placing optimal recovery high on their priority list to operate at this mileage.

As a second mistake, Jason mentioned the absence of faster workouts. This covers what was mentioned earlier in this chapter. Incorporating and adapting to various speeds will contribute to resilience, provided that the introduction is sensible without abrupt spikes in your TRIMP. As Jason put it:

> *"If you don't train fast, you'll never be able to race fast. A good starting point is implementing one faster running session per week. You can start with time-based repetitions, and once you become comfortable with these types of speeds, you can progress to more advanced workouts".*

A novice speed session might include one minute intervals spread throughout a shorter run. For example, a previously scheduled 20 minute jog might include a one minute faster effort every five minutes. This can eventually evolve into tougher, more creative sessions as your body begins to tolerate the high demand. You could assign yourself a rigid speed session structure, but if you thrive off variety, here are a few of my personal favourites. Remember, the 80/20 rule still applies even though speed sessions are progressed:

- Hill sprints: 5–10 repeats of 100m hills at 8–9 RPE
- Strides: 5–8 repeats of 100m efforts building up to 85–90% of max sprint

- Distance Intervals: 1K jog (3 RPE) / 1K fast run (6–7 RPE) for 6–10K's
- Time intervals: 10 repeats of 2 mins on, 2 mins off (RPE 3 and 7)
- Pyramids: 5K pyramid (RPE per kilometre 3,5,7,5,3)
- Time–trials: 3K, 5K or 10K
- Intervals + pyramid: 11K (RPE per KM 3,5,3,7,3,9,3,7,3,5,3)

The third and final mistake Jason mentions is when runners lose focus of their strength training. Jason said:

> "I don't even consider strength training as cross training. I consider it a part of the training process. If you want to get better, you have to do some strength training".

Strength training comes in many forms, of which some methods are more advantageous to running performance. Both Jason and I are big advocates of strength training, which will be discussed in more detail throughout Chapter 13.

Research on Training Plans and Performance

A paper published by Arturo Casado and colleagues analysed 85 world-class male runners specialising in five kilometre races, 10 kilometre races, half-marathons and marathons [87]. The performances of these athletes ranged from world-class to competitive national standards and the authors of this paper paid particular attention to their 10 week preparation leading into their goal race.

Casado gathered data from these athletes for seven years and recorded the total distance covered in each of these categories:

- Easy running
- Tempo runs
- Long interval training
- Short interval training
- Competition & time trials

For the purpose of this study, the final four categories were classified as 'deliberate practice' as the subjects of this study rated these activities with high values. After compiling the data, they discovered that the total training volume had the strongest correlation with performance. In other words, irrelevant to the quality of training, higher volume predicts performance outcomes.

Even more interesting, the overall duration spent with easy running was more correlated with performance scores than all 'deliberate practice' sessions combined. The authors concluded:

> "Although deliberate practice activities, particularly tempo runs and short-interval training, are important for improving performance, coaches should note that the non-deliberate practice activity of easy running was crucial in better performances, partly because of its contribution to total distance run".

These findings are aligned with the advice from Jason Fitzgerald earlier. Building a larger base of slow running will aid future performance. The same lead author co-edited a chapter on training volume and intensity distribution from the book *The Science and Practice of Middle and Long-distance Running*. To further comprehend the intensity distribution of training programs and what the research has shown, Casado details the intensity of training in three zones.

Zone Three: Involves high running intensities that surpass your lactate threshold. At intensities above threshold pace, lactate accumulates in the blood faster than it can be removed. The assigned RPE for zone three is between seven and ten.

Zone Two: Includes intensities at threshold pace, or an RPE of either a five or six.

Zone One: refers to intensities below the lactate threshold and can be considered an easy effort at an RPE between one and four.

Considering these training intensities, an athlete can formulate a training approach within a certain training model. Below is a list of three common training models described by researcher Stephen Seiler [89].

The Traditional Pyramidal Model

This describes 80% of training volume in zone one with 20% spent in Zone Two and three. This is what most people consider to be the classic 80/20 training model.

The Polarised Model

This model still involves 80% of training volume in Zone One but works primarily on both intensity extremes. In other words, while 80% is in Zone One, the vast majority of the remaining 20% is spent in Zone Three, entering Zone Two rarely if at all.

The Threshold Model

The threshold model includes a training schedule by which greater than 20% of training is spent in Zone Two.

With these training models implemented, researchers can study athletes to examine which approach fosters the best performance. A great systematic review titled *'The Effect of Periodisation and Training Intensity Distribution on Middle- and Long-Distance Running Performance'* captured 16 papers comparing these three training models and concluded:

> *"Current evidence describes pyramidal and polarised train-ing as more effective than threshold training".* [90]

One paper included in this systematic review, for example, came from Esteve-Lana and colleagues [91]. This study examined the effect of decreasing the training volume performed at threshold intensity on 12 sub-elite endurance runners. They did this while maintaining equal volumes of high intensity work between the two groups. In other words, Zone Three sessions remained the same between groups, but the amount of time spent in Zone Two was removed and added to Zone One volumes. Running performance was assessed five months later with a simulated 10 kilometre cross country race. The pyramidal group displayed a significantly better improvement in performance than the threshold group.

With emerging research, it seems an intensity distribution close to 80/20 will yield superior results and recreational runners should follow this as a template for their training. But this ratio isn't a hard rule. Instead, based on individual preference, it should be seen as a guideline to follow. Many recreational runners are not elite perform-ers wanting to squeeze out every ounce of potential they have. Some runners are content with always running slow, while others enjoy low volume running at higher intensities.

If performance is on your mind, start with the 80/20 intensity distri-bution and see its benefits. If you then decide to try something new, make a small adjustment in the intensity dial as a brief experiment and reevaluate with an honest assessment. The adjustment could be toward 85% low intensity, or it could be 75%. Everyone responds differently to training, so wiggle-room for individual variability should be encouraged. If you notice a decrease in performance, unusual fatigue, soreness, or injury, it may be worth adjusting to an 80/20 baseline.

Running Programs and Data Tracking

A runner of any ability has the option of several data tracking devices to help their training schedule. After all, with the correlation between training loads, injury and performance so closely related, it makes sense to use a device to track workload more accurately.

While devices serve to aid training, also consider that some runners may have a predisposition to become overly reliant on data. Particularly those Type-A personalities, which include traits of competitiveness, achievement-oriented and overly analytical, runners may lose sight of running to feel and adaptability. Runners should, therefore, self-reflect and assess if their data tracking is helping or hindering their training.

Tracking your running and gathering data can definitely assist runners and several options are available. This section will discuss the practical use and the benefits and limitations of each.

Tracking Your Speed and Pace

One of the most simplistic ways of recording your running is to track your pace with a watch or phone with GPS tracking. If your device is tracking your location against time, you can track your real time speed and split per kilometre or mile.

As Chapter two has explained, running speed will significantly influence the load of certain muscle groups and joints, so accurately tracking your speed can be extremely helpful for avoiding spikes in training load. In addition, tracking your pace can ensure you are hitting a predetermined target. For example, an interval session might require short running repeats at a specific speed, or maintaining a race pace across a certain duration.

One of the major limitations with relying on speed and pace is the influence of running with elevation. Level running will keep the pace consistent with intensity, but relying on pace alone will create an effort mismatch if hills are included. Say your goal is to maintain a five minute pace per kilometre throughout your run. Uphill running will raise your effort levels and increase the demand for the muscles and tendons required for propulsion. Circumstances such as this create a large discrepancy in the effort, which leads to data inaccuracy.

Monitoring your Heart Rate

Requiring slightly more equipment and complexity is training to your heart rate. Some watches may record your heart rate but vary in accuracy, while a heart rate strap worn around the chest is recommended and may provide a more accurate measure. Once you track your heart rate with a device, you can then train with certain heart rate zones, allowing greater accuracy than pace alone.

While tracking speed alone has limitations with hills, heart rate will elevate and therefore, can be extremely helpful when training with undulating terrain. So if hills are regularly involved, running within a certain heart rate zone can help maintain effort levels and accuracy to overall training strain.

Calculating your heart rate zones starts with estimating your heart rate max, which involves subtracting your age from 220. While this calculation is broad, it is the most recognised and easy calculation. From there, five heart rate zones can be assigned based on the percentage of your heart rate max (HR Max).

Heart rate max = 220 – age

- Zone 1: 50 to 60% of HR Max
- Zone 2: 60 to 70% of HR Max
- Zone 3: 70 to 80% of HR Max
- Zone 4: 80 to 90% of HR Max
- Zone 5: 90 to 100% of HR Max

Example: Age 35

Heart rate max = 220 – 35 = 185 beats per minute (bpm)

- Zone 1: 93 - 111 bpm
- Zone 2: 111 - 130 bpm
- Zone 3: 130 - 148 bpm
- Zone 4: 148 - 167 bpm
- Zone 5: 167 - 185 bpm

Running within heart rate zones can be great for training to a certain intensity distribution but does have its limitations. One of the major limitations is the other factors outside of exercise that influence heart rate. Common disturbances include outdoor temperature, humidity, and caffeine intake.

Acute high training volumes can also lower resting heart rate during exercise. I first learned about this during my conversation with Chris Schneider on the Run Smarter Podcast [92]. At the time of recording, Chris was a PhD student studying heart rate measures. Chris has contributed to several scientific papers relating to this topic and said:

"When you are doing high training volumes, it is a common phenomenon that heart rate drops. The more you work, the more you fatigue. Therefore, when you usually have an easy run at 130 beats per minute at low intensity, even a heart rate lower than 130 could be an overload when acutely fatigued due to high training volumes".

Power Training

The next option available to runners is allocating training zones based on power. This method usually involves a device that accurately measures your speed, acceleration, elevation and cadence for an instant reading of running power in watts. This device is commonly a foot pod attached to your shoe. In 2021, I hadn't had much experience with power training and decided to interview Nathan Fenton, a power-based running coach, to talk about the pros, cons and practical implementation of power training [93]. Nathan said:

"On a really basic level, power is just a measure of intensity. If you are used to running with heart rate, you can completely swap that out and run to power instead. The same goes for pace zones or RPE zones".

"The difference between the others is power is more objective, with fewer external factors coming into play. If it is hot, you are loaded on caffeine, or you're tired, your heart rate will be higher. There is also a lag. For example, if you did a 20-second hill sprint, your heart rate would only start to climb once you reach the top, whereas power is quick and within two to three seconds you have the reading on your watch".

> *"With pace if you're going up a hill you're fighting against gravity so you are going to have to work harder to get up the hill at the same pace. But, you can use power as an input into how much work you're actually doing, which is good for an undulating course while keeping a steady intensity".*

Once you have the necessary equipment, the first step is to perform a power threshold test. While you can choose several threshold tests, Nathan's favourite involves a three minute max effort and a nine minute max effort. After a warm-up, complete a three minute run as fast yet as consistently as possible. After this, rest but remain warm for 30 minutes and repeat a nine minute test. Once you capture the average power for each test you can calculate your functional threshold power abbreviated as FTP with this formula:

FTP = ((3 min power + 9 min power) /2) x 0.9

For example:
3-minute test: 260W ave
9-minute test: 230W ave

FTP = ((260 + 230) /2) x 0.9 = 220.5w (or rounded to 220)

Now you have an FTP score, you can assign intensity zones to your workouts in the same way you would for heart rate zones. While there is no universal model to follow regarding zones and FTP percentage, choosing and sticking to one model will help maintain consistency when training to power. Below is a model created by coach Steve Palladino.

ZONE	DESCRIPTION	LOWER	UPPER
1a	Easy recovery	50%	65%
1b	Easy warmup	65%	75%

1c	Easy run	75%	80%
2	Long run	81%	87%
3a	Tempo	88%	94%
3b	Threshold	95%	101%
4	Intervals	102%	105%
5	Max Intervals	106%	116%
6	Reps	117%	150%
7	Sprints	150%	300%

Your FTP will change throughout your career based on your level of fitness. For this reason, Nathan recommends retesting a threshold test every six to twelve weeks. That way, your training accurately reflects your fitness.

One major limitation of power training and all the other earlier data tracking suggestions is the lack of internal subjective feedback from the body. Some runners can become narrow sighted in their training and only focus on data, numbers and trends. Rather than holding data as the only factor to guide training, perhaps it should be used as a piece of a more complex puzzle.

Max Paquette and colleagues wrote a paper titled '*Moving Beyond Weekly Distance*', making reference to running distance as only one aspect contributing to training stress [94]. While they mention the importance of tracking data such as weekly distance, you should be cautious about solely relying on it. They mention:

> "It is increasingly evident that running distance should not be the sole training metric, as it can often misrepresent and significantly underestimate training stress".

> "For example, the same 10 kilometre of running distance can result in approximately 14% more foot strikes per

> session and approximately 6% greater accumulated peak vertical ground reaction forces when fatigued versus fresh".
>
> "One of the major limitations of measuring external training load is that it fails to account for how runners feel during a given training session, which is not only influenced by the external load of the training session but also by the runner's state of recovery and daily stress (eg, sleep, illness, relationships, etc)".

Even though this paper focuses on weekly mileage, the same can be said when training to pace, heart rate or power. Regarding the load versus capacity model, devices are becoming more accurate at measuring load but poor at measuring capacity. In addition, devices accurately predict external load to the entire body and are poor at measuring loads to a specific area.

It seems likely that the best approach combines external measurement with internal perception. In other words, combining accurate data such as power zones, with the internal perception of effort, with RPE measurements and TRIMP scores. With this combination, you measure the training loads but process signs of under recovery, fatigue, illness, and psychological stress. All this objective and subjective data can be factored into the decision making process of training.

Running Performance on a Tightrope

When a tightrope walker has progressed to performing outdoors, the weather conditions play a major factor in the performance and outcome. In this analogy, the speed and frequency of the wind represent the training volumes placed on a runner. More specifically, the abrupt changes in training volumes. In other words, if a runner trains at a volume and intensity they have already become accustomed to, then the conditions represent a light breeze. However, as the wind speed and abrupt gusts become more frequent and violent, the more you push the training load beyond your current capabilities.

Considering the 80/20 intensity distribution, this ratio provides enough high speed winds for the journey to be exciting, challenging and essential for skill building. After all, what runner doesn't want to run fast? The ratio also allows plenty of reprieve for the tightrope walker to regain balance, recover, reflect and resume. It would seem irresponsible and idiotic to subject yourself to high wind gusts throughout the majority of your journey. Even if you manage to remain balanced after the first few gusts, do not get overconfident and cocky. Like tightrope walking, running is fun and exciting but also comes with risks. Therefore the safety measures should be implemented accordingly.

Chapter 12 Summary

1. Training programs should avoid abrupt changes in weekly mileage and also abrupt spikes in accumulative TRIMP scores.

2. Improve your running performance by slowly building your running base while mixing in speed sessions at an 80/20 balance.

3. Data trackers such as heart rate monitors and power meters can be effective tools for training when combined with internal perceived efforts.

Action Items

1. Practice incorporating your RPE into your training.

2. Once comfortable with RPE measurements, start calculating your daily and weekly TRIMP.

3. Combine these calculations with real time effort levels and base your current and future training decisions on each method.

CHAPTER THIRTEEN

THE MISCONCEPTION OF HEAVY LIFTING

A few weeks passed, and Pete's running program was in full swing. His plan had him running four days per week with a seven kilometre run on the weekend. Almost all of his running called for an RPE of three to four out of ten and he was feeling happy with this approach. He enjoyed the low-intensity sessions, knowing it was the safest way to build a bigger base.

Once again, sitting in the physiotherapy waiting room, Pete was still unsure of Daniel's plan for the day's session. Daniel appeared around the corner and welcomed him through the clinic. They walked right past the consultation room and into the gym at the back of the studio.

Daniel explained that Pete had made a great start to increase his performance. A well structured progressive running program containing a well balanced intensity distribution was essential. However, the only strength training experience Pete had encountered was the rehabilitation exercises he had done to overcome an injury. This time, his strength training needed to focus on increasing running performance.

Pete looked around and saw a long line of racked dumbbells. Each set grew larger along the rack, each one more intimidating than the last. Every other piece of equipment was foreign to him. Daniel reassured him that he wouldn't be lifting heavy weights initially, and he would start slowly to make sure he was comfortable with all the assigned exercises. This session was designed to help him learn the basic movements.

Firstly, Daniel picked up a long thin wooden dowel, placed it across his shoulders and demonstrated a squat technique. Since squats would be a foundational movement throughout his running career, he wanted to make sure Pete was doing them correctly. With his feet placed wider than his hips and turned out, he found it easier to squat at a lower depth. Daniel ensured Pete's back was positioned well, and his hip and ankle mobility facilitated a good squat technique.

Next, they moved on to a deadlift. Daniel mentioned that a squat primarily strengthens the glutes and quads, while a deadlift strengthens the glutes and hamstrings. Daniel demonstrated by slowly hinging his hips backwards while holding the thin, wooden dowel across his mid-thigh. Simultaneously, the dowel brushed down his thighs and past his knees while keeping the shin bones vertical.

Daniel executed the deadlift perfectly, but it took several attempts for Pete to grasp it. Whenever he sat back into the movement, he felt off balance and often fell backwards. Daniel explained that the top half of his body needed to counterweight the action by moving forward. This felt unnatural for him, but he was determined to practice over the next few days.

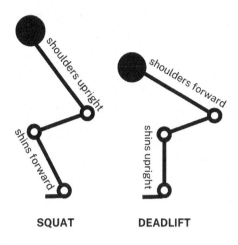

SQUAT   **DEADLIFT**

The lunge came more naturally to Pete. He was instructed to hold a dumbbell in each hand by his side throughout the set. They worked together to find a challenging yet achievable weight while completing eight repetitions on each side.

Last on the list was a single leg heel raise that Pete was familiar with during his achilles rehabilitation. Daniel warned Pete that every repetition needed to go through a full range of movement and perhaps performing in front of a mirror would be helpful. They found a challenging but achievable weight that involved 12 repetitions on each side.

Pete's running schedule was updated to include two strength sessions per week. One session doubled on top of a running day, leaving him with two remaining rest days. Daniel explained that the number of repetitions for each exercise ranged between 10 to 12. While these exercises were new, it was best to work within a higher repetition range with a weight that offers a challenge after 12 repetitions. However, as he got stronger, he could add more weight. Eventually, the goal was to surpass the 10 to 12 range and complete four sets of eight challenging repetitions for each exercise.

To avoid complacency, Daniel created a progression chart for Pete to follow. He was instructed to progress to the next assigned phase once the exercise became comfortable and didn't present significant muscle soreness the following day.

Pete was a bit confused, since he was training for a marathon, wouldn't lighter exercises with higher repetitions condition his body for endurance? Daniel told him that although it made logical sense, heavy strength training would trigger a different stimulus than running, which would then carry over to aid running performance. He mentioned adaptations such as higher propulsion force and stronger, stiffer tendons which would result in greater running efficiency. While endurance is an important quality to train for, Pete was already achieving this during his running sessions. While in the gym, it would be best to take the opportunity to diversify and build on existing resilience.

Pete trusted Daniel's guidance and agreed to start the next day. Daniel was happy to let him use the clinic gym facilities until he organised a local gym membership. On his way out, Daniel told Pete to book a session in four weeks and to bring his running shoes.

MON	TUE	WED	THU	FRI	SAT	SUN
Strength	5km run 3 RPE	Rest	6km run 4–5 RPE Strength	5k 3 RPE	Rest	8k run 3 RPE

Pete's Strength Program

1. Barbell back squats 3x12 with an empty barbell (20kgs)

2. Barbell romanian deadlifts 3x12 with an empty barbell (20kgs)
3. Alternate lunges 3x10 on each side with a 5kg dumbbell in each hand
4. Standing single leg heel raises 3x12 each side with a 7kg dumbbell

Strength training progressions: *progress every 2 weeks or as the body allows*

	SQUATS	DEADLIFTS	LUNGES	HEEL RAISES
PHASE 1	3x12 20kgs	3x12 20kgs	3x10 2x5kg	3x12 7kgs
PHASE 2	3x10 30kgs	3x10 30kgs	3x8 2x8kg	3x12 12kgs
PHASE 3	3x8 40kgs	3x8 40kgs	3x6 2x10kg	3x12 15kgs
PHASE 4	3x10 45kgs	3x10 45kgs	3x8 2x12kg	3x12 20kgs

Run Smarter Lesson 13

A strength and conditioning program is key for runners looking to increase their running performance. This does sound counterintuitive, but fortunately, there is good research to back up the performance benefits of heavy lifting. A runner can look at an interesting, well designed study released in 2019 by Fei Li and colleagues to highlight this point [95].

The participants in this eight week study included 28 collegiate runners, each with a minimum running experience of four years. The participants performed identical running schedules while the study was taking place. Next, they were divided into three groups matched by age, body composition, VO2max, and five kilometre running time.

1. Complex strength + endurance training (10 runners): This group incorporated heavy strength with power based exercises. They performed three sets of six exercises paired into three groupings. The first pair included a back squat and a drop jump from a 40 centimetre box. The second involved bulgarian squats with single leg hops. The last pairing included a romanian deadlift, with a double leg hurdle hop of 50 centimetres. These complex movements involved heavy loads (with 80–85% of their one repetition maximum) for five or six repetitions. The recovery time between sets was four minutes.

2. Heavy strength training + endurance training (9 runners): This group performed the same back squat, bulgarian squat and deadlift but excluded the power based exercises. To ensure that both groups had a similar workload, the heavy strength group added two additional sets for each exercise to match group one. The repetitions remained at five per exercise with a recovery time of three mins between sets.

3. Strength endurance training + endurance training (9 runners): This group performed the exercises as the other two groups but reduced the load to 40% of their one repetition maximum. As a result, the repetitions were 20 for the squats and deadlifts, while the Bulgarian squat called for 15 repetitions on each side. Like the heavy strength group, five sets were allocated.

After the eight week intervention, participants in the first and second groups demonstrated a significant improvement in running economy at 12 and 14 kilometres per hour. Only the complex group showed a significant improvement at 16 kilometres per hour.

For more tangible findings, both the complex training and heavy strength training groups showed a significant improvement in their five kilometre running performance, including an almost 3% improvement in the complex training group. When converted to time, this resulted in a 27 second improvement. The Fei Li paper is only one cherry picked example, but more robust literature has also been published on this topic.

In 2016, Benedito Denadai and colleagues conducted a systematic review focusing on strength training benefits for endurance athletes [96]. This review uncovered 16 previously published papers for analysis. Upon compiling the data, they concluded:

> *"During short-to-medium concurrent training periods, explosive training and heavy weight training seem to have similar positive effects on running economy of endurance athletes".*

But why do runners benefit from running once they implement strength training? It is only natural to think that we need to only train our muscles for endurance. When I talk about heavy strength training benefits, I envision having three energy buckets in my running inventory: an endurance bucket, a strength bucket and a power bucket. Because runners love running, they spend most of their weekly schedule filling up their endurance buckets. This desire continues into the weight room when a runner decides to commit to low weight, high repetition exercises. With this approach, the runner continues to fill up an already full endurance bucket, ignoring the other two, relatively empty buckets. As I continually reinforce with my clients, you should spend your cardio days training the body for endurance, but while you're in the gym, dedicate this time to tap into other energy systems. The result is a well rounded, resilient athlete with a full endurance bucket and a handy strength and power supply.

This was discussed on episode 85 of the Run Smarter Podcast when I interviewed physiotherapist and strength coach Trang Nguyen. Trang discussed the benefits of strength training for runners and eloquently said:

> *"Strength and conditioning is there to complement your running and is an adjunct to endurance training. It is there to achieve all the other attributes to help you thrive and perform even better as a runner. It is there to work on all the missing links or areas that endurance might miss out on. To fill in those gaps and develop a runner as a whole".* [97]

Does Strength Training Change Running Technique?

The rationale makes sense. Observe the running technique and if there are any obvious imperfections, assign strengthening exercises to correct them. This would seem important for running inefficiencies that look sloppy or show signs of poor control. These common traits include a contralateral hip drop, excessive pronation, and knee internal rotation introduced in Chapter five. The thinking process goes like this:

Strengthening the gluteus medius should:

- Reduce a contralateral hip drop
- Help a collapsing knee
- Widen a narrow step width

Strengthening the knee should:

- Fix internal knee rotation

Strengthening the foot and ankle should:

- Reduce the rate and magnitude of pronation

However, I am yet to see, and find it difficult to believe, that strengthening your muscles will create a visible change in running technique. From what I have observed, if I witness sloppy running traits and only assign a 12 week strength program, the runner jumps back on the treadmill and looks exactly the same. It seems the forces of running are too great to correct for most major joints in the body.

For example, if a runner has pain on the outside of their hip while running and upon assessment elicits a moderate hip drop, all the banded exercises, single leg squats, and lunges wouldn't stack up to meet the rapid ground reaction forces when hitting the ground during a running action. After committing to a tailored strength program, they would likely run with the same moderate hip drop. There may be a few rare examples that disprove my thoughts, but for most, the visible changes in running technique from strength training alone seem non-existent or negligible.

This shouldn't discredit strengthening exercises. While the supposedly insufficient running traits aren't corrected with strengthening exercises, the capacity of those tissues increases, and therefore, can tolerate greater running volumes. From an injury prevention and rehabilitation standpoint, this translates into tolerating higher running volumes without symptoms. Using the earlier example of the runner with hip pain, after 12 weeks of strength training, they may move in the same way, but they run with greater confidence and less pain across longer distances. Essentially, through strength training, the vulnerable area has become robust and has achieved a greater capacity to tolerate running forces.

This begs the question of what interventions can assist if you are exhibiting running inefficiencies. If the traits identified are minor and do not directly impact a current or past injury, I would be reluctant to change anything. However, if a running inefficiency warrants change, then gait retraining is the answer. In other words, if a runner displays a narrow step width, instead of spending 12 weeks building the hip abductors in the gym, simply try stepping wider. The process may require practice and visual feedback through video analysis, but the change is instantaneous without implementing strength training.

The decision to change your running technique may require guidance and clinical justification from a professional but can have profound effects, particularly on injured runners. In the case of a hip drop or internal knee rotation, gait retraining with a higher cadence may be of benefit. Research has shown that increasing the cadence in runners with knee pain significantly influenced hip and knee mechanics. Chris Bramah and colleagues manipulated the cadence of 12 participants and concluded:

> "A single session of gait retraining using a 10% increase in step rate resulted in significant improvements in running kinematics. This showed significant reductions in peak contralateral pelvic drop, hip adduction and knee flexion". [98]

How Does Heavy Strength Training Help Endurance Athletes?

Richard Blagrove is a running researcher and author of the book *'Strength & Conditioning For Endurance Running'* [99]. He lists several physiological adaptations runners produce when strength training. The first includes the ability to produce a higher force during the push-off action. This means the muscles primarily responsible for forwarding propulsion can generate higher forces if required.

Heavy Strength Training Benefit #1: Greater Force Production

When adapting to heavy strength training, the tendons of the lower limb become stiffer. Unlike the benefits of mobile joints, tendon stiffness provides tremendous advantages to running economy. Imagine running with strong metal springs under your shoes. The spring will compress and store energy as your shoe impacts the ground. This stored energy will then convert into propulsion during the push-off phase. If your shoe springs offer greater stiffness, they can perform more efficiently, and a stiff, rigid spring will yield better returns in energy.

Conversely, a spring with less stiffness will dissipate stored energy as it becomes misshapen and demonstrates unintended wobbles. The amount of stored energy will not equal the degree of output.

When I assess runners, a particularly helpful test I administer is 10 single leg barefoot hops on each side. As simple as this test may be, it can provide a lot of information. I can compare the height, confidence levels, launch strategies, landing strategies, and the overall stiffness of the lower limb. With this test, it is easy to separate those who offer an efficient, stiff spring and those who do not. For instance, listening to the hard impact of the heel hitting the ground may indicate the achilles tendon lacks recoil strength. Other indications of reduced stiffness include an increased ground contact time, increased knee bend and flailing arms for momentum. A runner who can consistently demonstrate a powerful hop and show minimal movement from their hip, knee and ankle translates into stiff and powerful tendons.

Heavy Strength Training Benefit #2: Greater Tendon Stiffness

Another benefit strength training offers is a greater speed reserve. Think of the mid-race mini-surges a runner needs to demonstrate to shake their competitors or the final sprint at the end. In 2018, I needed a change-up in my training. I managed a few mild running injuries and wanted to give strength training a go. At the time, I was recreationally attending sprint-distance triathlons and partaking in some home gym strength exercises, but I had never picked up a barbell in my life. Needing a change, I decided to sign up at my local CrossFit gym and had an instructor teach me the basic lifts.

After six months of squats, deadlifts, lunges, box jumps and all the other compound movements the gym offered, I felt stronger than ever. That winter, I signed up for my favourite trail running series and noticed a significant improvement in my uphill running. It would be the only time I'd be passing large groups of runners at once. It felt easy, and I felt powerful. I finished the series in third place for my age group, and the strength work I committed to played a huge part. Now, my commitment to strength training is stronger than ever. Here are some of my favourite exercises:

- Back squats
- Romanian deadlifts
- Single leg deadlifts
- Kettlebell swings
- Dumbbell lunges

- Bulgarian split squats
- Bent knee heel raises
- Banded crab walks
- Box jumps

Heavy Strength Training Benefit #3: Greater Speed Reserves

In episode 49 of the Run Smarter Podcast, my guest Jason Fitzgerald talked about his take on strength training. He said:

> *"If runners understood all of the amazing benefits strength training gave them, I am sure they would be in the gym a couple of times per week. Improving your form, your efficiency, recruiting more muscle fibres and sprinting faster at the end of a race. You are going to have stronger muscles, connective tissues and bones, and that is going to help protect you against the repetitive stress of running".* [100]

Greater force production
+
Greater tendon stiffness
+
Greater speed reserves
=
Better running efficiency
=
Better running performance

Common Strength Training Fears

1. Fear of starting something new: It is tough committing to something when you have zero experience. It is human behaviour to gravitate towards activities we are naturally good at. Making a start in strength training doesn't need to be

complicated. Learning a basic squat and deadlift action can only take a few minutes if provided with the right guidance.

Ask a personal trainer or friend with weight training experience if they can comment on your form, along with any corrections to be made. When I observe a runner who is initially reluctant to start strength training, I notice two outcomes. Either they start to enjoy their strength training sessions, or their motivation to strength train elevates when they see the carry over in running performance.

2. Fear of injury: The two main desires within the running population are to increase running performance safely and reduce injury risk. Getting injured is a horrible situation for a runner of any ability. It is, therefore, a big hurdle to overcome if you believe strength training will increase your injury susceptibility. However, strength training is safer than running if your approach is sensible.

   A survey from Brian Hamill published in the Journal of Strength and Conditioning Research found that two to four injuries occurred for every 10,000 hours of weight-lifting activities [101]. In comparison, Nielsen and colleagues reviewed all available literature and reported 25 to 74 injuries for every 10,000 hours in marathon runners [102]. For novice runners who run 30 to 90 minutes per week, this incidence rate dramatically increases to 330 for every 10,000 hours of training.

   To start a strength program safely, you must consider the same adaptation principles detailed in part one of this book. It is not uncommon for runners to develop low back pain when adding deadlifts into their training, for instance, or knee pain to develop after weighted lunges. For this reason, it is best to ensure good quality and a full range of movement of a particular exercise before increasing the weight. Once you increase the weight, ensure you allow enough time for your body to adapt. With a carefully regimented program, the risk of injury is low.

3. Fear of muscle mass: It is understandable to look at a typical gym going bodybuilder and conclude they are not built for running. This is true. Runners need to be lean to increase their running economy. But the likelihood of you putting on enough muscle mass to hinder performance is extremely small.

   Your body places a higher priority to adapt to cardiovascular fitness when it competes with other strength routines. In other words, if you participated in strength training twice per week and concurrently ran five days per week, your body would prioritise the endurance component when undertaking the adaptation process. While you will still get stronger in the gym, your body will hinder your ability to gain muscle mass.

   You may put on the necessary muscle mass required for optimal performance, but it will not be excessive with the correct training balance. This is why bodybuilders limit their cardiovascular input. However, if you're looking to increase your running performance, implementing both strength and cardio means you'll get the best of both worlds. Illustrated below is a bodybuilder's routine compared to a generic running strength routine. One routine fosters the development of muscle mass while the other develops strength without unnecessary muscle mass gain.

BODYBUILDER'S STRENGTH ROUTINE	RUNNER'S STRENGTH ROUTINE
Strength sessions 5+ days per week	Strength sessions 2 days per week
Typically 4–6 sets of 4–8 repetitions	Typically 3–4 sets of 8–10 repetitions
Very minimal cardio workouts per week	Vast majority cardio workouts per week
High caloric intake, High protein intake	Moderate caloric intake, well-balanced

4. Fear of muscle soreness: You may have experienced severe muscle soreness after a strenuous workout in the past. Delayed onset muscle soreness or DOMS is the essential rebuilding phase of the muscular system and can be particularly excessive when trying a new workout. If you have experienced this yourself, perhaps after a high intensity interval training (HIIT) class you have never attended before, it may impact your running performance for one to two days.

This is a fear a lot of runners have. They worry if they participate in strength training twice per week, the DOMS will carry over into their week and disrupt their running sessions. Here is a list of considerations to allay your fears:

- Expect excessive DOMS initially: Yes, you can anticipate greater DOMS than usual when attempting something new. Persist through this introduction phase with consistency and your body will make the necessary adaptations. After this initial phase, mild DOMS lasting one to two days is expected but should not disrupt your training.

- Ensure the right intensity: If you persevere through the introduction phase and your level of DOMS is above moderate and persists beyond two days, your strength training may require an adjustment. Either the level of intensity is too high, the weight you're lifting is too heavy, or your recovery is inadequate. Make the correct adjustments to ensure a non disruptive balance.

- Schedule your workouts carefully: Through trial and error, or with the help of a coach, you can schedule your workouts carefully throughout the week to ensure fresh legs during harder running sessions such as scheduling your strength training one day before an easy run. Another option is to design a more challenging run session in the morning and a strength training session that afternoon.

- DOMS won't impact performance: You may perceive DOMS to be debilitating, especially during an early morning warm up. But once an adequate warm-up has been performed, in most cases, DOMS has minimal hindrance on your running performance.

- Reduce the frequency close to races: As a general rule of thumb. You should commit yourself to two strength sessions per week. If you are preparing for a long-distance event, reducing the frequency to one session per week at the peak of your training can be helpful. This one session can maintain your strength while adding more recovery time or opportunities to add extra mileage.

5. Not having enough time: When I interviewed Dr Richard Blagrove on episode 14 of the Run Smarter Podcast [103], he carefully listed some suggestions if runners found it hard to

allocate time for strength training. Firstly, he mentioned that if a runner was running six or more days per week, it would yield better results to drop one or two running days and replace them with strength sessions.

Secondly, Richard advised runners to spread smaller training units throughout the week if time allocation is a problem. For instance, instead of finding time for one 60 minute strength session, allocating three 20 minute sessions throughout the week may be more manageable.

Strength Training Complacency

As mentioned above when discussing the fear of injury, you should ensure each particular exercise is executed correctly with a full range of movement before increasing the weight. This will reduce the risk of excessive strain and exceeding the adaptation zone of a particular area. However, you should always intend to progress your gym workouts once the body is ready.

Too many times I have encountered runners who strength train and maintain the same routine for several months without progression. They simply get stuck in a groove and find enough satisfaction in their workout to warrant their complacency. Like Daniel's approach with Pete, I often create progression charts for my runners to follow. Each phase contains a harder intensity and encourages the runner to progress once the body allows it.

Also mentioned above in the Fei Li paper [95], runners should be encouraged to progress their exercises by increasing their weight, not by increasing the repetitions. I believe hovering around a repetition range of 8 to 12 will return good running results for most runners.

I follow a particular progression for my squats, deadlifts, lunges, and heel raises.

I start with a weight I find challenging throughout three sets of eight. My subsequent progressions maintain this weight and progress to 10 and 12 repetitions. Once I achieve 12 repetitions of this weight, I increase the weight and drop back to 8 repetitions. This cycle serves me well and ensures I am always progressing. Other performance coaches argue a repetition range of 5 to 8 will yield better results. While I agree with their opinions, operating with such a heavy weight will require years of experience in the gym.

Developing a Strong Tightrope Walker

In exercise, the rule of specificity states that the body will adapt to the specific type of training undertaken. Following this rule, you'll often hear that in order to become a better runner, you should dedicate more time to running. While this is true for most runners, those already operating at a high mileage may spike their risk of an overuse injury if their solution to improvement continues to be more mileage.

The same argument can be said for your tightrope walking skills. If you are already committing the necessary hours of tightrope walking, you could further enhance your skills by supplementing other drills and routines that are transferable to performance. For instance, the longer the balance beam you hold, the easier it is to adjust balance when unexpected winds come your way. Building the strength of your arms and upper back in order to handle a longer, heavier beam will be of great advantage when executing a difficult walk. In addition, building upon foot strength to grip the rope and act as a sturdy foundation will be easily transferable to performance.

While in normal circumstances, constantly practising on a tightrope and falling offers little consequence, in this particular analogy, falling even during practice represents the birth of a running related injury. Therefore, minimal to no falling should be the priority.

The skills, drills and strength training may not look like the desired action. In the same way, upper body strengthening for tightrope walking may seem strange. Exercises like deadlifts, heel raises and squats look nothing like a running action. However, the transferability to a greater performance will still be achieved.

Chapter 13 Summary

1. Strength training is essential and complementary to endurance performance.

2. Once a runner has gained enough gym experience, heavier weighted exercises with an 8 to 12 repetition range will be superior compared to lighter weights with higher repetitions.

3. Provided a sensible approach with safe technique, the risk of injury when strength training is low.

4. The fear of muscle mass gain or severe DOMs inhibiting your running is unlikely provided the weekly schedule is well balanced.

Action Items

1. If not strength training already, start a minimalist strength program consisting of squats, deadlifts, lunges and heel raises.

2. Enlist the help of a personal trainer or friend if you are not confident in your technique or starting dosage.

3. Work two strength training sessions into your training week.

4. Find a nice schedule where one day of DOMS following a gym session does not disrupt your running workouts.

CHAPTER FOURTEEN

SHOE SELECTION

After receiving his strength program, Pete walked out of the clinic feeling strong and optimistic. Everything was coming together, and he was getting sound advice in multiple areas of his training. He had a progressive strength program to build upon his running performance and he felt all the pieces of the puzzle coming together to set him up for success.

While driving home from the physiotherapy clinic, Pete started thinking about other avenues to assist in his performance. Deep in thought, he lost concentration on the road and was late to recognise the changing traffic light. He slammed on the brake and halted to a stop. Feeling his foot pressed firmly on the brake pedal, he was struck with an epiphany. Advice on a perfect running shoe!

Pulling over to the side of the road, he got Daniel on the phone and asked him what footwear he recommended. Daniel advised him to check out a certain shoe store nearby and to ask for Jane once he got there.

Two days later, Pete walked into the shoe store recommended by Daniel. The two storey warehouse was full of high rise aisles containing thousands of shoes. He approached the counter and asked the sales assistant if Jane was available. After a friendly smile and a head nod, the sales assistant walked into the backroom to find Jane. Pete was excited to meet this lady. Looking her up online before entering the store, he discovered Jane was a running coach, a biomechanist, and a running shoe lover.

Waiting for Jane to appear, Pete casually walked around the store. He quickly spotted the section of the warehouse dedicated to running shoes. The display was overwhelming. If the vibrant colours of the shoes weren't distracting enough, the complexity of shoe types would have any novice runner scratching their head. Looking at the extensive selection, he picked up a shoe labelled for trail runners. He was surprised by the weight of the shoe. It was considerably lighter than his current running shoes. He also noticed the large width at the front of the shoe that housed the toes.

Another shoe that caught Pete's eye looked futuristic. It had double the material of the previous shoe, mostly stacked underneath and around the back of the heel. Upon picking it up, he was again surprised by its light weight. However, this shoe was incredibly stiff. He tried ringing it like a wet cloth and bending it in half. Despite his efforts, it wouldn't budge. Placing the shoe back on the shelf and taking a step back, he couldn't help but feel anxious. All these different shoes consisted of different weights, flexibilities and levels of support. It was all too much.

Then, Pete felt a tap on his shoulder. He turned around, and a bubbly, energetic young lady stood in front of him. He returned a smile and looked down at her name badge, which said 'Jane: Store manager'. Pete introduced himself and updated Jane on his goal to break his previous marathon time. Jane's eyes lit up and she spent five minutes probing into his circumstances. She asked about his past running injuries, overall running mileage and the primary running terrain. He updated Jane on his past achilles and knee injuries and detailed his training mileage and his love for occasional trail running.

Jane then questioned Pete about his current running shoes. Most importantly, if he found them comfortable. He was luckily wearing his running shoes and took them off to show Jane. He reported that he found his current shoes very comfortable and hadn't had any problems with them. She flipped the shoes upside down and took a careful examination of the outer layer of the sole. She handed the shoes back to Pete and disappeared into the back of the store.

During Jane's absence, he decided to inspect the soles of his shoes. He had never thought about analysing his shoes before. Looking closely at the grooves, he noticed a significant fade residing around the back of the shoe. The wear and tear seemed equal on both shoes, but he had no idea what this meant. Jane appeared holding several shoeboxes with a look of excitement on her face. She explained that since he was not currently injured and found his current shoes comfortable, she had selected pairs that were similar.

Pete had a look of disappointment. He was looking for a competitive edge with a high tech shoe. Jane could sense his disappointment and reassured him that similar is good because he had already adapted to these types and it would be risky to transition to a different shoe halfway through marathon training. Jane continued to explain that his current shoes weigh 350 grams which is quite heavy. However, the selection she had chosen were only 200 grams. This would go a long way to improving his running economy.

Pete spent the next 20 minutes finding a shoe he found most comfortable. They all felt similar to his old shoes but the lighter sensation was noticeable. He narrowed his decision down to one pair which Jane suggested he try on the treadmill. After sliding on the shoes and stepping on the treadmill, he felt an incredible surge of energy. The sensation of running with lighter shoes felt effortless. Compared to these, his old shoes felt like rubber bricks. He stepped off the treadmill with a big smile on his face and walked straight to checkout.

When paying for his new shoes, Jane explained the likelihood of injury was quite low when transitioning into these new shoes because they were similar to his previous shoes, but she still recommended a gradual transition phase to be on the safe side. She recommended running in these new shoes 5% of the time for the first week and added 10% each week thereafter. Once he has adapted to these new shoes, he could start a 50/50 rotation between his two pairs and commit to the newer shoes during his faster running sessions.

Pete was happy to take the patient, sensible approach. The risk of injury was not worth it in this training phase. When Jane handed over his brand new running shoes, he visualised his new and improved speed sessions, which sparked a question. He asked Jane for her recommendations on a good running warm up. As he asked his question, she was pulled away by another staff member and asked him to return tomorrow morning when the store was quiet. Pete walked out of the store, already wearing his new shoes. Once again, he felt one step closer to success.

Run Smarter Lesson 14

When concentrating on the equipment you have available to enhance your running performance, shoe selection is your one and only option. It is what I love about running: all you need is to slip on your shoes and head out the front door.

With so many different opinions, however, it can be difficult to identify what shoe is best for you. This book has already uncovered in Chapter five that businesses compete for your attention and money. In the world of running, there are no bigger companies than shoe brands. These big businesses put extraordinary amounts of money into marketing campaigns with the aim of making you desire the newest running shoe. Also highlighted in Chapter five was the poor regulation hovering over these companies when promising performance outcomes. They simply do not fall under the same scrutiny or regulations as research advisors. They can cherry pick flimsy studies and manipulate results to push whatever narrative they desire.

These intentions may also trickle down into smaller retail shoe stores. While some stores may have pure intentions to assign the best shoe for your circumstances, it is worth reminding yourself that their business survives off people buying their products. I often hear statements like *'your running shoes need replacing after 500 miles'* or *'you need to replace your shoes because they have lost their cushioning'*. These statements are too broad to decide if a shoe is worth replacing, but perfect advice if the goal is to buy more shoes.

Another factor you should consider before buying running shoes is the accuracy of information provided by staff members. The scope of knowledge will fluctuate throughout the industry, and the information provided may not hold up with the latest research. Like Pete, you may get lucky with a top tier biomechanist to assist, but most running retail stores have a novice salesperson assisting with your enquiries.

A common experience when walking into a shoe store is the staff checking your foot shape, arch height and walking mechanics before assigning a specific range of shoes based on their findings. Assigning stability shoes for those with flat feet is a classic example. The rationale behind this decision is that flat feet require support because the arch collapses and the foot overpronates when walking, therefore, providing a shoe that offers stability underneath the arch would make sense.

Like most of the misconceptions discussed in the book, they make intuitive sense. It may surprise you that research has failed to show a correlation between foot shape and the type of shoe required. In episode 52 of my podcast, I interviewed JF Esculier who is the Leader of Research and Development at The Running Clinic and a clinical assistant professor at the University of British Columbia [100]. Luckily for me, JF was also my first mentor in treating runners. On the podcast, we discussed running shoe misconceptions and shoe selection. Here is one quote from JF during our interview:

> *"I think every shoe has its purpose, but I am very conscious of the evidence. Trying to link research with the marketing of shoe manufacturers sometimes just blows my mind. Because they are promoting so many things and trying to make people believe that these shoes will prevent injuries or treat injuries sometimes and unfortunately it is not based on evidence".*

Foot Shape and Injury Risk

A large study by Rasmus Nielsen and colleagues looked at the running injury rates for many foot postures [105]. They gathered 927 novice runners and categorised them into five different foot postures:

1. Highly supinated (53 people)
2. Supinated (369 people)
3. Neutral (1292 people)
4. Pronated (122 people)
5. Highly pronated (18 people)

Once assigned to a category, participants were provided with a neutral running shoe and instructed to only run in this footwear. The researchers then followed every participant for one year and monitored their running mileage with GPS tracking. After 12 months, the researchers couldn't find any significant differences between the groups and their injury rates. Even more surprising, they found that runners in the pronated category were injured significantly less per 1,000 kilometres run than those labelled as having a neutral foot posture. The research paper concluded:

> *"The results of the present study contradict the widespread belief that moderate foot pronation is associated with an increased risk of injury among novice runners taking up running in a neutral running shoe".*

Should We Aim for Natural, Barefoot Biomechanics?

Runners and health professionals face multiple fallacies when it comes to shoe selection. Over the years, different philosophies have emerged and gained varying amounts of popularity. Minimalist shoes and barefoot running are still regarded highly as they promote natural, barefoot mechanics. Conversely, maximalist shoes are also finding their place in the market. These big, bulky shoes promote support and protection from harsh ground reaction forces theoretically reducing your risk of injury. With such contrasting philosophies arguing the same effect, it's difficult to decide what direction to take.

Chris Napier and Rich Willy released a clever and insightful editorial titled, *'Logical Fallacies in the Running Shoe Debate: Let the Evidence Guide Prescription'* [106]. As the name suggests, the authors break down these beliefs and follow the science. On the topic of minimalist versus maximalist shoes, these authors highlight the lack of evidence when considering any of these paradigms for injury reduction. They state:

> *"In light of the lack of evidence supporting traditional shoe prescription, we must be careful not to view alternative shoe paradigms as suddenly more effective".*

> *"For example, arguing that a greater degree of minimalism promotes natural foot motion may have substance, yet there is no evidence that a more natural foot motion is indeed effective in the prevention of running-related injuries".*

This made sense when I read the research and saw the poor correlation between shoe type and injury. Assessing a runner's foot shape and shoe type is one tiny piece of a large injury prevention puzzle. Remember, most running related injuries are due to an abrupt change in training. When this abrupt change occurs, it increases the likelihood of exceeding tissue capacity. When it comes to injury risk, any other seemingly insufficient abnormalities a runner possesses will be negligible as the body adapts.

For instance, if a runner with flat feet is put into a neutral shoe and asked to run for a year, provided abrupt training errors are absent, that runner will adapt to the shoe. Throughout the year, if the runner continues to build upon their mileage gradually, they will have a significantly lower risk of injury, no matter what type of shoe they were assigned. This is why researchers cannot see a correlation between foot shape, shoe type and injury, because these changes are not considered training errors if administered appropriately.

Running Shoe Selection for Performance

As mentioned above, my podcast conversation with JF Esculier focussed on running shoe misconceptions and shoe selection. The best advice he had for non injured runners looking to thrive in a shoe is to try a variety of different shoes and select the one they find most comfortable.

This follows advice from Benno Nigg and colleagues who published '*The Preferred Movement Path Paradigm: Influence of Running Shoes on Joint Movement*' [107]. The idea behind this paradigm is that everyone presents with different mechanics, mobility and habits. Based on your tailored circumstances, your body will factor in all your stiff points and naturally move through space in a particular way with the least amount of resistance. Essentially, we all have a different preferred movement path. When walking and running in different shoes, some will foster this movement path while others will hinder it. Therefore, selecting the most comfortable shoe is a safe bet once you have tried several different types. Keep in mind that this comfort theory hasn't been tested for reducing the risk of injury but is still highly recommended by JF, myself and many other health professionals to guide shoe prescription.

When it comes to running performance, it is often best to find a comfortable shoe that is also lightweight. Work done by Wouter Hoogkamer and colleagues reached the same conclusion in their 2016 paper [108]. Their study recruited 18 elite male runners who were already performing well and completed a five kilometre race in under 20 minutes.

All the runners that participated were told the primary research objective was to establish a predictive equation for performance based on VO2max and running economy. Each runner would need to participate in weekly three kilometre time trials to gain this data while maintaining a similar diet, sleep, and training pattern. These instructions, however, were deceptive as the runners needed to have an unbiased approach to each trial. Instead, the researchers aimed to study their running economy with different weighted shoes.

The control shoe had no added mass and ranged from 202 grams (size nine) to 225 grams (size eleven) per shoe. For the second pair in each size, the researchers cleverly added 100 grams of lead beads into the tongue of each shoe. For the third pair, the lead remained in the tongue with an additional 200 grams of lead beads in medial and lateral side pockets, which were inconspicuously sewn inside the shoe uppers in the midfoot area. These weight alterations were unbeknownst to the runners performing the three kilometre time trials.

After gathering all the data, the results showed that adding mass to the shoes significantly increased metabolic rate by over 1% per 100 grams. So, adding 300 grams delayed their finish time by 15 seconds for a time trial that averaged 10 minutes and 25 seconds in the control shoes. Other studies have shown similar results. Joel Fuller and colleagues randomised 61 trained runners into a control group and an intervention group. The intervention group participated in a six week program that transitioned into lightweight minimalist shoes. After the six week program, both groups participated in a five kilometre time trial. They found the intervention group had small improvements in running economy at 11 kilometres per hour and moderate gains at 13 kilometres per hour. They concluded:

> *"This study demonstrated that training in minimalist shoes caused small improvements in time-trial performance and moderate improvements in running economy compared with training in conventional shoes. The minimalist shoe group improved time-trial performance by an additional 21 seconds when compared to the conventional shoe group".* [109]

Collectively, it does seem that lighter shoes can carry performance benefits. However, before you rush out to buy the most lightweight shoes possible, it is essential to consider the risks when transitioning your running shoes.

Transitioning Your Running Shoes Safely

Runners will rarely develop an injury because of the shoes they are wearing. Remember, running related injuries are due to abrupt changes in training loads. But if you have adapted to a certain type of shoe and begin running in a different shoe, this could present as an abrupt change. A lot of traditional shoes share similar characteristics such as weight, heel drop, cushioning and support. If this is the case, a gradual transition phase is rarely necessary. However, there are shoes on the market that offer a wide spectrum of characteristics and shoe technologies.

You may be familiar with barefoot or minimalist running shoes. These are often extremely lightweight but commonly sacrifice support. On the other side of the spectrum are the bulky maximalist shoes. These shoes offer high levels of support, and while some foam technologies are emerging as an exception to the rule, they are generally heavier than a traditional shoe. This spectrum is often referred to as the minimalist index and places barefoot qualities closer to 100% and maximalist shoes at 0%.

To transition into your new running shoes safely, you'll need to know where on the minimalist index your body has adapted to, along with the percentage difference with your new shoes. If you are impatient and speed up the transition process, you could put yourself at high risk of injury. This is because a change in shoe quality will shift the demands of your muscles and tendons, increasing the likelihood of overload. Generally speaking, shoes that display barefoot qualities increase the demand for structures below the knee. With less support offered by the shoe, the plantar fascia, bones of the feet, achilles tendon, shinbone and calf muscles need to take on higher requirements. Conversely, a supportive, bulkier shoe will offer a reprieve for these structures but more load accumulates at the knee and hip joints.

A study by Matthew Salzler and colleagues observed this risk first-hand [110]. They recruited 14 runners who were previously running in traditional running shoes and fitted them with five-toed barefoot shoes. After providing them with these shoes, they provided educational material on transitioning the shoes and advised them to make a slow transition according to the recommended guidelines. The researchers discovered that 12 out of 14 runners had sustained an injury during the followup period, with 10 of these injuries involving the foot or calf complex. More importantly, when questioning the runners afterwards, they learned that not one runner complied with all industry recommended guidelines.

This is a prime example of how you shouldn't operate with new shoes. First, these runners were accustomed to traditional shoes, which are placed around 50% on the minimalist index. Next, they forced their bodies to adapt to five-finger barefoot running shoes, which is an extreme adjustment as these shoes are placed close to 100% on the minimalist index. Lastly, all runners displayed a lack of patience and diligence in the transition process. This combination of training errors created a recipe for disaster, resulting in 86% of the group developing an injury.

My own experience with minimalist shoes almost resulted in the same fate. It was two years into my running career when I learned about the positive effects of lightweight shoes. At this time, I was pretty oblivious to a safe transition process and the Run Smarter principles. I bought a pair of Inov-8 minimalist shoes weighing 150 grams. In hindsight, I was transitioning from a shoe that was 40% to a shoe that was 80% on the minimalist index, and when I say transition, I'll use that term lightly. At this point, I had just completed my first half marathon and was moving ahead into full marathon training. My weekly mileage was 40 kilometres, and my long run was approaching 25 kilometres. With such a solid running foundation to work with, I committed to a four kilometre tempo run in my new shoes. This was the first time I had ever worn them.

During the tempo run, I felt amazing and fast, and like Pete on the treadmill, it felt effortless. After three kilometres, I began to notice my calves and feet burning with fatigue. This was quite foreign to me but I persisted through the remaining kilometre. At the end of my run, my calves began to tighten up. For the next three days, I experienced severe DOMS in my feet and calf muscles. I was easily able to manage two hour long runs in my traditional shoes, but fell apart with a 16 minute tempo run in my minimalist shoes. I believe my calf complex was quite strong from my basketball days, and with my long list of injuries, I haven't had one achilles or calf issue. If that wasn't the case, I think that tempo run would have resulted in an injury.

After I learned my lesson, I took my minimalist running more gradually. I have since grown accustomed to the minimalist qualities and run most of my mileage in these shoes. On days my feet or calves require some downtime, I have my traditional shoes on standby.

The take home message is that runners need to take the transitional process carefully. To assist the process, there are clinical guidelines offered to those who want to transition to minimalist footwear. Joe Warne and Allison Gruber released a paper titled '*Transitioning to Minimal Footwear: a Systematic Review of Methods and Future Clinical Recommendations*' and produced a helpful list that concluded [111]:

> "*Given the individual responses to all factors, as well as the difficulty in combining all factors in the determination of being transitioned to minimalist footwear, we may have to accept that no clear timeline can be established using a single scientific method*".

1. We suggest that a transition period of no less than four to eight weeks should be used because of general muscular adaptation to training, taking this period of time.

2. Given the dramatic change in the demand of the foot structure and musculature with minimalist footwear use, a period of preparation could include some light walking and every day, non uniform loading whilst wearing minimalist footwear or going barefoot may be of benefit before any running activity has begun.

3. We suggest that the initial overall running volume is decreased in the region of 10 to 20% in the first two weeks to reduce the risk of bony injury from unfamiliar repetitive loading.

4. We suggest starting at 10% of your daily running volume or up to a maximum of 10 minutes in your new shoes. This can be increased by 5 to 10% per week.

5. Females and males over 85 kilograms in weight should perhaps consider a more conservative programme.

6. It is suggested that some proportion of running takes place in different footwear and on numerous different surfaces to help develop the ability to deal with multiple stressors in various environments. This way, we may develop more resilient runners and combat the dramatic injury rates seen today.

When is it Time to Buy New Shoes?

You will find a wide array of opinions if you search for an answer for the right time to replace your old shoes. As mentioned above, some are based on the number of months running in the shoe (i.e. you need to replace your shoes every eight months). While this may be a helpful guideline, this advice doesn't contain enough information to warrant a replacement. Two runners could buy an identical pair of shoes on the same day. Suppose the first runner runs six times per week averaging 50 kilometres. In that case, their shoes are expected to be replaced a lot sooner than the second runner, who runs three days per week and only accumulates 10 kilometres.

Another, more accurate piece of advice is based on the total mileage of the shoe. For example, you need to replace your shoes every 500 kilometres. This holds more information than the first opinion but lacks some crucial details. For instance, your running technique, sole material, and running terrain all directly impact the life of a shoe. A great example was the Inov-8 minimalist shoes I mentioned previously. When I purchased those shoes I was still living in our family home which meant my running took place on loose gravel walking tracks. Every shuffling step I took created a sound of gravel sliding underneath my shoes. This is not great terrain for shoe longevity.

I was also a mid-foot runner with a narrow step width which subjected the sole underneath my fifth toe to most of the ground impact. We will discuss shoe wear and tear patterns further in Chapter 16, but suffice to say the gravel ate through the entire sole of my shoe within five months. Fast forward several years later, and I am running with an identical pair of shoes with a few changes. I now commit those shoes to roads and footpaths. Additionally, I have since widened my step width to dissipate the loads across my midfoot evenly. As a result, my Inov-8 shoes have lasted over three years to date.

The third opinion on shoe replacement is to retire shoes when they lose cushioning or support. The idea behind this decision is that once the cushioning diminishes, it could place higher ground reaction loads on the runner and increase injury risk.

Pui Kong and colleagues conducted the first ever longitudinal study to describe the kinetics and kinematics of running in new and worn shoes. They randomly assigned 15 males and 15 females to air-cushioned, gel-cushioned and spring-cushioned shoes and analysed the running mechanics of each runner in these new shoes and retested them after 200 miles. They found that as cushioning qualities degrade, despite the type of cushioning, the runner unconsciously increased their stance phase when running. In other words, they changed their mechanics to keep ground reaction forces consistent. They concluded that:

> *'Worn shoes cause kinematic changes but do not influence force variables.'*

So, what guidelines should you follow if a shoe mileage or degraded cushioning isn't enough data to warrant shoe replacement? In episode 52 of the podcast, my guest JF Esculier attempted to clear this up [104]. His advice followed two simple guidelines. First, you want to change your shoes if they become uncomfortable. This follows the *'Preferred movement path'* rationale when initially selecting a shoe. In my experience, it takes significant shoe wear and tear before running becomes uncomfortable. Secondly, you want to replace your shoes if the old shoes abruptly alter your mechanics. This requires an abrupt change due to wear and tear, different to the gradual shift in the stance time like the Pui Kong study. For example, I have caught myself changing foot strikes in the past because the shoe undersurface became too thin. It became too uncomfortable when running over stones and tree roots. As a result, I adopted a more careful gait pattern which warranted a shoe change.

Shoe Replacement Guidelines that Lack Enough Information

1. Replace your shoes across a certain timeframe.
2. Replace your shoes across a certain mileage.
3. Replace your shoes when they lose cushioning.

More Sensible Shoe Replacement Guidelines

1. Replace your shoes once they become uncomfortable.
2. Replace your shoes if the wear and tear change your running mechanics.

Carbon Fibre Super Shoes for Performance

Super shoes have exploded in popularity and are breaking records in all running distances worldwide. A 'super shoe' is constructed with high tech foam, carbon fibre plates, extreme stack heights and pronounced rockers. Its role is to return as much energy as possible and convert it into propulsion which results in a more efficient running performance.

In July 2020, I interviewed world renowned podiatrist Simon Bartold on episode 80 titled '*Is a Carbon Fibre Shoe Right For Me?*' Simon discussed the unprecedented advancements in shoe technologies and all the major shoe companies rushing to compete with the record-breaking Nike Vaporfly super shoe [112]. In his expert opinion, Simon suggests these shoes are designed and recommended for elite runners. However, he has witnessed a performance gain regardless of running ability. I asked Simon if these shoes would be beneficial if a recreational runner wanted to improve their marathon time? Here is his response:

> "Probably not, you have to have adequate technique and strength to exploit these shoes properly. I think many recreational runners are seeing an improvement in their marathon times with these shoes, but I am a bit suspicious that it may well be a placebo effect because these shoes are aimed squarely at people who are very good runners".

Another common misconception about super shoes is that they act as a spring to return energy efficiently. With a stiff carbon plate inserted into the shoe, you can see why this is a prominent belief. Simon revealed that the stiff carbon fibre plate does not act as a spring. Instead, it acts as a lever at initial contact. This differentiation makes a big difference because a heel striker will take greater advantage of the shoe than a midfoot striker.

Work done by Emily Farina and colleagues has confirmed that a stiff, curved plate within the midfoot of a shoe can reduce net energy loss without increasing mechanical demand [113]. With this research finding, they can better understand the interaction between plate stiffness and running geometry and can tune the mechanics to enhance running performance.

Lastly, Simon directed listeners to the high technology foam built into the shoe. Returning as much energy from impact into propulsion is critical when it comes to running efficiency. Within a shoe, the type of foam that is squashed underfoot can play a key role. Apart from a super shoe having a stiff carbon fibre plate acting as a lever, it also contains extremely lightweight, economical foam. Again, here is what Simon had to say:

> *"All of these shoes are using very technical foams which are quite different to the ones in the past. They have started using a material called Pebax which they then turned into a foam 20% lighter than the next best material. It also has about 30% more rebound than the next best foam. So, this shoe will return about 87% of all input energy. The next best is about 61% so you can see that the foam is super important".*

In science, super shoes are relatively new, and while they are breaking records repeatedly, the research is playing catch up. Based on my current understanding, I think runners of all abilities can consider running in super shoes if they so choose. Provided that the transition into a new shoe is gradual and all other training components are well balanced, the rewards seem to outweigh the risks.

Chapter 14 Summary

1. There is no correlation between your foot shape and the type of shoe to reduce injury risk.

2. A lighter shoe is recommended for running economy and performance.

3. Super shoes may be supplemented for performance provided all other training elements are well executed.

Action Items

1. You do not need to replace an old shoe until it has significant wear and tear, resulting in a change in mechanics or becoming uncomfortable.

2. When purchasing a new shoe, try several types and be guided by comfort.

3. Use the minimalist index and recommended guidelines to evaluate a safe transition phase between shoes.

CHAPTER FIFTEEN

THE PERFECT WARM-UP

The following day Pete woke up early to complete his six kilometre run. He was excited to run in his new shoes but wanted to follow Jane's recommendations. He started running in his new shoes but placed his old pair at the doorstep for quick access. As he hoped, the new shoes felt amazing. He didn't realise shoes could feel so light! In comparison, he felt like all his previous running shoes had been caked in mud. He resisted the urge to complete the run with his new pair and after two kilometres, he swapped them over. He also decided to walk in his new running shoes throughout his day to become more accustomed and help the shoe adapt to his foot shape and movement path.

After an easy run and a shower, Pete set off to Jane's shoe store. It opened at eight o'clock, giving him enough time to chat before heading to work. He arrived 10 minutes before the store opened. He wanted to spend as much time with Jane as possible and was looking forward to her insight. Not only was Jane the store manager, but she also studied biomechanics. Surely she would have helpful information on warming up, stretching and other running preparations.

Pete was the first customer to enter the store when the doors opened. Jane was there to greet him as he updated her on the new shoes. She agreed that walking and strength training in the new shoes was a good decision. That way it would allow his body to adapt to the shoe and also the shoe to adapt to Pete. It seemed like every lesson required patience and a systematic progression. He could easily see why so many runners get injured. His natural urge was to spend all his time running in these new shoes. Not only did it take dedication, but it also required the right advice.

Jane cut straight to the chase with enthusiasm and asked Pete about his current warmup routine. A wave of guilt washed over him. At the start of his running journey, he would do the bare minimum to prepare for a run—few seconds of stretching for each muscle group along with a few leg swings. Recently, his warm-up was non existent, and he would start his run with a slow jog until his body eased into a fluent stride.

Sharing this with Jane, she asked if he had tried any other warm-up routines in the past. He couldn't recall any moment that he dedicated to stretching throughout his adult life. She explained that a stretching routine before running might not be as crucial as some runners believe. The purpose of a warm-up routine is to prepare the body for what it's about to undertake. However, for easy running sessions, the body doesn't require a large range of movement. Additionally, easy running poses little risk of muscle strain and will rarely justify an extensive warm-up routine.

Pete remembered back to his last Parkrun. He recalled the majority of runners participating in some form of preparation. Some runners participated in static stretches, either pulling their heels back to their glutes or bending over with straight legs to stretch their hamstrings. Others were incorporating more dynamic stretches. They would actively swing their legs from side to side, jogging on the spot with

high knees or lunging from side to side. With most runners participating in some form of warmup, there was surely some benefit.

To probe deeper into Jane's rationale, Pete mentioned that some
high performance runners at his local park have strict warmup and
stretching routines that seem to benefit. Jane explained that runners
present different running biomechanics, mobility levels, fitness
levels and physiological responses to exercise. Therefore, she recommends that runners try a wide variety of warm-up routines. Your
warm-up could involve an extensive 10 minute routine, a 10 second
shakeout and everything in between. You could even compare it to
no stretching at all.

Pete tried to comprehend the recommendations Jane provided. It
seemed quite broad. He expected the best warm-up routine to assist
in a marathon personal best, or a deep insight that would give him
a secret edge over his competition. Instead, these warm-up recommendations were disheartening. The way Jane was talking, it almost
seemed like stretching wasn't important. To allay Pete's confusion,
Jane explained that a proper warmup and stretch routine can be
necessary and useful for a runner, but everyone responds differently.
It is up to the individual to establish their routine based on the
planned workout.

For example, an easy run might require different preparation than
a two kilometre time trial. Another important aspect to consider
is while a warmup may be less relevant for some runners, it isn't
harmful either and if someone enjoys the feeling of stretching, there
is no harm in continuing.

Jane walked over to her desk and sorted through her files. She
returned with a handout that demonstrated several different war-
mups. She suggested Pete try a combination of warm-ups to find a
routine that felt best. Throughout the next seven days, he planned to

execute a different routine every run to hone in on his most beneficial warm-up routine.

Jane's Warm-up Handout

Static stretches:

- Calf stretches
- Quad stretches
- Hip flexor stretch
- Hamstring stretch
- Glute stretch

Dynamic stretches:

- Walking lunges
- Leg swings
- Heel flicks
- High knees
- Side lunges

Run Smarter Lesson 15

My career involves talking to runners every day which gives me insight into different training philosophies, reasons for getting injured, and thoughts behind their warm-up routines. I often hear statements like *'I am always injured because I don't stretch'* when talking to an injured runner. In fact, published research by Bruno Saragiotto and colleagues investigated such beliefs [117]. After interviewing 95 people, one of the primary responses, when asked about injury risk factors, was *'not stretching'*.

The purpose of warming up before a run is to prepare the body for what it's about to undertake. For instance, if a dancer wanted to prepare for a routine, their warm-up would involve several stretches through a joint's full range of motion. If a 100 metre sprinter wished to prepare for their event, it would require power based, ballistic preparations.

However, for lower intensity, long distance running, preparations may not be as necessary. Firstly, the running action doesn't require large, complex ranges of movement, nor does it involve explosive muscle activation. In fact, some research argues that stiffer runners perform more efficiently. This refers back to Chapter 13 when discussing leg stiffness and running mechanics. Keep in mind that every run is different, and preparing for a harder effort, such as interval training or hill sprints may require different preparation than an easy, slow run. Remember, the purpose of warming up before a run is to prepare the body for what it's about to undertake.

Will Stretching Help My Constant Tightness?

Firstly, I'd like to address the runners who constantly feel the need to stretch. Regardless of the perceived benefits of stretching, some runners have a deep compulsion to stretch due to continually feeling stiff. In these cases, I believe that the perception of tightness is a signal of muscle soreness, not legitimate tightness. It is reasonable to confuse the two, after all, the day after my heavy workouts, I still catch myself complaining about how tight my hamstrings feel. To add to this tightness belief, you can elicit the same soreness by stretching it. It is only reasonable to think that the muscles must be tight and require stretching. I think stretching can provide relief in these circumstances, but it is only short lived. The problem some runners have is the misinterpretation of their symptoms and not addressing the underlying problem of why they are sore in the first place.

For example, before I became a long distance recreational runner, my body was built for basketball which required explosive movements like jumping, 20 metre sprints, side shuffles and constant changes in direction. When I transitioned into low intensity, continuous running, my calves struggled with the adjustment. I still remember returning home after 30 minutes of easy running and feeling like my calves were about to explode. Throughout the next 24 hours, I would constantly stretch my rock hard calves to try and get some relief. Even though the stretches may have been beneficial for a fleeting moment, I look back now and realise they weren't tight at all. In fact, they were sore from being overworked. Fastforward five months later, and my calves had adapted to long distance running. Stretching was more of a want than a need as my calves didn't feel tight at all. All it took was patience for my body to adapt.

All runners should recognise the distinction between muscle tightness and body soreness. If you are a runner compelled to stretch regularly, here are four tips that might help:

Be patient: Like me and my sore calves, I had to train sensibly and allow my body time to adjust to the demands of endurance running. With frequent training, this could take up to three months.

Appreciate rest days: If you're constantly sore and exercise more than five days per week, your body may require rest. You cannot expect your body to recover if you exercise every day. Allow one to two days of complete rest or low intensity cross training, and observe for changes in soreness.

Adjust your intensity distribution: Chapter 12 covered the benefits of the 80/20 intensity distribution. Dedicating the bulk of your training to low intensity running will enhance recovery time and result in fresher legs for harder efforts.

Enhance your recovery: We will cover an optimal recovery in Chapter 19. However, monitoring your sleep, nutrition and stress levels is recommended and may require adjustments if you identify lacking areas.

Stretching to Reduce Injury Risk

Based on Saragiotto's research paper and my own experience, we know there is a common belief linking running related injuries to lack of stretching. However, it is worth repeating that most running related injuries are due to an abrupt change in training load that exceeds your ability to adapt. Let's test out this philosophy by looking at another research publication.

David Behm and colleagues released a systematic review titled '*Acute Effects of Muscle Stretching on Physical Performance, Range of Motion, and Injury Incidence in Healthy Active Individuals*' [118]. A systematic review is one of the highest quality publications released in journals. This paper covered a wide population of athletes and was not exclusive to runners but does contain relevant results. They concluded:

> *"Overall, the current research indicates that pre-activity stretching may be beneficial for injury prevention in sports with a sprint running component but not in endurance-based running activities with a predominance of overuse injuries".*

In other words, your body doesn't care how flexible you are when it relates to an overuse injury. Provided you train within your adaptation zone and avoid exceeding its maximum capacity, your risk of injury is low regardless of stretching beforehand.

Results from the Behm study have also been supported through additional papers. More specific to long distance runners, Claire Baxter and colleagues investigated the impact of stretching on the injury risk of long distance runners in their 2017 review. They state:

> *"The majority of studies suggest that stretching has no impact on the risk of chronic injury in endurance runners".* [119]

Stretching For Rehabilitation

If you have faced an injury in the past, a health professional may have prescribed a series of stretches. Conversely, perhaps you have intuitively started stretching your injury to help the recovery process. For some reason, as humans, we like stretching a sore area and eliciting a mild pain response in the hope that it releases the area. Similar to the above rationale of someone who is constantly stiff, the rationalisation process usually goes like this:

- When I stretch my injury, it brings on my pain
- Therefore, the injured structure must be tight
- Consequently, I need to stretch

- When I stretch the area, I get momentary relief
- Therefore I should stretch more often

Unfortunately, stretching rarely helps with healing an overuse injury. Given the right circumstances, it may create less pain momentarily, allowing more freedom to execute other proactive measures. For instance, briefly stretching your hips may decrease gluteal muscle pain, allowing you to execute your strengthening exercises with reduced discomfort. Keep in mind, however, that the goal of rehabilitation is to build strength and restore capacity. Strengthening, in turn, allows you to tolerate the demands of running. Stretching does not offer this. It does not strengthen your body and serves less purpose in the rehabilitation process.

One of the most common structures recommended to runners to stretch is their Iliotibial band or ITB. A thick and fibrous structure, this fascia plays a supportive role in keeping the leg and hip level when standing on one foot. Stretching and foam rolling the ITB are standard practices and highly recommended when injured. But like any other structure, it falls victim to the same false rationale explained above.

In fact, a randomised control trial by Pepper and colleagues studied the effects of foam rolling and stretching on ITB stiffness [120]. After the randomisation process, they asked the foam rolling group to perform a detailed foam rolling release technique for one minute and repeat it five times after a 30 second rest period. The stretching group executed a seven second submaximal contraction of their hip abductors followed by a 15 second stretch in an elongated ITB position. They repeated this three times. The third randomised group was a control group. After the intervention phase, the results revealed no statistically significant differences among the three groups. They concluded:

> *"A single episode of stretching and foam rolling does not affect short-term ITB stiffness. The lack of ITB stiffness changes may be from an inadequate intervention stimulus or indicate that the interventions have no impact on ITB stiffness".*

Stretching the ITB may not produce tangible improvements in flexibility, but I believe it can be justified if it delivers momentary pain relief. I recommend runners try a variety of stretches, foam rollers, massage balls, thera-guns or whatever they have access to. If a device helps settle pain, then continue in mild dosages. If you don't feel any immediate benefit, it is a waste of time. Patellofemoral pain, plantar fasciitis and gluteal muscle pain are examples of injuries that these devices may or may not assist. The runner must carefully trial stretching versus not stretching to test any potential benefit.

Alongside stretching, pre-activation exercises can be beneficial for tendon pain. For example, slowly loading the achilles tendon with two sets of heavy eccentric heel raises can reduce pain and reduce apprehension. Finding the right warmup loading exercises along with the correct dosage may require professional guidance. For those injured runners who opt-in for stretching, you must accompany your stretch routine with strength training and rehabilitation exercises to restore capacity.

In some circumstances, stretching may be detrimental and even prolong recovery. A condition known as proximal hamstring tendinopathy or PHT is a prime example. This is a pathology of the hamstring tendon as it inserts high up onto the sitting bone and leads to localised pain when running, sitting and bending forward. PHT is considered an insertional tendinopathy as the pain is located close to its bony attachment. Runners suffering from this injury will experience the same temporary relief from stretching as explained above. However, excessive stretching may, in fact, contribute to long term pain and pathology. With so much confusion around stretching versus non stretching, I always advise seeking the help of a health professional if your symptoms do not improve week by week.

Does Stretching Help Running Performance?

When analysing a runner's performance, there are two elements to consider. The first is the amount of force they can generate during propulsion and the second element is their running economy. An economical runner will utilise energy more efficiently and this correlates strongly to running performance.

When considering force production, we can draw information from Claire Baxter's work, already mentioned earlier in this chapter. The paper is titled '*Impact of Stretching on the Performance and Injury Risk of Long-distance Runners*' and is relevant to this topic. When it comes to force production, this review concluded:

> "It has shown that long-term stretching can potentially increase the compliance of the muscle-tendon unit and may allow greater force production at longer muscle lengths which may be relevant to other sporting disciplines; however, for endurance running, these potential benefits are not clinically beneficial". [119]

For instance, if a volleyball player needs to produce a high amount of vertical force from a deep squat, then stretching may assist. However, as we have already discovered, long distance running isn't an explosive, dynamic activity that demands complex ranges of movement.

The second element of performance is running economy. Running economy is defined as the steady state of oxygen consumption at a given running velocity, reflecting the energy demand of running at a constant submaximal speed. As discussed previously, the running economy depends on lower limb stiffness, not flexibility. The argument is that efficiency increases with a tighter musculotendinous system and is favourable for endurance athletes, not a loose, flexible musculotendinous system.

For example, one study investigated the effect of short and rapid stretching on running economy and found that inflexibility in the hip and calf regions was associated with an improved running economy and required less energy for muscle stabilisation [121]. Continuing with the Baxter review, they could not find any studies to suggest that stretching immediately before an endurance running event could improve the running economy.

When translated directly into running performance, a trial by Mayara Damasceno and colleagues looked at the effects of stretches during a three kilometre time trial [122]. The study involved 11 male, recreationally trained long distance runners executing different mobility tests, treadmill tests and time trial tests. Most importantly, one session involved a three kilometre time trial without stretching and the other with stretching. Each static stretch involved three sets of 30 seconds and included:

- Straight leg stand toe touch
- Standing quadriceps stretching
- Hamstring stretching
- Back stretching
- Hurdler's stretching
- Standing calf stretching
- Assisted hip stretching
- Assisted thigh stretching

After performing the time trial with and without stretching, the researchers found no significant difference in total running time. Interestingly, they detected those who stretched started the first 100 metres significantly slower. In addition, the stretch group reported a significantly higher RPE for the first 800 metres.

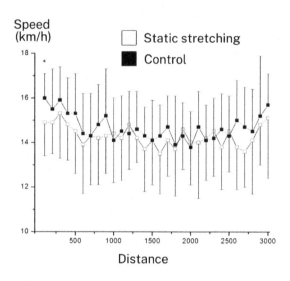

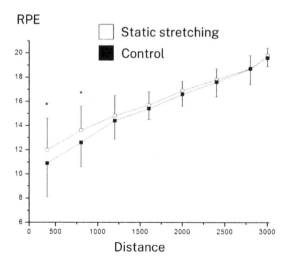

These findings support the idea that a stiffer runner is more efficient and economical. The stretching may momentarily hinder the rigid leg that a runner strives for, which is why there was a discovery of increased RPE and a speed drop. However, it is reasonable to suspect this inefficiency would quickly mitigate as the body adjusts and returns to the natural running rhythm. Apart from the initial differences in speed and RPE, both groups performed similarly, highlighting that stretching is not detrimental to performance.

Most recreational runners are not regularly pushing themselves through a three kilometre time trial, so these findings may not be applicable but are still worth mentioning. My general advice is to try several preparation routines just like Pete and decide on your best method through trial and error. For example, throughout my basketball career, I was constantly told the importance of stretching before games. This advice continued into my life as a recreational runner. Before a casual five kilometre run, my routine involved 30 seconds of static stretching for each main muscle group. As the years progressed, my stretching time reduced. As I reduced my stretching time, my running remained unhindered, and the sensation of running was identical. With this realisation, my warmup and stretch routine became minimal. Upon waking early in the morning, all my body would require was five seconds of stretching for each muscle group before heading out the door.

This method changed when I started implementing harder running sessions. Anything that included short, fast intervals, I would dedicate five minutes for hip and ankle mobility exercises. After I headed out the door, I'd dedicate another five minutes to a gradual buildup of intensity. Once I honed in on this routine, my speed sessions felt more fluent. Remember, the goal of a warmup is to prepare the body for what it is about to undertake. My rationale was that running at faster speeds generates higher loads on your body and pushes some joints like your hips through a greater range of motion. Therefore, the mobility work would assist in a more fluent experience. My preparation may also change as I get older and my body changes, and I am determined to continue experimenting with different warm-up routines to observe any changes in outcome.

Will Stretching Aid Muscle Soreness and Recovery?

Most runners have witnessed the scene at a marathon finish line. Some will celebrate, and some will stumble across the finish line as they push themselves to the limit. Once the adrenaline rush subsides, the stiffness and ache throughout the entire body emerge. As a result, I have witnessed a sea of exhausted runners, all stretching their aching bodies for temporary relief. While it may feel good at the moment, will it contribute to recovery?

A systematic review by Rob Herbert and Michael Gabriel gathered five previously published articles to answer this question [123]. This paper was published in 2002 and titled '*Effects Of Stretching Before And After Exercising On Muscle Soreness And Risk Of Injury: A Systematic Review*'. The total stretch time per session varied from 300 seconds to 600 seconds, except for one study where the total stretch time was only 80 seconds.

The results of these five studies imply that stretching reduces soreness within 72 hours after exercising by, on average, less than two points on a 100 point scale. Most athletes will consider the effects of this magnitude too small to make stretching to prevent later muscle soreness worthwhile. Therefore, this study concluded:

> *"This systematic review finds clear evidence from five studies of nominally moderate quality that stretching before*

or after exercising has no effect on delayed onset muscle soreness".

Nine years later, Rob Herbert and colleagues published another review to provide updated recommendations [124]. Instead of yielding five papers like the last review, this search collected 12 articles for analysis. '*Stretching to Prevent or Reduce Muscle Soreness after Exercise*', and Rob's research, returned similar results. The authors suggested that:

"Muscle stretching, whether conducted before, after, or before and after exercise, does not produce clinically important reductions in delayed-onset muscle soreness in healthy adults".

Publications like this set out to investigate the pure physiological effects of stretching. However, there is another element of stretching that runners should consider. Based on the individual, stretching after exercise can have mental calming effects. These psychological benefits can help switch the body into recovery mode and aid the recovery process. This book describes certain exercise and recovery hormones in Chapter seven, but it is worth a brief recap:

"Once you stop exercising, the mind and body calm themselves, and these hormone levels settle. When this process happens, your body can easily enter recovery mode. Lowering these stress hormones is vital for recovery and injury prevention because an athlete won't get stronger during a workout. Instead, they get stronger after the workout during relaxation". [Chapter 7]

These psychological benefits are based on the individual because some runners may not find stretching relaxing. It is purely subjective and isn't recommended unless you see a benefit personally. On episode 94 of the Run Smarter Podcast, I had the pleasure of interviewing Professor Shona Halson, a world leading expert on recovery. Her take on stretching after exercise followed a similar path. When I asked her about the benefits of stretching post exercise, this was her response:

> *"There hasn't been much research on stretching to help recovery, but the evidence that has been done suggests that there are no pure recovery benefits. But I certainly know there are a lot of athletes who feel like stretching in the recovery period does help them, whether it's psychological or not. Maybe if you are one to always feel tight or have areas of soreness and it just makes you feel better, then it wouldn't be something that is harmful".* [125]

In conclusion, similar to stretching for running performance, the evidence is yet to reveal any tangible, physical benefit, and my advice remains the same. Try several different routines and look for potential benefits. If you identify benefits, whether they are physical or psychological, it may be worth pursuing. However, if you cannot see any difference, it might be more worthwhile to explore other alternatives or none at all. We will dive further into optimising your recovery in Chapter 19.

Dynamic Warm-ups

I have witnessed a small percentage of runners who are so physically rigid in their mechanics they cannot execute a fluent running motion. Particularly for runners beyond the age of 50, the stiffness in their ankles, hips and lower back may interfere with running biomechanics. In these rare cases, I would recommend prioritising a warm-up routine.

The ankle, hip and big toe joints require particular focus for these rigid runners. However, the goal isn't to increase muscle flexibility, which addresses the muscles. Instead, the goal is to increase the articular movement within the joint. This is where a dynamic warmup has its advantages. Instead of holding a static stretch for a desired length of time, it would be better served to take the body through a series of movements.

A great example of a dynamic warm-up is a walking lunge, emphasising hip extension, ankle bend and big toe extension. These are exercises that any runner can try, but it is more important for those runners who require extra joint mobilisation to achieve a fluent running action. Repeating 10 walking lunges on each side would assist in restoring the necessary range of motion. Other exercises include jogging on the spot with high knees and flicking up your heels or A, B, and C skips.

As mentioned above, my running preparations change before a hard interval session compared to an easy run. These exercises mainly focus on joint mobility rather than muscle flexibility. Some of my favourites involve kneeling in a deep lunge position and rocking forwards and backwards. I find this opens up my hips and makes me feel less restrictive when running at higher speeds. I have discovered this process through trial and error, not to help me improve my performance or reduce my risk of injury, but to feel better while running.

Unfortunately, when it comes to dynamic stretches, the research is lacking. Most of the publications have focussed on static stretches, which means we cannot rely on science for recommendations. The review mentioned several times in this chapter by Claire Baxter briefly mentioned that dynamic stretching is limited and requires further examination. Unless further research emerges that will shift our current understanding, the recommendations of dynamic stretching follow a similar trend to static stretching. If it feels good, do it. If you find no benefit, your time would be better spent elsewhere.

Active Recovery

Active recovery refers to a deliberate practice immediately after your exercise session to assist the recovery process. Some popular methods involve hydrotherapy, hot/cold water therapy, sauna exposure or light cardiovascular alternatives such as swimming and cycling. I believe this process is less critical for recreational runners unless you had multiple events on one day or are committed to back to back performances over consecutive days.

The purpose of this process is to gently settle the body back into a resting state. Physiological responses involve lowering body temperature, heart rate, respiratory rate and sweat rate. However, because you're making it an active process, the body can circulate nutrients efficiently while removing byproducts. On the podcast, when I asked Shona Halson about her recommendations on active recovery, this was her response:

> "It depends on what you have access to. It could be as simple as walking. It might be getting on the stationary bike, getting in the pool, or anything that is low intensity. More 'time off legs' can be good, but you want a bit of blood flowing and a bit of movement. You don't want to add any more fatigue or use any more fuel than you really need to. So just

> *do something short, something that is low intensity where*
> *you've got your breath back, and it just helps you wind down*
> *from the session".* [125]

So an active recovery might help your recovery if you're facing back to back performances. Similar to static stretching, it can also have profound advantages on your psychological recovery. Use it as a tool to physically and mentally unwind in a short, low intensity manner.

To Stretch, or Not to Stretch

For every runner who loves dedicating time to stretching, another will loathe it. No matter which camp you fall into, it is important not to convince yourself of its effects. As this chapter has shown, stretching before and after running will not impact your performance, nor will it reduce your risk of injury. I highlight this point because I have interacted with many runners who tell me they are always injured because they do not stretch enough. This false narrative continues throughout their career while they remain oblivious to the real reason they are getting injured, such as rapid fluctuations in training intensity.

If you love stretching and mobility workouts, try participating in yoga several times a week. Yoga will not be detrimental to running. However, if you are injured or looking for running resiliency, strength and stability will trump flexibility and mobility. Here are my three recommended scenarios on when a runner should stretch:

1. If it feels good: Try a wide variety of warm-up routines and settle in on one that results in the best feeling during the run.

2. A high degree of joint stiffness: If you are within the small percentage of runners with joint stiffness that altered your

running biomechanics, dynamic stretching and mobility exercises may be required to restore fluent running.

3. Potentially for high power based workouts: Research has shown stretching may help activities requiring ballistic movements. This research disqualifies recreational running but may apply to short intervals, hill sprints, strides and other power based workouts. In these circumstances, dynamic warm-ups may be more effective than static warm-ups.

Chapter 15 Summary

1. Research has shown that static stretches do not reduce your likelihood of injury or increase your running performance.

2. Stretching will not aid a physical recovery, but can have profound psychological recovery benefits.

Action Items

1. Try a wide variety of warm-up routines and compare them with no warm-up routine. Select which routine feels the best.

2. Higher intensity running sessions may require different warm-up preparations.

3. If struggling to unwind mentally from exercise, try stretching or a brief low intensity cool down session and observe any positive changes.

CHAPTER SIXTEEN
ENHANCING RUNNING ECONOMY

Pete's marathon preparations were in full swing. After consulting with Jane, he was on a mission to find his own optimal warm-up. The first step of his mission was to identify his next four running sessions dedicated to low intensity. He then assigned a different warm-up to each session and documented the outcome after each run.

Warm-up #1: 5 minute Dynamic Warm-up

Comments: "Noticed an improvement in my running action. I felt more efficient at the start. Within 30 seconds everything felt normal".

Warm-up #2: Static Stretches 8–10 Minutes

Comments: "The act of stretching felt nice. I could notice my flexibility improve throughout the warm-up session. Once I started running, I didn't notice any benefits. Not entirely sure if 10 minutes is worth it".

Warm-up #3: 5 Minute Combination Static and Dynamic

Comments: "This has produced the best result. I enjoyed the sensation of the stretching beforehand, and after mixing static with dynamic, I noticed a benefit in my running action for one to two minutes".

Warm-up #4: No5 Stretching

Comments: "Went straight out the door without any preparation. My running and performance were very similar to previous attempts. Hard to notice any profound changes".

After Pete's experiment, he concluded both dynamic and static stretching didn't possess any profound benefit to his running. If he had the time available, he'd dedicate a few minutes to stretching beforehand due to the nice sensation it created. However, most of his weekday night runs were time sensitive and he rarely had the luxury. He also administered the same systematic process to his harder training sessions. Every Friday for four weeks, he would administer a different warm-up routine and concluded that a combination of static and dynamic stretches for five to ten minutes was worth continuing. Not only did stretching free up his body for a greater range of motion, but the interval sessions were typically shorter in duration, so he could fit this preparation time in comfortably.

Pete was now ready for his third and final physiotherapy session which was two days away. Since Daniel asked him to bring his running shoes, he suspected they were going to look at his running technique to assist his performance. Surely a running assessment was the next and final missing piece to the marathon PB puzzle. He decided to research running forms to get the upper hand and prepare for his session. While browsing on his computer, he came across consistent information about running techniques to increase performance while lowering injury risk. He wrote down four tips:

1. Maintain an upright posture with a slight forward lean.

2. Run with a relaxed upper body, shoulders, arms, and hands.
3. Activate your glute muscles during push-off.
4. Pick your feet up while swinging your legs.

Pete discovered another tip across multiple websites. He even found videos of running coaches condoning it along with numerous testimonials. They suggested:

> *"To increase your running efficiency and prevent injuries to your lower body, use a mid-foot strike, and avoid hitting the ground with your heel. This allows your foot to land directly under your hip as you drive your body forward. A heel strike may cause unnecessary braking force, causing you to run slowly and generate stress on your knees".*

Pete's eyes widened as he dug into a rabbit hole of information promoting non rearfoot running. Not only was this technique adjustment designed to increase running performance, but also lowered injury risk. One video approached the argument from an evolutionary standpoint. They highlighted the fact that our ancestors ran with a midfoot contact before footwear. Another article took a pure biomechanical angle, claiming that mid-foot runners generate less ground reaction force. Each piece of information contained a clear rationale, and each point was compelling. Pete decided to test out this new running technique tomorrow and report back to Daniel on his experience the following day.

The next day, Pete's training schedule called for a seven kilometre run at a three RPE. He decided to run his first five minutes with his normal stride, figuring this approach would help warm his body up before switching to a foreign midfoot contact. After the warm-up phase, he made the awkward adjustment and removed his heel strike. Initially, he unknowingly started speeding up. His legs fired like pistons underneath his body, and he couldn't help but accelerate. Pete was amazed and figured he was generating unnecessary braking force all along.

The adjustment in stride took a few minutes to coordinate, but Pete soon found himself in a fluent stride. He knew today's running session called for an RPE of three, so he reduced the overall speed despite every urge to sprint the remaining five kilometres. After 10 minutes of his newfound stride, he started to recognise a buildup of fatigue, particularly in his calves. This fatigue was a familiar sensation that he experienced when running up hills, but this was occurring on level ground. Thinking he might be travelling too fast, he adjusted his speed, and the fatigue level plateaued.

Persisting for three more kilometres, Pete's calf fatigue formed into a mild, manageable pain. He thought perhaps this was an innocent niggle that would quickly resolve. He checked his watch and saw he had one kilometre remaining. Even though the pain was mild, he took the cautious approach and switched back to his old heel striking pattern. With this correction, the pain dissipated, and only the fatigue sensation remained. After surviving the run home, he assessed the damage. His calves were tight and felt like balloons stretched to their limit. He felt like he had just hiked up the steepest mountain he could find. After a warm shower, all the soreness and tightness settled. Perhaps Pete's guess of an innocent niggle was right?

Pete slept well and awoke to the sound of his alarm. Before hopping out of bed, he pointed his toes up and down, assessing the degree of tightness. Both calves seemed tight but not enough to raise concern. Once he stood up, he felt a mild shot of pain in his right achilles. This troubling sensation felt similar to his previous achilles tendinopathy pain. Pete was devastated but thankful he had his appointment with Daniel to resolve the issue and get his marathon preparations back on track.

Run Smarter Lesson 16

With the desire to increase running performance so prevalent within the running community, it is understandable that analysing your running technique would be a logical area to explore. While Chapter five covered the elements of technique that may influence injury risk, this chapter will focus on running economy and performance. You may find these two chapters have overlapping content because if you are running efficiently, it should theoretically assist in performance and injury risk.

Understanding Running Economy

Running economy is the ability to metabolise energy aerobically and is a prerequisite for superior endurance performance. When performing an endurance based exercise such as running, you consume oxygen and remove carbon dioxide which in turn, helps your body perform. Therefore, running economy is determined by how well you are able to utilise the oxygen consumed and translate that into forward momentum at submaximal speed. Put simply, runners with a good running economy use less energy and therefore less oxygen than runners with a poor running economy at the same velocity.

There is a strong association between running economy and running performance, with running economy being a better predictor of performance than VO2 max scores in elite runners [126]. Despite two runners having identical VO2 max, one runner could show superior efficiency at slower speeds which would lead to better running performance.

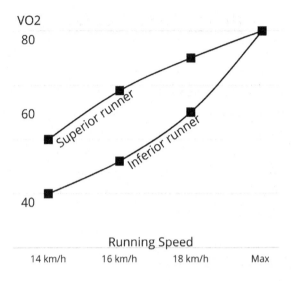

My guest Christos Ziliaskoudis explained the definition and its effects on the Run Smarter Podcast. As a researcher on running economy, Christos explained this concept in relation to car fuel economy. Here is what he said in episode 68:

> "When I describe running economy, I use the example of a car and its gas consumption. Let's say we have two different cars both travelling at 50 miles per hour. The more economical car will cover a greater distance before running out of gas. It doesn't matter which car has the greatest maximum speed or engine power. The same goes for running, at a certain running speed, each runner will have a different energy consumption rate".

> "If we have two runners at a similar fitness level and both of them are running at the same pace, the more economical runner would be able to keep moving for a longer period of time. If the same two runners were asked to cover the same

> *distance as fast as possible, the more economical runner will be able to sustain a faster running speed and will be the winner".*
>
> *"There are so many variables that can affect your running economy. Cadence is one of them, another one can be the environment and lower limb stiffness".* [127]

While fitness levels have a strong influence on running economy, many other factors play a role also. Christos mentioned the environment which relates to temperature, humidity and elevation, as well as lower limb stiffness which includes the ability for the leg to act as an efficient spring and return a healthy amount of energy. Research from Philo Saunders and colleagues has compiled extensive research on running economy influences and is displayed below [126].

RUNNING ECONOMY				
Training	Environment	Physiology	Biomechanics	Anthropometry
Plyometrics	Altitude	VO2 Max	Flexibility	Bodyweight
Resistance	Heat	Metabolic factors	Elastic stored energy	Limb morphology
Speed, volume		Adolescent development	Mechanical factors	Muscle stiffness and length
Intervals, hills			Ground reaction force	Body composition

What Information Can We Gather From Our Shoes?

Your running shoes are the only piece of equipment required for running, and they can be a source of valuable data relating to your style of running. If the shoes have experienced higher mileage and are dedicated to only running, you can gather more accurate information. If you have spent a long time walking in your running shoes, this could produce inaccurate results. When Pete purchased his shoes from Jane, she inspected his old shoes by flipping them upside down. This is called the outsole and is where the shoe makes direct contact with the running surface. In most cases, the part of the shoe that makes contact first will encounter the highest load and, therefore, fade quicker than other sections of the shoe.

Looking at the diagram below reveals four areas of interest. If your shoe shows a fade of the outsole tread in Zone 1 or 2, most likely, you will make a non rearfoot strike. Conversely, if the tread is more worn in zones 3 or 4, you most likely run as a heel striker. Continuing one step further, the outsole can also gather evidence on your step width. Showing a significant fade in either Zone 1 or 4 would indicate a high likelihood of a wide step width. On the other hand, a tread worn around Zone 2 or 3 will indicate a narrow or crossover step width.

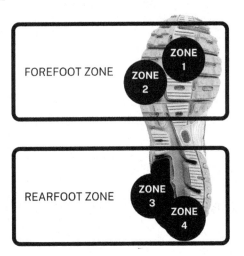

A faded outer zone is often mistaken for excessive supination. However, if a runner directs their foot across the midline, the outside of the shoe makes first contact. Remember, the section that contacts first will be exposed to the highest load and will fade quicker. Here is a breakdown of each zone:

- Zone 1: You are most likely a NON REARFOOT runner with a WIDE step width
- Zone 2: You are most likely a NON REARFOOT runner with NARROW step width
- Zone 3: You are most likely a HEEL STRIKER with a NARROW step width
- Zone 4: You are most likely a HEEL STRIKER with a WIDE step width

Forefoot strike   Heel strike

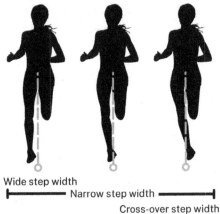

Wide step width

Narrow step width

Cross-over step width

Not only do shoes reveal information about your running pattern, but they also reveal the balance of impact between the right and left foot. If one shoe has degraded quicker than the other, odds are it is impacting the ground at a higher velocity. On the other hand, if your shoes show no difference in wear and tear, you are more likely to have an even impact.

Below is a photo of my trail shoes after three years of running. As you can see, almost all of my wear and tear is generated at zone two. Ever since my basketball days, I had been running with a forefoot strike, which carried over into my long distance running. As you can see, the sole around the heels seems virtually untouched. Additionally, in my first few years of running, I also adopted a narrow or crossover step width, leaving Zone 1 with mild wear and tear and Zone 2 with significant loss of tread. Interestingly, the shoe displayed on the right (left foot) shows greater wear and tear than the opposite. This gave me crucial insight to help overcome a certain injury which I'll explain later in this chapter.

Running Techniques to Increase Performance

Like the correlation with injury, changing your running technique to increase performance is under debate among researchers and health professionals. Most would agree that running inefficiencies could increase the likelihood of injury and may also hinder performance. An overstride pattern is a clear culprit. If a runner over-reaches their foot when making contact with the ground, this will produce unhelpful braking forces. This can drive high loads through the body, contributing to injury while hindering the running economy. If a runner elicits this trait, it is like trying to drive a car while holding the handbrake.

Runner's centre of mass

Runner's reach at initial contact

Carrying over from injury risk, traits such as a crossover pattern, excessive knee rotation and hip drop may negatively impact performance. This idea is still open for debate but makes sense if a trait that generates unusually higher loads on the body would also produce a poor economical stride. There are two main theories regarding optimal performance and a perfect running technique with the debate continuing.

One theory suggests that runners self-optimise their running style based on their body shape and capabilities. If this theory is correct, it would mean that once someone passes the novice phase and the runner has developed the correct coordination through repetition, they would develop an innate, unconscious, automatic response to their most economical running style. In addition to this theory, any attempt to change their running style comes at a metabolic cost. Unless this change is built-in through repetition and becomes automatic, the metabolic cost will hinder performance.

The second theory suggests the possibility of training runners the same way we train any other athletic skill. For example, a popular running retraining method is pose running. This method is designed to improve a runner's efficiency by reducing overstride, increasing cadence and leaning your upright body forward during the running action. While I believe some runners should make adjustments to improve efficiency, the majority of runners are not operating with extreme inefficiencies. It is all about taking the individual runner and basing recommendations on their individual circumstances.

For instance, Marcus Dunn and colleagues taught a small group of runners the pose method and matched them with a control group [128]. The 10 runners in the intervention group attended three x two hour retraining sessions all designed to correct their current running form into a more economical stride. At a six week followup, a number of technique changes occurred in the intervention group, including:

- Reduced stance time
- Reduced take off distance
- Increased ankle flexion at push-off
- Increased cadence

However, this study found no change in the running performance after a five kilometre time trial event. While the sample size in this study was small, perhaps these runners were already running in an efficient manner and didn't warrant a change in the first place? Here is the paper's final statement:

> *"It was concluded that following pose running retraining, retrained participants adopted a running style that was different to their normal style without changing specific, biomechanical factors associated with lower limb injury or compromising performance".*

The Dunn paper is just a small example to illustrate the lack of performance benefits when changing your running technique. For a more robust paper, you need look no further than a systematic review from Dr Izzy Moore. '*Is There an Economical Running Technique? A Review of Modifiable Biomechanical Factors Affecting Running Economy*' aims to identify any technique changes a runner might require to increase their running performance [129]. As we have already established, running economy is closely related to performance, therefore, any change a runner can make to improve their running economy will lead to better running times. However, determining what changes carry over into economic improvements is tough to uncover. Dr Moore supported the findings from Marcus Dunn's work and in her paper stated:

> "Interventions concerned with instructing runners to retrain their running biomechanics towards a specific global running technique, such as Pose, Chi and midstance to midstance running, has generally resulted in either no improvement in running economy or a worsening of running economy".

> "Whilst these techniques are often advocated as efficient forms of running, and all the interventions led to modified running biomechanics, currently, there appears to be no evidence to substantiate the claims that they benefit running economy".

More recently, in 2021, researchers conducted another systematic review and meta-analysis to determine if altering someone's running biomechanics could impact running performance, pain and injury. They analysed 19 studies from 16 independent cohorts involving 673 participants and concluded that:

> "Running gait retraining approaches in this review were effective at increasing step rate, reducing average vertical loading rate, and increasing knee angle at initial contact, but

> *did not have any negative or positive effects on measures of running performance"*. [130]

If you recall from Chapter six, work by Amy Schubert and colleagues found that running at a higher cadence reduced ground reaction forces and reduced braking impulse. However, increasing a runner's cadence would only be beneficial if their starting cadence is below optimal. This is because increasing your cadence has diminishing returns and may be detrimental to the running economy if elevated higher than optimal. This is where Dr Moore's findings are important. She discovered that runners appear to naturally choose a cadence that is economically optimal, or at least very near to optimal. This sides with the self-optimisation theory mentioned earlier. Dr Moore writes:

> *"An experienced runner's naturally chosen stride length is self-optimised to within 3% of the mathematically derived optimal. Deviating between naturally chosen and mathematically optimal will only have a negligible effect on running economy".*

> *"However, novice runners have not acquired the running experience necessary to self-optimise as effectively. Therefore, a short-term running training program for novice runners can lead to running biomechanics being modified to benefit running economy".*

This goes back to my philosophy on tailored intervention. There are no absolutes or blanket statements that will apply to every runner. A clinical justification should be made based on the injury history, running goals, level of strength, footwear and various other factors relating to the individual. There may be obvious scenarios in which changing your technique is warranted, such as running with a low cadence or presenting with a severe overstride, but such presentations are not common.

The work by Dr Moore also covers foot strike patterns and performance. As experienced by Pete, it is a common belief that rearfoot striking is unhelpful, and all runners should adopt a non-rearfoot strike to improve their running efficiency. This systematic review was unable to identify such beliefs. Empirical evidence shows no difference in running economy between rearfoot and forefoot striking at slow, medium and fast speeds. In fact, some studies have shown rearfoot striking to be more economical than non rearfoot striking at slow running speeds [129].

I believe this heel strike misconception is based on two inaccurate assumptions. The first assumes all heel strikers are overstriding, which is not the case. The second assumes runners need to remove a heel strike to make initial contact underneath the hips. This assumption is also untrue. If a heel striker elicits an unhelpful overstride pattern, they simply need to reduce the overstride, commonly by increasing their cadence while remaining a heel striker.

In my mind, there must be a clear justification for a gradual transition from a heel strike to a non heel strike. Certain circumstances may justify such a transition and will be discussed later. Clinicians, coaches and health professionals need to be very careful with over-prescribing and over-promising the effects of non rearfoot running because of the associated risks which we will now discuss.

Risks Associated with Changing Technique

As established multiple times in this book, a running related injury is most often caused by an abrupt change in loading that exceeds the capacity of a certain structure. It is then worth considering the dramatic changes in the load that will occur if you decide to change your running technique to something unaccustomed. Despite what you may have been told, changing your running technique will not reduce the load placed on your body. Instead, the load shifts to a different area. Take foot strike as an example. Transitioning from a heel strike to a non heel strike is one of the most common changes I have witnessed. This change shifts loads away from the hip, and knee, and towards the ankle. If this transition is too abrupt, an overload may occur in structures such as the plantar fascia, bones of the feet, achilles and the calf complex.

I have treated runners multiple times who have read about the many benefits of non rear foot or barefoot running. Inevitably, after experimenting with the new style, they have ended up in my clinic with an achilles or calf strain injury.

With Dr Izzy Moore's publication revealing a lack of performance benefits and with the potential risk of injury, is changing your technique worth it? When it comes to foot strikes, research from Laura Anderson and colleagues helps point runners in the right direction. This 2020 systematic review titled '*What are the Benefits and Risks Associated with Changing Foot Strike Pattern During Running?*' analysed 53 papers and concluded:

> *"Considering the lack of evidence to support any improvements in running economy, combined with the associated shift in loading profile, changing strike pattern cannot be recommended for an uninjured rearfoot strike runner".* [131]

Changing your foot strike has also been shown in some studies to be harmful to your running economy. Particularly with experienced runners, any shift in running technique that disrupts your current natural coordination and breaks your muscle memory motor pattern requires energy. This added energy required to make such adjustments can make it more difficult to perform economically. This high energy cost will continue until the new motor pattern is repeated over several weeks and the body establishes a new natural rhythm.

If a runner still wishes to change their running style and adopt a new strike pattern, my advice is to do so gradually. Like any other variable in your training, your focus should be to train within your adaptation zone and avoid abrupt changes that exceed your body's capacity to adapt. Similarly to a walk-run program for a beginner, a change in technique might require short intervals of a new running pattern, leaving the remainder of the run at the previously adopted style.

The advice by Moore and Anderson is purely focused on runners who are not injured and would like to increase their performance. But some exceptions should be made. As a physiotherapist working with runners, I have seen first hand the profound and immediate effects changing a running technique can have on an injured runner.

Circumstances to Change Your Technique

As stated previously, changing your running technique won't decrease the total load on your body. Instead, it merely shifts or spreads the load to different areas. This can sometimes be useful for a runner, especially if they are injured. If a new running pattern redirects loads away from a vulnerable, painful area and towards another body part, that could be a crucial step toward recovery.

Such a decision requires sound clinical reasoning, and a proficient health professional can guide the runner during the rehabilitation process. This is because the advice given will change depending on the type and state of the injury. For instance, take the work done by

John Willson and colleagues relating to cadence and foot strike on patellofemoral pain, also known as runner's knee:

> "Patellofemoral joint kinetics per step was 10 to 13% less during forefoot strike conditions and 15 to 20% less with a shortened step length. Patellofemoral joint kinetics per kilometre decreased 12 to 13% using a forefoot strike pattern and 9 to 12% with a shortened step length".
>
> "To the extent that patellofemoral joint kinetics contribute to symptoms among runners, these running modifications may be advisable for runners with patellofemoral pain". [132]

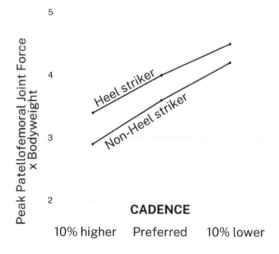

Another common running related injury is ITB syndrome, a persistent irritation of the ITB on the outside of the knee joint. A study by Stacey Meardon and colleagues investigated the load through the ITB structure when altering a runner's step width [133]. Here is what they found:

> "We conclude that relatively small decreases in step width can substantially increase ITB strain as well as strain rates. Increasing step width during running, especially in persons whose running style is characterised by a narrow step width, may be beneficial in the treatment and prevention of running-related ITB syndrome".

As stated before, the idea is to redirect some load away from the injured site and toward stronger areas that can better handle running loads. Multiple running technique adjustments are beneficial for different injuries and are summarised well in a paper by Christian Barton and colleagues titled '*Running Retraining to Treat Lower Limb Injuries: a Mixed-methods Study of Current Evidence Synthesised with Expert Opinion*' [134].

My first experience as a runner had its setbacks. As I have already mentioned in this book, my calves were sore and stiff after every run I completed. Growing up playing basketball, my natural running mechanics involved a forefoot initial contact. One thing I didn't mention was I changed my mechanics predominantly to a heel strike to give my calves some reprieve. This adjustment only lasted two weeks but was enough recovery for my calves to catch up with the rest of my body. I then slowly adjusted back to my natural forefoot strike and while my calves still encountered mild soreness, I was grateful I made the initial decision and reduced my risk of a calf overload.

The next adjustment I made was a permanent one and came four years later when trying to overcome a persistent tendinopathy located behind my knee. As you can see from my old shoes above, I ran with my natural forefoot strike but displayed a very aggressive narrow step width. This hadn't caused me any problems in the past but when I made the adjustment to a wider step width, I could run a lot further with less tendon pain. This adjustment helped me overcome my injury and since then, my wear and tear pattern has moved away from Zone 2 and into Zone 1.

I have also witnessed non injured runners who required immediate technique changes. As the information above highlights, an overstride pattern and cadence lower than 160 are valid reasons to change a runner's technique. I have also come across other unique situations that warrant an immediate change. For example, a runner reached out to me for online coaching when preparing for a marathon. Their goal was to finish the marathon in the best possible time and required my input to give them the best possible chance. After reviewing the running videos they sent me I noticed an obvious, loud smack on the ground during every step. When I questioned this runner about the sound I realised they convinced themselves that running involved hitting the ground with a firm, hard strike. In their eyes, running quiet and soft wasn't running, and a firm contact was a more effective workout. After explaining the high risk of injury and the parameters of running economy, this runner made an immediate shift to a lighter, quieter foot strike.

Lastly, I wanted to touch on circumstances where changing running form might apply to performance. When weighing up all the available research, it seems that changing your running technique won't carry over to improving your running economy. However, I do believe short distance running athletes and more elite individuals may benefit from repetitive running drills to improve their performance. For professional and track athletes already executing well balanced training, and looking for a small benefit to one-up their competitors, they may have merit. Therefore, running drills and technique training may have clinical justification and yield performance benefits. However, for long distance recreational runners, the juice might not be worth the squeeze.

If running performance is your main focus, then building on all other aspects in this book will pay greater dividends compared to changing your running technique. For instance, strength training and transitioning to lighter shoes. The other major component is building upon your overall mileage safely. It is clear that building a large base consisting mainly of slow mileage will lead to better performance come race day. Jason Fitzgerald explained on episode 49 of the podcast:

> *"The number one way for a runner to run faster is to run more, with the bulk of this training being slow mileage. Running is a sport where the more you do it the better you get and so running more weekly mileage is going to make you more economical and efficient. It's going to build more mitochondria in your muscles and that will improve your general endurance and build upon a bigger running foundation".* [135]

Manipulating the Width of Your Tightrope

Coming back to our tightrope walking analogy, this chapter pays particularly close attention to the width of the rope used on your journey. If you were to cross the gorge with a thicker rope, your odds of successfully negotiating faster winds are increased. This is how I imagine a runner with optimal cadence, step width and mechanics. It creates a small buffer in the presence of tougher training conditions, but will still result in a fall if the abrupt change is too much. I believe this is one of the reasons why some runners are slightly more resilient and can handle larger increases in training volume without injury. The width of the rope may not be a major certainty when everything is going well, but if you are continuously falling off throughout your journey, it may be worth changing your approach and changing the rope for something thicker.

Chapter 16 Summary

1. Most experienced runners will naturally self-optimise their running technique.

2. Research suggests that transitioning from a heel strike to a non rearfoot strike will not improve running economy or reduce the risk of injury.

3. Runners may choose to change their step width, posture, hip angles or dorsiflexion under clinical justification.

Action Items

1. Inspect the soles of your running shoes to gather information about your running technique.

2. If you display a cadence under 160 or a significant overstride, it may warrant a change.

3. If you choose to change your strike pattern, do so gradually and systematically.

4. If injured, a change in technique may be warranted but the guidance of a health professional is recommended.

CHAPTER SEVENTEEN

GOOD PAIN, BAD PAIN AND PERFORMANCE NIGGLES

Pete's achilles discomfort was bothering him, but perhaps the psychological worry played a role too. The different outcomes kept circling in his head. Is this a slight niggle or something serious? Can he continue running or will he have to halt his marathon training plan? From the runners he had talked to since his journey began, he heard it was common to experience niggles during a marathon training block. He was hoping Daniel could help decipher this issue.

Symptoms didn't seem to improve throughout the day. While walking, Pete placed his pain at three out of ten. As his workday finished, he drove to Daniel's clinic and walked through the front door with a mild limp. Daniel was already at the front desk and witnessed Pete's reluctant walk of shame. They both slowly made their way into the treatment room as he updated Daniel on the recent technique change along with symptoms over the past 24 hours. Daniel reported that his current symptoms made sense. Today was a session to assess his running form, but this recent issue would take priority.

Daniel got to work with some clinical tests to determine the extent of the damage.

He instructed Pete to repeat the loading tests from his previous achilles injury. Jogging on the spot produced a mild three out of ten pain while jumping raised the pain to four and hopping spiked it to seven. Daniel then palpated the structures surrounding the achilles, asking for feedback on the most tender areas. After the testing, they both sat down, and Daniel delivered his findings. He advised Pete that his achilles tendinopathy had resurfaced and that his recent change in foot strike has significantly increased the demands on the calf complex.

Pete's head sank into his hands in frustration. He had learned from his past injuries that rest wasn't the best answer and wanted to spring into action. Daniel reviewed Pete's current training schedule and advised him to avoid running for the next three days. In the meantime, he could continue his strength routine without the calf raises, which would need to be reintroduced gradually. Concerning his cardio options, Daniel created a progression chart that Pete could progress through based on symptoms. Sensing Pete's frustration, Daniel assured him that these symptoms would dissipate quickly with the correct management in place.

Physiotherapy Instructions:

1. Start: 45 minutes spin bike every second day (low to moderate intensity).

2. Once able to walk pain free, reduce the spin sessions to 30 minutes and add 30 minutes on the elliptical trainer.

3. Once able to jog on the spot for 60 seconds with symptoms less than two out of ten, begin a walk-run program.

Walk-run Schedule:

Phase 1: 8x (2 mins run, 2 mins walk)
Phase 2: 12x (2 mins run, 2 mins walk)
Phase 3: 10x (3 mins run, 1 min walk)
Phase 4: 12x (4 mins run, 1 min walk)

Progress to the next stage of the walk-run schedule if symptoms are less than 4/10 and return to baseline in less than 24hours.

4. Once completed the walk-run program, resume a regular running schedule and heel raises.

Pete was happy to incorporate the spin bike and elliptical at his local gym until his tendon could tolerate running. This alternative enabled him to maintain his fitness levels and exercise other body parts so the return to running in the near future would be less risky. He was excited to start his new plan forward, but he was confused by one thing. He asked Daniel how he could work out the difference between an injury and a niggle that other runners talk about.

Daniel sat in silence for a few seconds, thinking about his response. He advised that some sore spots are expected during hard training cycles and in most cases, it would be delayed onset muscle soreness the day after a hard workout. Other times it might include an intermittent sharp pain that fades away as quickly as it appears. These pain signals can be confusing and might require tailored advice in each circumstance, however there are some general guidelines to follow. He promised that he would send Pete an email to help guide his future decision making.

Pete walked out, optimistic about his recovery. Even though he was still in pain, he always felt at ease with a plan in place. In fact, Pete believed that having a clear plan played a direct role in decreasing his pain levels. On his way home from work, he stopped at the gym for a low intensity 45 minute spin session. Initially, his achilles pain was three out of ten but quickly settled to one, which remained throughout the session. Later that night he checked his inbox and opened up Daniel's email.

Daniel's Email

Delayed onset muscle soreness (Good pain):

- Onset 24–48 hours after an intense or new exercise
- Often involves a vague location in the muscle belly
- Elicited pain when stretching or activating the muscle
- Resolves in 2–4 days
- If it resolves in less than 4 days, no assessment is required
- If persisting beyond 5 days, seek an assessment

Injury soreness (Bad pain):

- Onset can be during or after exercise
- Is often more localised and painful than DOMS
- Can have constant or intermittent symptoms
- If symptoms persist >4 days, get medically assessed

Niggle (Bad pain that doesn't require a medical assessment):

- It can be a sharp or dull sensation
- Typically lasts either seconds, minutes or severe cases, hours
- Once resolved, it never returns
- Each fleeting niggle is worth documenting, in case it returns
- If the same fleeting niggle continues to occur, seek an assessment
- If one niggle persists >4 days, seek an assessment

Run Smarter Lesson 17

When constructing the principles designed to increase your running performance safely, it is necessary to discuss the nature of pain and what action you should take. The body can deliver pain in many forms. It could be a fleeting, sharp pain that lasts a few seconds, never to return, or it could be a pain of a longer duration. Ultra marathon runners and high mileage runners experience this regularly. It is uncommon to complete a brutal race without some new, random pain. In most cases, these pains will disappear shortly after the event.

On the other hand, low mileage recreational runners can also experience a wide array of pain signals. For the uninitiated, it can be tricky to assign a level of seriousness. Some stubborn runners convince themselves that their pain is nothing to worry about, even if it has persisted for months.

In my years as a physiotherapist, I have discovered that the level of pain isn't enough to trigger a runner to seek help. Instead, it is all about motivation levels. For instance, if a runner is training for a marathon and develops knee pain, they are likely to continue running if the pain is manageable. The decision to continue running with pain occurs because the injury is not severe enough to disrupt their training in a significant way. They might need to avoid speedwork or hills but can still gradually build upon their weekly mileage. In this instance, their motivation to seek medical help is low, even if the pain persists for months. However, if the injury becomes severe and the runner cannot run because of pain, they book in for an assessment immediately as their motivation has completely changed.

On the other hand, I have seen runners who get every injury assessed when pain arises. This type of runner, in particular, may have had several injuries in the past and may have learned their lesson the hard way when it comes to injury management. In this instance, this runner is highly motivated early in the pain process.

This subject can be tough to navigate because every pain signal and injury presentation should be considered a unique situation. Consider the below recommendations as a loose guideline rather than an absolute. If you are struggling to determine the seriousness of your injury, there is no harm in being on the cautious side and seeking advice from your rehabilitation team. However, educating runners on pain and symptom behaviour can help guide the decision making process.

Good Pain Versus Bad Pain

Discussing good pain versus bad pain essentially separates pain signals into DOMS, injury, and innocent niggles. As explained in Chapter 13, DOMS refers to delayed onset muscle soreness and is the essential rebuilding phase of the muscular system. When you complete a hard training session, the muscles require time to repair and, depending on the severity level, can result in a high level of discomfort. I can recall several cases where a runner has booked an appointment, which upon assessment, turned out to be a severe case of DOMS. Even though discomfort can be severe, this type of pain is widely considered good pain because it is necessary to get stronger and will not develop into a long term injury.

As stated above, every pain presentation should be considered unique. However, delayed onset muscle soreness does have some key characteristics to help you decipher it from something more threatening. Firstly, this type of pain will arise 24 to 48 hours after a training session that is either new or more intense than what you are used to. Because this pain affects the muscle, the pain distribution is often vague throughout the muscle belly. In other words, instead of pinpointing the pain with one finger, you have to trace your finger across a large area to describe the location.

Most importantly, DOMS will resolve within a few days as the muscle adapts. This timeframe can be a significant distinction as injuries often persist beyond the DOMS recovery time. In most cases, the pain will completely subside in two to three days. DOMS may take five to seven days in severe cases, but this is rare.

Next, we have pain characteristics that resemble an injury or a niggle. Some of these symptom behaviours overlap those of DOMS but can have key stand alone features. Unlike DOMS, which always has a delayed onset, symptoms resembling an injury can happen during or after exercise. For example, an ankle sprain or high grade muscle strain will immediately produce pain during the activity. In addition, low grade muscle strains and other inflammatory conditions can develop minutes to hours after exercise. However, similar to DOMS, certain bone stress injuries and tendinopathies can develop the day following exercise. Bad pain that is also delayed in its onset can be confusing because it has overlapping characteristics with DOMS. This is when the location and behaviour of the pain become important.

Remember, DOMS is often a vague, widespread pain within the muscle belly. Conversely, tendon soreness is more often a focal point of pain, located with one fingertip. Additionally, DOMS symptoms often resolve in two days. Therefore, you can rule out DOMS if symptoms persist beyond one week. Both the location of the pain and duration of symptoms can be key characteristics when deciphering good pain from bad pain. If there remains confusion, a medical professional will administer diagnostic tests to reach a definitive answer. Hopefully, you now have some understanding of good pain versus bad pain. However, I also like to separate bad pain into two further categories. That being overuse injuries and performance niggles.

Overuse Injuries Versus Performance Niggles

A niggle is not a medically defined term. Instead, it is an ambiguous term that runners should recognise. I believe some symptom behaviours can be classified as bad pain that is still less of a concern and doesn't require medical attention. Therefore, this section of the book is my interpretation and understanding of the term niggle. Across my physiotherapy and podcast career, I have talked with runners of different skill levels, experiences, and preferred race distances. Over this time, I have come across different stories about painful yet innocent niggles. While compiling these niggle stories, I thought the easiest way to separate them is to categorise niggles based on their symptom duration.

1. Niggles lasting a few seconds: This can either be an unpleasant sharp sensation, dull ache, throbbing, painful tightness and any other nasty irritation that quickly fades. This is common among distance runners, particularly trail runners who navigate through challenging, uneven terrain, ascending hills, and changes in surfaces. These niggles can happen anywhere within the body, but some common areas include the foot, knee and hip. The reason behind these pains is beyond me, but due to their low level of severity, I don't think an explanation is too important.

2. Niggles lasting a few hours: Similar to the above classification of niggles, these can produce a wide array of symptoms. Niggles that continue for a few hours are more commonly experienced during long distance races. In these circumstances, athletes are pushing their physical limits, and the body can

be subject to random alarm bells. Rather than develop into injury, these symptoms significantly decrease once the race is over and always completely subside by the following day. When resuming your training after the race, symptoms do not resurface.

3. Niggles lasting a few days: In most cases, if a niggle persists >24 hours after a race, you're flirting with the niggle and injury middle ground. This is when a runner should be cautious and assess whether their niggle carries over or is exacerbated by the next bout of exercise. Say you compete in a marathon and slowly develop knee pain throughout the race. You see if it is a niggle by assessing the symptoms the following day. If pain completely subsides, it is likely a low threat level, and assessment is not required. However, if your running resumes three days later and the knee pain resurfaces, I would categorise this as an injury.

Regardless of the niggle duration, runners should log their occurrence if any similar symptoms happen in the future. Based on the location and nature of the niggle, it is also worth noting certain details of the exercise, such as the duration, surface and footwear. I recommend this process in case a niggle is occurring on more than one occasion, is recurring more frequently, is more severe, or persists over a longer duration. If you notice the symptoms come back with higher severity, it is important to change your approach to the exercise and eliminate any other future episodes. If attempts to modify the exercise don't change the onset, or if you are letting your niggle dictate your training parameters, I'd suggest further investigation with a medical assessment.

In my first year of running, my body was desperately trying to adapt to long distance running. Within 10 months, my long runs had stretched beyond two hours. It was at this stage that I fell in love with running. I'd head out from my parent's house and run along a dirt track behind Melbourne's Tullamarine airport which consisted of bushland filled with singing birds and hundreds of kangaroos. It was this time in my training that I recall one major niggle. I was 10 minutes away from home after completing 20 kilometres across the beautiful morning bushland. My legs handled the run well but upon straightening my arm, I encountered a severe, sharp pain in my elbow. I was shocked! I couldn't explain it. Out of all the joints in my body, I never expected to encounter pain in my elbow (and when I say pain, I'd place it close to a seven out of ten!).

With such bizarre symptoms, I figured my elbow was unhappy while being locked in a 90 degree position for such a long period of time. The remainder of my run consisted of a painful bending and straightening of my arm until I reached my front door. Throughout that time, the pain slowly dissipated. I made sure to shake out my arms during the next two scheduled long runs, and the pain never returned. Just like my elbow symptoms, niggles can come in a wide variety of symptoms. With such an ambiguous, ill-defined phenomenon, I understand there may still be uncertainty about when to take symptoms seriously. Let's try and clear a few things up.

When is it Time For an Assessment?

Generally speaking, the longer you've had an injury, the more difficult it is to overcome. As previously mentioned, stubborn runners often delay medical attention. For some reason, running with pain isn't enough motivation to prompt investigation. Only when the injury severely disrupts running are runners highly motivated to seek a health professional. I do not blame runners for this behaviour. It seems to be human nature unless you've decided to learn from past mistakes. After all, I was once the type of person that only got my car serviced when there was an issue and only went to the dentist when I was in pain. There are many circumstances when it is acceptable to manage pain without escalating the urgency to a health professional. However, misinterpreting the seriousness of some injuries can have consequences.

If a runner waits too long and pain becomes highly irritated, it can create several rehabilitation problems. Firstly, you are likely to face longer recovery times. Secondly, you will severely limit your exercise and rehabilitation options. For example, if a runner presents with mild knee pain, they may still tolerate low levels of running, cross training and challenging strength exercises such as lunges, step ups and squats. On the other hand, if a runner presents with severe, irritable knee pain, they may have to cease running and be restricted to low level rehabilitation exercises such as wall sits.

Below is a basic flowchart to help decide what may warrant a medical assessment. These guidelines are basic, and exceptions to these rules will apply. They should act as a foundation framework:

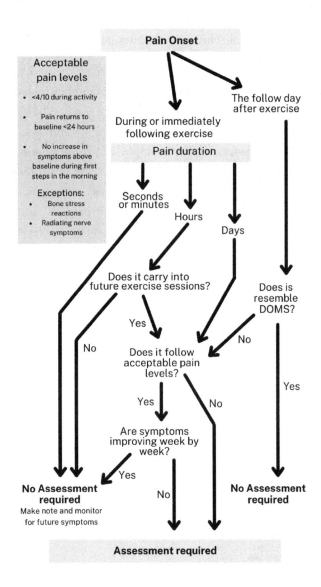

Injuries That Aren't Getting Worse or Better

In January 2022, I released a solo Run Smarter Podcast episode titled '*What to Do When Injuries Aren't Getting Any Worse, or Any Better*' [137]. Once released, many runners realised they needed help which prompted them to reach out. Sometimes, injuries can be mild and lay low in the background. They can even fall within acceptable levels of pain, but, if an injury persists beyond a few weeks, I want you to answer two questions honestly:

1. Are you getting better across a longer time scale?: Humans naturally live day by day and can convince themselves of inaccurate trends. It isn't until they take a step back that a more accurate picture comes into focus. For instance, an injury could improve across two weeks, but the third week sparks a flareup. This is followed by three good weeks only to encounter another flareup. Only once the timescale changes does a more accurate, bleak realisation appear.

    The truth is, if you haven't had an injury assessed and it persists beyond three weeks, you should take action. If you look back over several weeks or months and cannot recognise a linear recovery, my advice is to take action. If a drastic change is not made in your management, the likelihood of the injury continuing on this fluctuating path without resolution is high.

2. Are you getting better or retreating further?: This is a process that may be unconscious or extremely gradual that goes by undetected. When running with an injury, certain parameters may increase the likelihood of a flareup. For instance, speedwork can irritate a hamstring injury or downhill running for ITB issues. These aggravating variables can play on the runner's mind and instead of addressing the problem with rehabilitation, they retreat to safety. As the weeks continue,

the injury further dictates the distance, speed, and terrain to which the runner subjects themselves.

With this pattern of behaviour, on the surface the injury can seem to be improving, but in reality, the runner is continuously retreating to safer waters. In this scenario, an injury assessment is also advised. Once a well structured progressive rehabilitation plan is in place, the runner will bridge the gap between the current capacity and desired running dosage. You should run with freedom and not let current or past injuries dictate your exercise beyond a few weeks.

Chapter 17 Summary

1. Delayed onset muscle soreness is considered good pain.

2. The characteristics of bad pain should be monitored carefully.

3. Recognising the difference between a niggle and injury is crucial for runners.

4. Your injury should show signs of improvement week by week.

Action Items

1. Document your fleeting niggles and look for recurring trends which may elevate urgency.

2. If you have been holding onto an injury longer than three weeks, get an assessment.

3. If niggles or injuries are dictating your exercise program, get an assessment.

CHAPTER EIGHTEEN
OPTIMISING RECOVERY

Pete's recent achilles flareup recovered quickly. As instructed, he spent three days cycling at an intensity that sat within acceptable pain levels. During this recovery phase, he had several cross training options to maintain his fitness and continue with a sense of progression. Day by day, his symptoms improved, and he swiftly negotiated the walk-run program. When attempting phase one of the walk-run program, he was cautious. Symptoms initially hovered at two out of ten but settled to a one on the pain scale within five minutes. The following day, he recognised the same mild level of pain and stiffness. Since there was no irritation above his normal baseline levels, he was permitted to progress.

Pete tolerated the walk-run program so well that he transitioned through all four phases over the first four running attempts. However, phase four seemed to test his tolerance. Like before, he would initially rate his pain at a two before it faded to a one out of ten. However, by the end of phase four running program, the pain would increase to three. This pain remained within acceptable levels, but he remained cautious. The symptoms had returned to baseline within 24 hours, but he did notice a mild increase within the first few minutes upon waking.

When he called Daniel to discuss these symptoms, Pete was advised that he was on the borderline between acceptable and unacceptable levels. Pete needed to repeat the same walk-run dosage until the symptoms were within acceptable parameters. Taking a deeper look at his running plan, Daniel suggested incorporating intervals and strides once a week when Pete was back to running pain free. This approach would continue to build upon his running resiliency and allow his achilles to adapt to several intensities. Pete was happy with this suggestion. He had invested time in strides and interval sessions in the past and found them beneficial.

Stride and Interval Phases

PHASE	# OF STRIDE REPEATS	% OF MAX SPRINT	INTERVALS	AVE RPE (FOR RUN)
1	4	75	5x (1'run/1'jog)	7
2	6	75	4x (2'run/1'jog)	7
3	8	75	5x (2'run/1'jog)	8
4	6	90	4x (3'run/1'jog)	8
5	8	90	5x (4'run/1'jog)	8

Within two weeks, Pete's original marathon training plan was back on track. Attributing his swift recovery to his strength training, he made sure to reintroduce calf raises into his strength program and was motivated to progress the weight. Once all achilles symptoms subsided, he introduced phase one of interval training and stride sessions. He progressed through each phase week by week, provided that his body had adjusted to the change in intensity.

MON	TUE	WED	THU	FRI	SAT	SUN
Strength	12k 3RPE +Intervals	Rest	15k 4RPE +Strength	8k +Strides	Rest/ Cross train	30k RPE 3

Several weeks had passed, and race day was quickly approaching. Looking through his training schedule, Pete realised he only had six weeks until the big day. His mileage had continued to increase, and the weekend run progressed to 30 kilometres. Once his achilles pain resolved, he visited Daniel for the long awaited running assessment. Daniel assured him that his cadence and technique were fine and didn't require adjustment.

As the weeks rolled on, Pete noticed more fatigue in his training. He expected this with the increase in running volume, but it started to impact his training progression. While it didn't feel like an injury was developing, the first 10 minutes of every run presented with hip tightness, and calf soreness, with his overall energy levels lacking. Looking at his training program and dreading the 32 kilometre run scheduled next weekend, he wondered if marathon training was meant to feel like this. He sent Daniel an email asking for advice. The next morning, he opened up his inbox and read Daniel's reply:

> *"Hey Pete, I am glad you reached out. I have just the person for you to call. She is a friend of mine. Her name is Claire, and she is a researcher on recovery and an ultra marathoner.*
>
> *P.S. Your marathon is quickly approaching. I have attached some contact details at the bottom of this email. When your race is three weeks away, give the number a ring. You can thank me later".*

Pete didn't hesitate and picked up the phone to call Claire. He explained his situation and described the stage of his marathon plan, the overall soreness and the low energy levels. Claire suggested that perhaps he needed to enhance his recovery and asked how much sleep he was getting each night. Pete explained that he slept quite well and would get eight hours on average. He mentioned there was no change in sleep patterns since the start of the marathon training.

Claire reassured Pete that eight hours is the recommended average sleep for adults, but if he continued to train harder, he'd need to recover harder. Claire went on to explain that sleep is hands down the best recovery tool in his arsenal. She shared that most of her ultra running friends slept more than nine hours per night with multiple naps planned throughout the week. With training loads so high, they need to match it by elevating their recovery.

Pete was on the phone with Claire for 40 minutes. They discussed Pete's stress levels, nutrition and training intensities. Apart from recommending extended sleep and napping, Claire also recommended dropping a strength session in this phase of his marathon training. She highlighted that twice a week is a great frequency to build strength in the peak training season. However, if he required additional recovery, it could be a good option to drop back to once a week. That way, he would still be maintaining the strength he had accumulated over the past several months. Additionally, she recommended continuing with strides and interval sessions while listening to his body to decide what phases he'd like to implement. For instance, some weeks he could even drop down to easier sessions, and since his body was telling him it needed more recovery, this would be a perfect time to make these adjustments.

Claire also detailed that generic soreness was normal in marathon training, but the bigger the weekly mileage, the more runners should be prioritising recovery and optimising it the best way they can. Pete was happy with all of Claire's suggestions. Dropping the strength training frequency to once per week opened up another rest day. He also found himself going to bed 30 minutes earlier, finding some time for weekend naps, and ensuring that rest days were dedicated entirely to rest.

Pete's Notes and Updated Routine

- Sleep more
- Ensure the bedroom is cold when sleeping
- Avoid electronic devices 90 minutes before bedtime
- Rest on rest days
- Strength train once a week
- Stay hydrated
- Ensure good nutrition
- Meditate if stressed

MON	TUE	WED	THU	FRI	SAT	SUN
Rest	12k +Intervals 3RPE	Rest	15k 4RPE Strength	9k +Strides	Rest	32k RPE

Run Smarter Lesson 18

To train hard, you need to recover hard. Finding the balance between the two can make the difference between a stellar performance and a flop on race day. Before diving into the factors that enhance recovery, it is worth repeating the importance of a well balanced training load. I say this because some runners may constantly seek recovery aids due to never ending stiffness and soreness. In their eyes, once they find the right concoction of stretches, foam rolling, massage guns, trigger point release and manual therapy, their symptoms will reduce. In reality, the problem will most likely lie with their training such as having the wrong intensity distribution, as explained in Chapter 12. However, if the training loads are sound and the volume increases gradually, these strategies below will come in handy.

Runners should never underestimate the importance of lifestyle factors outside of their training. Chapter seven of this book already explored the impact of stress and sleep on injury prevention. It is worth reviewing how factors such as quality of sleep and emotional stress can inhibit your body's ability to rejuvenate. From an injury prevention perspective, this means altering your body's adaptation zone. From a performance perspective, it is manipulating the overall recovery availability. We can now review a paragraph from Chapter seven with this new perspective in mind:

> "While hormones such as cortisol and noradrenaline circulate through our bloodstream, the body prepares for exercise. Once you stop exercising, the mind and body calm themselves, and these hormone levels settle. When this process happens, your body can easily enter recovery mode".

> *"Lowering these stress hormones is vital for recovery and injury prevention because an athlete won't get stronger during a workout. Instead, they get stronger after the workout during relaxation. Imagine your body holds an important stress cup. When you exercise, the level of physical stress begins to fill the cup. If the cup starts overflowing with contents, the body can easily malfunction, becoming overloaded and increasing the likelihood of injury. However, when the body enters a relaxed state, it can begin processing the activity and slowly drain the contents within the stress cup".* [Chapter 7]

While the stress cup was introduced originally with injury prevention in mind, it can now be used to enhance your performance safely. However, there are various recovery methods for runners to try. Here is a short list of popular strategies I often come across when talking with runners:

- Active cool down and stretching
- Compression garments
- Cross training and hydrotherapy
- Manual therapy, dry needling, massage
- Foam rolling, massage balls and massage guns
- Sleep, downtime and napping
- Nutrition and hydration

It would be challenging to implement all of these strategies when preparing for a race. After all, squeezing in the weekly running mileage and strength sessions around your busy life can have its challenges. However, if the goal is to remove the contents of our stress cup, what is the most efficient way?

Signs and Symptoms of Poor Recovery

If a runner has analysed their training output and established the correct intensity distribution, the next step is to analyse their recovery. In reality, some runners may not recognise the signs of poor recovery. Below is my shortlist of the most common symptoms.

1. Constant muscle soreness: While some soreness during training is common, soreness throughout most of the week is not. Either you are overloading your body with too much training, or you are under recovering.

2. Feeling tired and lethargic: This could be a clear sign of overtraining or lack of sleep. Other emotional signs include mood swings, irritability and feeling jittery. A prolonged lack of motivation throughout the training process can also be a clear psychological sign.

3. Repetitive injuries: Some health professions consider injuries a question of under recovery rather than overtraining. In other words, if your recovery is optimal, it'll be very difficult to create an overuse injury. If you are seeing three or more injuries within 12 months of training. Self-reflect on your recovery methods.

Objectively Tracking Your Recovery

The importance of circulating hormones has already been discussed in relation to promoting or hindering recovery. However, another element that interplays with the release of hormones is your sympathetic and parasympathetic nervous systems. Rather than hormones circulating and eliciting a response, neurons are fired to either trigger the body for action (sympathetic) or prepare you for rest and recovery (parasympathetic). The parasympathetic nervous system in particular, when dominant in recovery mode, adjusts the rate of your heartbeat with subtle cues. For example, when you breathe in your heart rate increases and vice versa. As a result, even though your heart rate will beat at 80 beats per minute, it doesn't necessarily mean each beat is timed evenly. In fact, a large variation between heartbeats may be an indication that your parasympathetic nervous system is dominant and therefore, you are primarily in recovery mode.

This process is called heart rate variability and was introduced on the Run Smarter Podcast by biomedical engineer Simon Wegerif [138]. His website contains useful information about heart rate variability (HRV) and states:

> *"Generally speaking the more relaxed and unloaded (free from fatigue) the body is, the more variable the time between heartbeats. HRV data can indicate the impact of fatigue due to prior exercise sessions, hydration levels, stress and even the degree of performance anxiety, nervousness or other external stressful influences".* [139]

In theory, when you are stressed, anxious, overworked or sick, your body enters fight mode and will use the sympathetic nervous system to elicit the appropriate response. Therefore, measuring your HRV can identify these readings sometime before the athlete's knowledge. In other words, it may help to detect the hidden dangers that influence your capacity described in Chapter seven. Such data can then help an athlete make smarter training decisions for injury reduction and enhanced performance. Research from the Experimental and Therapeutic Medicine journal found that:

> *"Findings resulting from multiple studies suggest that HRV parameters are relevant in the analysis of stress that the body experiences during training and to increase insight into physiological recovery after training".*

> *"Referring to athletes, changes in the patterns of their autonomous nervous system reflected by altered HRV may serve as useful parameters for managing their physical fatigue and establishing their exercise intensity".*

> *"Information regarding the extent to which the body recovers after training may provide useful data for the personalisation of sports training, training loads and recovery times, targeting goal of improvement, avoiding overtraining and non-functional overreaching".* [140]

Detecting the variation between heartbeats requires a device to gather a large amount of data per second. A lot more than a standard heart rate monitor, and devices on the market vary in accuracy. Most devices gather data when worn on a finger, wrist or around the chest. Once HRV is documented, it can be used as a helpful piece of the puzzle to guide training. When I asked Simon about the practicalities of these devices and associated phone applications he said:

> *"People should train as they would normally, and then when their heart rate variability starts to dip, the algorithm would suggest you modify the workout to a lower intensity or shorter duration. If your HRV pops back up again tomorrow, then it can be a relatively higher loaded day".*

> *"Most apps will assign a traffic light system. Green means you're sufficiently well recovered and do what workout you*

have planned for that day. Amber means that there is likely to be an imbalance between your training and your recovery. However, it doesn't mean that your performance is going to drop off yet. But if you carry on creating a persistent imbalance between training and recovery it will mean at some point that your HRV will go down and your resting heart rate will go up".

"A red colour code should be taken seriously, it can mean you're sick or your body is really telling you that you need rest and you should not ignore that". [138]

Athletes should also consider the surrounding influences of HRV which may alter results. Particularly if only measuring HRV in one snapshot in time. For instance, body position, temperature, humidity, altitude, state of mood, hormonal status, drugs and stimulants all have an effect on HRV. It is, therefore, sensible to follow an average HRV score over hours, days and weeks as opposed to one moment in time. Martin Buchheit and colleagues wrote a paper on HRV and stated:

"Environmental conditions can exert a marked influence on HRV parameters".

"Quiet, slow-wave sleep recordings characterised by a regular respiratory rate, have thus been proposed as an optimal recording condition to accurately assess parasympathetic function from HRV analysis". [141]

I have been monitoring my HRV for years and during a bout of high volume training, I take HRV into consideration when choosing my training. I track this data by wearing a ring to bed each night. Through the night, my heart rate, HRV and sleeping metrics are recorded and on waking, assign a sleep score and readiness score. One interesting pattern I have noticed is my HRV stays low overnight for up to four days following an intense competition such as a triathlon event. Even when I physically feel recovered, my HRV tells me otherwise. Since this has been consistent with every hard race I have participated in, I have chosen to follow this trend and resume my regular training once my HRV returns to normal.

The HRV reading is a useful score among other health metrics and should not dictate training. Instead, it should be used as a piece of the puzzle to guide training. Subjective measures such as your internal perception of effort, enthusiasm, fatigue and soreness should also help guide the decision making process. Such recommendations were made by Daniel Plews and colleagues in a 2013 study:

> *"Reductions in HRV have been associated with fatigue and/ or non-functional over-reaching in recreationally trained and well-trained subjects. However, conclusions from past literature reporting isolated HRV values should be viewed with caution".* [142]

Managing Your Recovery Pyramid

Shona Halson is a world leading researcher on recovery and has worked with Olympic and sporting athletes across multiple disciplines. When I interviewed Shona Halson on the podcast, she introduced the concept of the recovery pyramid [143].

The recovery pyramid involves various layers of recovery methods, with each higher level representing either a less effective or less researched method. The concept of a pyramid illustrates the importance of establishing a solid foundation before moving up. In other words, your recovery strategy is sub-optimal if you implement higher pyramid levels without properly executing the fundamentals. Let's unpack each layer so you can self-reflect on your recovery methods:

Shona Halson's Recovery Pyramid

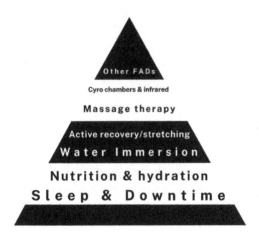

Sleep and Downtime for Recovery

As far as the body is concerned, psychological stress such as worry, frustration and anxiety are the same as physical stress. If you cannot let go of both the physical and emotional stress in your day-to-day life, you'll struggle to empty your stress cup as described in Chapter seven. This is why good quality sleep and downtime are the most crucial pieces of the recovery puzzle.

Christie Aschwanden concurred during my conversation with her on episode 95 of the podcast [144]. Aschwanden authored the book '*Good To Go: How To Eat, Sleep And Rest Like A Champion*' and commented:

> *"The benefits of sleep cannot be overstated. It's hands-down the most powerful recovery tool known to science. Nothing comes close to sleep's recovery-enhancing powers. You could add together every other recovery aid ever discovered, and they wouldn't stack up".* [145]

Research by Daniel Bonnar and colleagues helps bring a scientific approach to this concept. Their 2018 systematic review titled '*Sleep Interventions Designed to Improve Athletic Performance and Recovery*' is the first review to summarise the effects of sleep on athletes. They stated:

> *"Insufficient sleep can have a significant effect on athletic performance, with a particular decline in sports-specific skill execution and submaximal sustained exercise bouts".*
>
> *"Consistent with previous research, the results suggest that sleep plays an important role in some, but not all, aspects of athletes' performance and recovery. However, it remains unclear as to how much additional sleep is sufficient to produce these outcomes, as sleep needs vary considerably between individuals".* [146]

Laying the base of the recovery period, sleep must be highly prioritised over all other forms of recovery. I have heard of runners waking up 30 minutes early to squeeze in a foam rolling session before their run which is counterproductive. If you are foam rolling purely for the recovery benefits, you are best to remain in bed. Kenneth Vitale and colleagues released a 2019 review listing several sleep hygiene recommendations for optimising the recovery of athletes. I have included their ten recommendations [147] along with the most relevant tips and tricks for runners.

Sleep Hygiene Recommendations

1. Don't go to bed until you are sleepy. If you aren't sleepy, get out of bed and do something else until you become sleepy.
2. Build a regular bedtime routine or ritual to help the body prepare and relax for sleep.
3. Try to get up at the same time every morning, including weekends.
4. Try to get a full night's sleep every night, and avoid naps during the day if possible. If you must nap, limit this to one hour and avoid napping after 3:00 pm.
5. Use the bed for sleep and intimacy only. Avoid any other activities such as TV, computer or phone use.
6. Avoid caffeine if possible. If you must use caffeine, avoid it after lunch.
7. Avoid alcohol if possible. If you must use alcohol, avoid it right before bed.
8. Do not smoke cigarettes or use nicotine, ever.
9. Consider avoiding high intensity exercise right before bed. This may raise cortisol, which impairs sleep.
10. Make sure your bedroom is quiet, as dark as possible, and cool.

Other Tips and Tricks

1. Avoid blue light emitted from screens at least two hours before bed. Examples of these devices include smartphones, laptops and monitors. Blue light suppresses melatonin production that is needed to induce sleep. Avoid text messaging, social media, games and app use.
2. If you must use your computer at night, consider installing colour adjusting and blue light reducing software or wear blue light blocking glasses.

3. Don't hit the snooze button. It does not improve sleep quality.

4. Salt baths containing topical magnesium or oral magnesium may help if you are deficient.

5. Melatonin naturally occurs in foods such as tart cherry juice, raspberries, goji berries, walnuts, almonds, and tomatoes and may potentially improve sleep, but avoid artificial melatonin supplements.

6. Recovery from exercise should not only focus on muscle recovery. Reducing mental fatigue is just as important for healthy sleep. Actively try to reduce external stressors in your life.

While sleep is the number one recovery tool available to runners, you should also recognise the need for downtime. Downtime is another strategy to help manage daily stress if runners need an extra helping hand to empty their stress cup. As this book has discussed previously, your body reacts the same way to emotional stress as it would to physical stress. Consequently, it is best to monitor your psychological recovery when preparing for an event. Here is another statement from Shona Halson on the Run Smarter Podcast.

> "In athletes, we see that they have physically recovered, but mentally they can be drained. So downtime is a way to have some time without physical exercise and just relax".

> "These days we are so connected, whether that's with social media or phones and Netflix. We have lots of stimulation, and downtime is that period when you can be a little distracted from the world because we know the brain and the body are so well connected".

> *"We need to make sure the brain is recovering and feeling mentally fresh. For some people, it might be meditation or whatever helps you switch off for a bit".*

When my partner Megan and I moved house in 2021, my sleep reduced dramatically. A few elements played a role in this. Firstly, moving house is stressful, and selling Megan's house to move into our lovely new home added extra stress. I am usually calm when it comes to life-changing events like this, but not Megan. And it bothered me that it bothered Megan. The weeks before moving were filled with stress that disrupted our sleep, and once the move was complete, my disrupted sleep cycle continued.

In addition to the stress of moving, our bedroom curtains and blinds would not be installed for another six weeks. This resulted in our top floor east facing bedroom filling with morning sun, and as we were coming into summer, the sun would rise at 5:30am. Finally, as I mentioned in Chapter seven, my biggest cause of sleep disruption is excitement. Particularly when I have exciting business ideas swimming around in my head. Well, not only were Megan and I moving into our dream home, but the ground level of our house was being converted into my very own physiotherapy practice. Three years prior to moving, I treated runners online from my bedroom. So moving into a dedicated studio was a big, exciting business transition. Building a treatment room, podcast space, and rehabilitation studio sent my imagination into a frenzy. As a result, my sleep took a huge hit.

It took about two months for my normal sleep pattern to return. Over that time, I made the sensible decision to back off my running mileage and avoid testing my limits. My strength training continued to progress, but this time of my life was not the time to push the envelope in my running. I am sharing this story because runners should carefully weigh up the risks of pushing their running when dealing with similar life events. Many of us run for mental health, and running is often used for stress relief. If you are running while stressed, my advice is to maintain a low intensity and avoid pushing the limits.

Nutrition and Hydration

The next level on the recovery pyramid is nutrition and hydration. Yes, the food you consume provides fuel for performance, but a well balanced diet also provides the building blocks as you build your running mileage. If you are trying to find what foods will assist in your performance or which diet will yield the best results, this is not the book for answers. Firstly, I am not a dietician, and secondly, people react differently to various foods. Rather than positioning on a particular stance, I make a conscious effort to interview qualified nutritionists and dieticians to understand their interpretation of the evidence. To date, here is a list of my previous guests:

- Episode #26: *Gut Health for Runner Performance with Chloe McLeod*
- Episode #38: *Inflammatory Diets Impacting your Running with Vicky Kuriel*
- Episode #125: *Safe Weight-loss Methods for Runners with Dr Nick Fuller*
- Episode #140: *How Safe is Exercise While Fasting? With Kira Sutherland*
- Episode #174: *Running Lean with Food and Mindset with Patrick McGilvray*
- Episode #202: *How Safe is Fasting for Runners? With Meghann Featherstun*
- Episode #233: *Race Weight, Fueling and Helping GI Issues with Stephanie Hnatiuk*

While runners react differently to different foods and dieticians have various opinions, the practical steps a runner should make can be confusing. However, most people can decipher what a healthy meal looks like. A good balance of protein, fruits, and vegetables while reducing processed fats and sugars seems like the most sensible approach for most. Keeping with healthy, nutrient dense foods will supply the body with the building blocks for performance and recovery as you gradually increase the running weekly mileage and intensity.

When not training for a big event, you may pass with a sub-optimal diet. But if your goal is to thrive through higher mileage, you may need to up your nutrition game. Don't let old habits limit your potential. Even worse, some runners opt for a worse diet when training for a race such as a marathon. Whether due to cravings or self-justification, I have encountered runners eating copious amounts of food high in sugar and fat once their mileage increases. Be careful of this trend and keep healthy, nutrient dense foods on top of mind.

Active Recovery and Water Immersion

Chapter 15 discussed the effects of active recovery and stretching as an effective cool down method. Rather than aid in long-term recovery, these particular methods are beneficial for an immediate bounce-back to action. Unless you're competing in back to back events across consecutive days, these strategies won't be high on the priority list.

A similar stance is on water immersion techniques. As you can see on the recovery pyramid, water immersion is highly regarded as an effective recovery method. However, this pyramid was constructed with all athletes in mind, not just recreational runners. I believe recovery methods like these are studied with elite athletes in mind, particularly those competing multiple times a day or across consecutive days.

The evidence is looking good for cold water immersion with the proposed benefits of reducing post exercise inflammation with both temperature difference and pressure-induced changes. A systematic review conducted by Jonathan Leeder and colleagues revealed the effectiveness of cold water immersion [148]. They found temperatures ranging between 15 and 5 degrees celsius and immersion duration between 10 to 15 minutes to be an effective strategy for reducing delayed onset muscle soreness. While these findings are positive, the mechanisms for these effects remain elusive.

These particular strategies may not rank highly for a long term recovery optimiser, but they can provide well needed mental recovery depending on the individual. Like stretching, if you need downtime and water immersion therapy provides that need, it should remain an integral part of your recovery strategy.

Massage Therapy, Infrared and Cryotherapy

Toward the tip of the recovery pyramid are massage, infrared saunas, cryotherapy and other recovery FADs. While Shona doesn't specify all the examples of FADs, I'll include aids such as massage guns, TENS machines, foam rollers, massage balls, dry needling and similar devices. These forms of recovery have either been shown to be less effective, ineffective or absent when compiling high quality evidence. The book has already covered the marketing ploys companies use to sway the public in Chapter five. Some of these devices belong in this category. Advertising gadgets and using biassed and cherry picked data to pass products off as scientifically tested. These devices may still benefit some individuals but don't stack up in larger populations or compared to placebo trials. However, some of these methods are in this category due to the lack of available evidence, and therefore, emerging research may change our professional recommendations in the future.

I advise runners to continue implementing these recovery tools provided two elements are achieved. Firstly, the recovery method needs to have a profound positive effect on recovery. This effect may be subjective and will differ from person to person. Foam rolling is a great example. Some runners consider foam rolling an unpleasant, painful, unnecessary process, but they do it anyway because of the benefits they believe it will have. Others love the feeling of foam rolling, and while the sensation may be unpleasant at times, they finish their session feeling relaxed and recovered. Like stretching, the evidence may suggest ineffective physical benefits, but it can still provide psychological benefits. Each runner is unique in their response. Therefore, the advice to foam roll should be based on the individual.

Secondly, if you choose to implement these strategies into your recovery routine, you need to prioritise the lower tiers of the pyramid first. Consider the higher tiers as supplementary methods once the foundation is well established. There is no point in attending infrared sessions and using your massage gun if you're not managing your stress levels and not getting enough sleep.

Some runners rank massage therapy highly in their recovery list. This manual therapy treatment can be delivered in a wide array of options. For instance, it can be used as a relaxation tool with soft, calming strokes designed for your muscles to switch off as you sink into the bed. Conversely, it can be used as an unpleasant, firm technique that supposedly breaks up scar tissue, frees muscle knots, and releases active trigger points. While received as conventional wisdom, these proposed effects are, in my opinion, buzz words designed to oversell the effects and exploit the placebo effect.

I invited Alice Sanvito onto the podcast to help clear up this message. Alice is a massage therapist trained in trigger point massage, remedial massage and sports massage. She has spent several years practising and lecturing massage concepts, including trigger point therapy. Early in her career, Alice discovered that massage techniques didn't remove lactic acid, nor was lactic acid responsible for muscle soreness. It wasn't until several years later that her career fundamentally shifted. Alice stumbled upon a group of physiotherapists and science minded massage therapists who challenged her deep seated beliefs on trigger point therapy. Here is Alice talking about her turning point on the podcast:

> "It was, on the one hand, exciting but a little unnerving. The crisis came when someone challenged my thoughts on trigger points because I was very invested in them".

> "Early on, I had seen holes in the hypothesis, but because no one else around me seemed to recognise them, I forgot about them. But I started being challenged on them and came to realise we were being taught hypothesis as if it were fact".

> "There are a lot of holes in the trigger point hypothesis. We recognise that people have sore spots that can radiate pain and other sensations elsewhere, but it's the explanation about why that is happening has some serious flaws". [149]

Despite the harsh reality surrounding the mechanisms of massage therapy, it still has the potential for profound benefits. As a physiotherapist, I have personally witnessed countless clients lying on my treatment table in pain, only to stand up feeling amazing after a massage. Like Alice Sanvito, I'll continue using massage therapy as an effective treatment tool for those suitable clients. However, the big distinction is the language therapists use along with the narratives behind certain treatment effects.

For instance, I was working as an online therapist with a runner to help rehabilitate her proximal hamstring. At the time, she had successfully completed her walk-run program and was progressing into continuous running, strides and running at faster intervals. In between our catch up calls, she had received a manual therapy session with a practitioner which resulted in confusion and reduced confidence in her recovery.

During our next call, she listed off several findings this therapist had found as a potential cause for her ongoing issues. The biggest concern was a leg length discrepancy which was alarming at the time, along with a twisted pelvis, one glute not firing and poor activation of her core muscles. For her, it was a mental letdown after making good progress. Fortunately, I was able to rationally walk her through each finding and reassure her against any alarming narrative. I reminded her of the recent progress she has made and the continuing benefits that are expected when continuing on the same rehabilitation path. Unfortunately, many runners encounter these manual therapies without a medically rational explanation which results in low confidence levels, raised anxieties and a fear their body is letting them down.

In reality, the positive effects of manual therapy are created by many complex neurological and psychological processes. As runners, whether it is for pain reduction or recovery, if it feels good, do it. However, avoid falling into false narrative traps.

On the recovery side, runners should consider the benefits of a relaxation massage. Remember, while the physical effects are negligible and theoretical in the eyes of critics, you cannot ignore the profound psychological effects. After all, downtime is considered one of the foundation tiers on the recovery pyramid. If you love the psychological downtime associated with a relaxation massage, then place it high on your priority list.

Balancing Training and Recovery

Recovery methods need to match training output. Just as physical and emotional stress flood contents into your stress cup, your recovery needs to work just as hard to remove it. Remember, if the contents of the stress cup overflow, it significantly increases your risk of injury, illness or poor performance. Balancing these two aspects of training is important to consider when aiming for higher feats because runners commonly rely on old recovery habits to negotiate ever growing running demands.

For example, if your preferred weekly mileage was 20 kilometres per week and your weekend run stretched to 10 kilometres, you may be able to handle this mileage with poor recovery strategies successfully. In this scenario, you may get by with seven hours of sleep and a poor diet. These strategies may still be effective enough at removing the contents within your stress cup. If your running goals change and you start training for a half marathon, your recovery will also need to be adjusted to meet the demand. Likewise, these habits will need to be modified again with the jump to a full marathon or ultra distances.

It is worth giving thought to your current training load, internally analysing your body's response to that load, and considering if your recovery strategies need to change. Just like balancing a seesaw, you cannot let stress outweigh recovery. Another element of recovery is implementing a recovery week also known as a deload week which will be discussed in the next chapter.

The Recovering Tightrope Walker

Understanding the ramifications of recovery fits well with the tightrope walker analogy. So far, this book has discussed aspects of running technique that can continuously impact the thickness of the rope to walk along. What hasn't been discussed yet is the manipulation of the balance beam. The constant changes in sleep, nutrition and stress management throughout the training cycle, can be reflected in the fluctuating length of the tightrope walker's balance beam. This piece of equipment is vital for negotiating and counter balancing changes in wind and wobbles in the centre of mass of the walker. The longer the beam, the easier it is to balance and handle unexpected circumstances.

Throughout your marathon training, your balance beam needs to be constantly adjusting. If caught off guard or not recognised, a seemingly innocent running session could be enough to aggravate an injury. When all aspects of recovery are enhanced and maintained, your training balance beam provides the ability to handle and negotiate harder training loads. Conversely, moments of poor recovery should follow up with cautious training decisions.

Chapter 18 Summary

1. If you want to train hard, you need to recover harder.

2. Physical, psychological and emotional stress contribute to filling up your stress cup.

3. The most effective strategies you have to empty your stress cup are sleep, naps, downtime, and nutrition.

4. Massages, stretching, foam rolling, and water immersion can be effective adjuncts for some individuals once other effective strategies are well established.

Action Items

1. Study the recovery pyramid and make sure your recovery priorities are in the correct order.

2. If showing trends of under recovery, inspect your training loads, if the ramp up and intensity distribution are well balanced, look to enhance your recovery.

3. If poor sleep or stress is overwhelming and unavoidable, make necessary adjustments to your training program. Start by dialling back the weekly volume and the weekly intensity.

CHAPTER NINETEEN
THE PERFECT TAPER

Pete began implementing the recovery methods recommended by Claire. After two weeks he could feel his body slowly bouncing back. As a result, he had a spring back in his step which rejuvenated his motivation levels. The weekly mileage was still challenging and the weekend run had climbed to 30 kilometres which he felt was reaching his limit. Each Monday was a struggle as his legs were heavy, and the scheduled strength session required a lot of warmup time. With his recovery enhanced, the heaviness only persisted for 24 hours and the remainder of the week was easily negotiated. While the Sunday run was leaving him depleted, the strength training and interval sessions made him feel stronger and faster than ever.

After week 17, Pete felt quietly confident about his marathon target. He had never run at a weekly mileage this high before, and running consistently without setbacks began to excite him. Looking ahead to week 18, he noticed a strange drop in mileage during his scheduled Tuesday run. Wondering if it was a mistake he looked further ahead and realised the reduced mileage must be intentional. Week 18 contained a small reduction in mileage, but the following week was a drastic change.

WEEK	MON	TUE	WED	THU	FRI	SAT	SUN	TOT
16	Rest	12k +interval 3RPE	Rest	15k 4RPE Strength	8k + strides	Rest/ Cross train	30k RPE 3	65
17	Rest	13k +interval 3RPE	Rest	15k 4RPE Strength	10k + strides	Rest/ Cross train	32k RPE 3	70
18	Rest	13k +interval 3RPE	Rest	12k 4RPE Strength	10k + strides	Rest/ Cross train	25k RPE 3	60
19	Rest	8k +interval 3RPE	Rest	8k 4RPE Strength	7k + strides	Rest/ Cross train	12k RPE 3	35
20	Rest	6k +interval 3RPE	Rest	3k +strides	Rest	Race day 42km		

Pete assumed this was intentional but decided to learn more. Rather than bothering Daniel, he decided to look up this particular approach. He searched 'reduce mileage before a marathon' and quickly found a blog entry titled, 'How to Taper for a Marathon.' He had heard the term taper before but never put it into context. With his past marathons, he had intuitively reduced or stopped running for several days to feel fresh, but perhaps there was a more fine tuned method. He decided to search the definition of a marathon taper and came across an explanation:

> "A taper refers to the reduction of exercise before a race. Tapering can be considered one of the most important parts of training and is key to peak performance. Research has even shown that it leads to improved function of fast-twitch muscle fibres, which can result in faster race times".

Learning more about the taper was a relief for Pete. The weeks containing the hardest mileage were behind him, and he had tolerated this difficult phase without major disruption. While he felt relief and a sense of achievement, he couldn't help but feel a sense of anxiety begin to surface. Week 18 still contained a relatively high workload, but the following week scheduled a dramatic reduction. He began to worry that he would lose fitness. After all, two weeks of tapering is a long time.

Pete's concerns prompted him to call Jake, a friend from work who was also an experienced marathon runner. He took a screenshot of his plan and sent it to Jake. To Pete's relief, Jake was happy with the strategy. He explained that every experienced runner has a particular approach to tapering. For some reason, different runners respond differently, so they usually follow the standard recommendations and make micro adjustments every season before reassessing. Since this was Pete's first attempt at a taper, the standard approach is the way to go.

The reassurance was music to Pete's ears but he also expressed his worry about losing fitness. Jake laughed and mentioned that this phase is not only beneficial but necessary to perform at your best. Besides, Pete was still running four days a week to maintain his running rhythm. Thanks to Jake's wisdom, Pete would abide by the training plan throughout the next two weeks and trust the process.

Run Smarter Lesson 19

When preparing for a race, the training plan gradually introduces greater physical demand. If the ramp up is programmed correctly, your body will adapt to the ever growing demands. When race day approaches, the method of progression needs to alter as the goal shifts to prioritise peak performance on race day. Hence, the taper reduces the training load before a race to aid recovery and optimise performance. Administering the taper phase in your training is crucial. You don't want to dedicate several months gearing up for an event, only to make mistakes over the final weeks that jeopardise your chance of success.

Several running components will need to be considered during the taper process. Primarily, the training frequency, overall intensity and running volume. These individual components may need to be manipulated throughout the taper to create fresh, fast legs at the right time. In addition to these components, the overall duration of the taper will need to be taken into consideration.

Each component within the taper period requires precise adjustment. The goal is to perfectly balance the alleviation of training fatigue whilst maintaining physiological adaptation. If the balance is weighed and timed perfectly, the runner should feel physically and mentally fresh without losing fitness.

Does a Taper Affect Performance

Like Pete's anxieties, runners who haven't experienced the benefits of a well structured taper can have their doubts. One of the main reasons runners continue to run through an injury is fear of losing fitness. So when a running program calls for a steep reduction in workload, these same fears and anxieties can surface. However, good quality studies can reassure runners that the process is not only beneficial, but necessary if your goal is to race at your best.

A 2018 systematic review was published by Gerasimos Grivas investigating the effects of tapering on performance in elite endurance runners. His work observed that:

> *"Correct tapering would improve marathon performance up to 3%".*
>
> *"Tapering is an essential training strategy for improving performance and bringing success in a major competition".* [150]

Even though this systematic review focussed on elite runners, we can extrapolate these findings to Pete's scenario. With a sub four hour marathon in mind, a taper that delivers a 3% improvement will have Pete completing his race seven minutes quicker. To uncover why athletes see such an enhanced performance, we need to investigate the physiological and psychological effects.

Physiological Benefits of Tapering

If everything goes well within your marathon training cycle, you should be coming off the back of a challenging workload. Over subsequent weeks, the overall weekly mileage steadily increases along with the long run duration. As a result, there is an accumulation of fatigue. Every runner will experience the back end of this phase differently depending on the training intensity and volume. Some may encounter physical fatigue, leg stiffness, and an overall energy drop. The taper is designed to rejuvenate these physiological effects.

Work by Mujika and colleagues investigates the physiological and psychological effects of the taper period, emphasising its importance and necessity. Their paper titled '*Physiological Changes Associated with the Pre-event Taper in Athletes*' concluded that several significant physiological changes could occur with a well designed taper [151]. One particular finding is the increase in muscular strength. Mujika writes:

> "Studies suggest that muscular strength and power production is usually suppressed by chronic intensive training, but most likely recover during the taper when the training load is markedly reduced".

> "From a neuromuscular perspective, the taper usually results in markedly increased muscular strength and power, often associated with performance gains at the muscular and whole-body level".

In addition to increased muscular strength, Mujika and colleagues also report improved running economy, increased circulating testosterone, and maximal oxygen uptake. In other words, due to the effects of the taper, your body is physically more geared for performance.

Psychological Benefits of Tapering

With such a profound improvement in performance, it is hard to suggest the improvements of the taper are caused by physical effects alone. After all, performing at your physical best is severely limited if your mental game is not up to scratch. Mujika explained:

> "Competition performance is the result of a conscious effort, and it would be a major oversight to obviate the paramount

> *contribution of psychological and motivational factors to post-taper athletic performance".* [151]

Below are 3 of the psychological benefits uncovered during the taper process:

1. Improved mood state: Most studies indicate that tapering induces positive changes in the athlete's mood state, contributing to decreased levels of perceived fatigue, depression, anger and confusion accompanied by increased levels of vigour [151].

    During the ebbs and flows of training, your emotional state can significantly affect your performance and the likelihood of injury. For example, those who display high levels of frustration, performance anxiety, anger and depression are more likely to dismiss the body's signals, leading to overtraining and running through an injury. When it comes to race day, an improved mood state may also help with pre-race anxieties, as this emotional state is common across runners of all abilities.

2. Improved perceived effort: The perception of effort during exercise is influenced by several physiological and psychological variables, some of which are presumably affected by a taper. Patrick Neary and colleagues looked at cyclists and observed a 4.5% decline in the HR:RPE ratio after a seven day taper and a 5% increase in performance [152].

3. Improved sleep quality: We have already established how important sleep is for recovery. With reduced exercise load, slow wave sleep pressure is reduced, resulting in lower levels of slow wave sleep and increased rapid eye movement sleep. In addition, the number of movements during sleep was reduced

by 37% after a taper [151]. These findings indicate less sleep disruption than in previous periods of higher training loads.

The Right Taper Volume

The volume refers to the mileage or duration of your running. With the taper in mind, it refers to the rate of mileage reduction. For instance, some runners may reduce their weekly mileage by 15% during the taper period. It might seem negligible, but this could be enough to clear any accumulated fatigue. On the other hand, a runner may opt for a 90% reduction or no running at all. These are two extremes but highlight the spectrum of options available during the taper process.

While the response to a taper varies among athletes, general guidelines emerge based on research. Bosquet and colleagues published the effects of tapering in a meta analysis. They uncovered 27 articles and constructed the best taper guidelines based on their findings. The paper states:

> "Maximal performance gains are obtained with a total reduction in training volume of 41 to 60% of pre taper value. Training volume can be altered through the decrease of the duration of each training session and/or the decrease of training frequency. It seems that the first strategy should be preferred because decreasing training frequency does not result in a significant improvement in performance". [153]

Below is the graph for the Bosquet paper, which shows the 41 to 60% reduction displaying the greatest effect. This percentage range may serve as the physiological sweet spot between the recovery of chronic fatigue and maintenance of physical performance. However, there are many other elements to consider within the taper to ensure the sweet spot is reached.

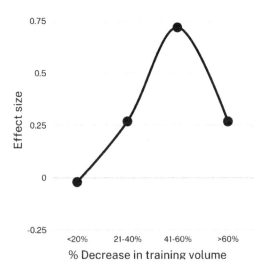

The Right Taper Intensity

While a reduction in overall training volume can be achieved, another important element is training intensity. Shepley and colleagues took nine highly trained cross country runners and randomly assigned them to one of three different seven day taper procedures [154]. The study had each subject perform each of the three tapers, separated by four weeks of training.

Before entering the taper period, each runner had completed an eight week training block. Each athlete ran six days per week in the final two weeks before the taper period, accumulating 80 kilometres. Within this training cycle, 30% was dedicated to high intensity interval training at 95 to 100% of VO2 max. The remainder of their running was spent at lower intensities.

The first taper method administered was the high intensity, low volume taper. During this taper phase, the volume of running was dramatically reduced. However, high intensity interval training was maintained. Conversely, the second method called for low intensity running without interval training. Lastly, the rest taper required no running throughout the entire taper duration. Below is a description of each seven day taper.

Taper number one: High intensity, low volume taper

- Day one: Rest
- Day two: 5x (500m fast intervals + 6 minute walk-recovery) + 800m finish 50% Vo2
- Day three: 4x (500m fast intervals + 6 minute walk-recovery) + 800m finish 50% Vo2
- Day four: 3x (500m fast intervals + 6 minute walk-recovery) + 800m finish 50% Vo2
- Day five: 2x (500m fast intervals + 6 minute walk-recovery) + 800m finish 50% Vo2
- Day six: 1x (500m fast intervals + 6 minute walk-recovery) + 800m finish 50% Vo2
- Day seven: Rest

Taper number two: Low intensity taper

- Day one: Rest
- Day two: 10km run at 57–60% Vo2Max
- Day three: 8km run at 57–60% Vo2Max
- Day four: 6km run at 57–60% Vo2Max
- Day five: 4km run at 57–60% Vo2Max
- Day six: 2km run at 57–60% Vo2Max
- Day seven: Rest

Taper number three: Rest taper

At the start of the study and at the end of each taper period, athletes were asked to complete a running test on a treadmill. After a warm-up period, the athletes were placed on a treadmill moving at a velocity matching their best 1,500 metre race of that year. The athletes would run on the treadmill until exhaustion as evidenced by stumbling or grasping the handrail.

The high intensity taper group improved their treadmill test by 22% as opposed to the low intensity group, which saw improvements of 6%. The rest group displayed a 3% reduction in time on the treadmill test. The authors of this paper made the following conclusion:

> *"We conclude that highly trained middle-distance runners can improve their performance as a result of a taper where intensity is maintained and volume greatly reduced".* [154]

The paper's conclusion was also supported in the Bosquet meta analysis. They state:

> *"It seems clear that the training load should not be reduced at the expense of training intensity, probably because it is a key parameter in the maintenance of training-induced adaptation during the taper".* [153]

Another useful resource was Kate Spilsbury's chapter in the book *'The Science and Practice of Middle and Long-distance Running'* [155]. Kate's chapter within the book describes tapering and peaking for a racing event. She writes:

> *"Whilst large reductions in training volume are necessary to alleviate accumulative fatigue from a heavy period of training, the preservation of training intensity during the taper is*

> *fundamental to maintaining physiological adaptations and preventing a decline in performance".*

By analysing the research, it seems that cardiovascular endurance is easily preserved if you maintain short duration, low intensity exercise. This can be reassuring for runners who shy away from a taper period due to fear of fitness loss. If you were not exercising or if you were bedridden, the rate of cardiovascular deconditioning would occur a lot quicker. However, while cardiovascular endurance is easy to maintain, it seems there is a quicker deconditioning in the neuromuscular response to maintain power, stiffness and running economy.

Practically speaking, the taper could consist of one to two stride sessions per week and one to two short interval sessions per week while the overall mileage drops dramatically. These guidelines, however, will depend on the level of high intensity exercise achieved before the taper.

The Right Taper Frequency

The frequency refers to the number of training sessions administered per week and is an element that intertwines with training volume. For instance, a runner could halve their running mileage by reducing the frequency of running from six to three days. If some running sessions concluded with strides, it would abide by the previous taper recommendations. However, your taper can become more effective if you follow the correct taper frequency guidelines.

Jason Fitzgerald was a repeat guest in episode 220 of the Run Smarter Podcast [156]. The episode was titled *'Finding the Right Taper and Recovery Week Strategy'*, and Jason imparted his wisdom and expertise on the topic. He agreed to the above taper volume and intensity recommendations and added his take on training frequency:

> *"There is a certain value to running more frequently, certain aspects of muscle memory, getting your body to use fuel more efficiently and fine-tuning that neuromuscular connection between your brain and your muscles".*
>
> *"So I still like to see athletes running the same number of days per week. Maybe the week of their race they cut it by a single day".*

Bosquet's work supports Jason's advice and recommends maintaining a training frequency close to 80% or more of the pre-taper value. Part one of the book has already discussed the adaptation advantages of high frequency training, which is also considered during tapering.

The Right Taper Duration

The taper duration refers to the overall time spent tapering before a race. Personally speaking to many experienced runners all over the world, I came across a wide variety of preferences. Some runners prefer a long three to four week taper, while on the other side of the spectrum, I have witnessed a taper cut down to only four days. While there is wiggle-room for individual preference and individual response to the taper duration, the available research can help novice runners with general guidelines.

Similar to the training volume graph, Bosquet's meta analysis has also compiled a taper duration graph with the 27 articles included in the paper. Bosquet concluded:

> *"We found a dose-response relationship between the duration of the taper and the performance improvement. Duration of 8 to 14 days seems to represent the borderline between the positive influence of fatigue disappearance and the negative influence of detraining on performance. Performance improvements can also be expected after one, three or four-week tapers".* [153]

Taper Guidelines

DURATION	VOLUME REDUCTION	INTENSITY	FREQUENCY
14 days	41–60%	Maintained	80–100% of Pre-taper

Recovery Weeks

Physiological and psychological benefits can also come from a recovery or deload week during a mid training cycle. Unlike the taper, a recovery week isn't designed to achieve peak performance on a certain day. Instead, it is designed to give the runner a physical and mental reset while fostering adaptation across a greater timescale. While the scientific literature on this topic isn't as robust or popular compared to a taper, we can extrapolate the research alongside expert opinions.

As mentioned earlier, I interviewed Jason Fitzgerald on this exact topic, and he described the intention of a recovery week perfectly:

> *"So the purpose of the recovery week is two-fold. Number one, we want to physically recover from all the hard work that we are doing. We want to make sure that our bodies*

> are absorbing all that hard work, and that we are getting all those adaptations that we are looking for".

> "The other reason why you would want to take a recovery week that doesn't get talked about enough is the psychological component. There are certainly a lot of mental benefits you can have when taking a recovery week".

> "I want runners to be excited about training. I want them to be motivated and driven to train hard. It is really hard to do that if you are not giving yourself the rest and recovery that you need". [156]

While the taper produces well defined guidelines, the recovery week is more subjective. Individual factors will significantly influence the frequency of a recovery week or the degree of reduction. For instance, the amount of good quality sleep a runner gets can significantly change the response and adaptation to high volume training. In addition, training volumes, intensity distribution, nutrition and stress management can all influence overall tiredness and soreness. If all these factors are optimised, a runner may never feel the need to take a recovery week.

We have already discussed in Chapter 18 that you don't get stronger during a hard workout. You get stronger after a hard workout once you have provided your body enough recovery time. A recovery week can be considered in the same way but across a grander scale. Instead of the 'train-recover-adapt' cycle that occurs each session, consider the same adaptation process across several weeks. The accumulation of chronic fatigue due to high workloads can take its toll. If the recovery week is administered correctly, it can keep motivation levels high, limit mood swings and generate a new spring in your step.

How often a recovery week should be implemented requires methodical testing and accurate interpretation of your body signals. You may have a sudden, unexplained mismatch in your perceived effort levels to running speed, or you may have muscle soreness stretching over several days. You may also encounter psychological disruption, either a loss of training motivation or irritability. A recovery week could rejuvenate your body without major training disruption if you listen to your body and accurately interpret these signals. Body signals can also be misinterpreted. For example, a few days of muscle soreness may not indicate a recovery week, and instead, all that is required is a rest day. This is where practice is needed to recognise familiar patterns and make the right decision accurately.

With a recovery week, you can adjust the training volume, intensity, and frequency slightly differently compared to a taper period. This is because the intention of a recovery week is different. Jason explained:

> "We are not getting ready for a peak performance like we are at the end of a taper. A lot of the things we do in the taper are designed to maintain our muscle tension and a lot of that is maintained by the intensity in our training".

> "In a recovery week, we don't necessarily need to prioritise high muscle tension for our goal race, because the goal is just extra recovery, extra adaptation and a psychological break from hard training". [156]

When training is building, Jason suggests a recovery week every four to eight weeks as a rough guideline. As opposed to the abrupt reduction in volume in the taper, the recovery week can be a simple, mild adjustment. Dropping one run within the week or one interval session may be all that is required. The frequency and reduction will depend on how the body feels, the current training volume, the overall recovery and just as importantly, the reaction to past recovery weeks.

Taper Guidelines

DURATION	VOLUME REDUCTION	INTENSITY	FREQUENCY
14 days	41–60%	Maintained	80–100% of Pre-taper

Recovery Week Guidelines

Duration	Volume reduction	Intensity	Frequency
5–7 days	Mild decrease	Mild decrease	Mild decrease

Taper and Recovery Week Variability

Several individual factors go into a perfect taper or a well designed recovery week. Unfortunately, the perfect recipe at an individual level is impossible to ascertain through science. Instead, the goal is to begin with genetic guidelines before making micro adjustments season to season to measure if a small improvement is made.

The intention of a taper is to perfectly balance the alleviation of training fatigue whilst maintaining physiological adaptation. Due to the complex nature of this balance, it requires a systematic approach alongside intuition. A micro adjustment will also be required based on different races. Keep in mind the individual variability of the response to a taper. Whether it is genetic makeup or individual muscle physiology, certain runners will respond differently to a change in training load. Due to these individual responses, you should treat each taper like an experiment. With each experiment comes a different hypothesis worth testing, and over time you start to learn your individual preferences.

The advice to experiment may seem too daunting and require too much patience, but as runners, we need to think long term if peak performance is the goal. Instead of leaping from race to race in a narrow sighted manner, take a broader perspective. Imagine your tenth race from now. How do you envision race day going? If you hope to have perfect preparation with everything falling into place, then use your next race as an experiment to help bridge the knowledge gap.

Chapter 19 Summary

1. The taper is designed to have your physical and mental performance peaked on race day.

2. General guidelines suggest a 14 day taper that halves volume while maintaining intensity and frequency will yield the best results.

3. Recovery weeks can be vital for training longevity, enhancing the adaptation process and maintaining high training motivation.

4. Recovery weeks may require a mild reduction in training volume, intensity and frequency.

Action Items

1. If you are challenging your capabilities during a build up phase, pay close attention to the body and assess if a recovery week is needed. If so, make small adjustments in volumes and intensity to bounce back stronger.

2. If you are aiming for peak performance on race day, follow the generic tapering guidelines and observe the effects.

3. Experiment with micro adjustments beyond these guidelines to allow for individual variability and different race conditions.

CHAPTER TWENTY

RACE DAY PERFORMANCE

O ne final step was looming over Pete's head. A few weeks ago, Daniel emailed him to provide Claire's contact details, but he attached one other detail:

> *"P.S. Your marathon is quickly approaching. I have attached some contact details at the bottom of this email. When your race is three weeks away, give the number a ring. You can thank me later".*

The day arrived, with three weeks until the marathon, Pete picked up his phone and dialled the number. A deep male voice answered and Pete sheepishly explained the situation about Daniel providing this anonymous number. A warming laugh boomed in reply. Pete could tell this person knew Daniel and his mysterious manner. He introduced himself as Steve, a sports performance psychologist. He was keen to dive into Pete's preparation and see if there were any strategies that would help him succeed.

Pete's excitement peaked. He had run three marathons before and recognised the brutal mental game a marathon plays. In fact, Pete had personally witnessed and experienced races falling to pieces when runners were physically prepared but not mentally equipped. Pete shared his A, B and C goals before Steve asked to rate his belief and capabilities to achieve his A goal.

The question caught Pete off guard. He had never thought about assigning a measurement to his self-belief. He thought his training was going really well and had come a long way, well beyond what he had expected. He was feeling faster than ever and had never successfully completed such high mileage. In addition, he had received expert advice in many facets along the way. Pete replied confidently with an eight out of ten.

Next, Steve wanted to dive deeper into Pete's primary goal and motivation levels. Steve prompted him to think about why he wanted to finish this marathon in under 4 hours. Again, this was a tough question to answer. He took some time to think about it before mentioning that he just loves running. While this response was a good start, Steve encouraged Pete to dig deeper. They both conversed back and forth each time diving deeper into Pete's deep seated motivations. Every response was followed up with Steve asking why, prompting more self-analysis:

"Because I want to push myself and see what I am capable of"
"Because if I achieve running goals, I'll build confidence to tackle other life goals"
"Because if I succeed in life, I will become a good role model for my family"
"Because my family is my number one love in this world"

Over the phone, Steve stopped prompting Pete. He had finally reached his deep seated motivation behind this mission. Pete had never thought about this on a conscious level before but he spoke from the heart and suddenly his motivation to see this plan through was ignited. Steve was pleased and advised Pete that family and love are enormous driving factors and that is what he should think about in those tough moments during his marathon. Regarding the sub four hour plan, Steve asked about his particular pace strategy for race day.

Pete tried to reply confidently, but he hadn't given it much thought. He mentioned he had researched the average required pace which was under 5 minutes and 40 seconds per kilometre and figured he would set out at this speed and reassess his situation every hour. For the remainder of the call, they worked together to adjust his pacing strategy. They also talked through race day tactics to sharpen Pete's mental game. Pete took notes throughout the call.

Pete's Notes: Mental Game Boost on Race Day

Self-talk:

- Invent a deep seated mantra to spark motivation

Useful self-distractions during tough moments of the race:

- Talking to other runners
- Taking in the scenery and atmosphere
- Counting steps to 50, and repeating
- Finding 10 things to be grateful for

Useful inward focus strategies to stay focused and on task:

- Focus on breathing
- Focus on posture
- Practice quiet running
- Maintain a relaxed arm swing

Steve made sure Pete had everything written down but still had one more thing to cover. He asked how many more long runs Pete had to complete before the marathon. Pete opened the schedule on his phone and saw a 25 kilometre run scheduled this weekend. While it would have been ideal for longer runs, Steve recommended he try these strategies during his next run. He also recommended Pete visualise race day with as much detail and incorporate as many senses as he could. He advised Pete to live the experience to prepare his body, mind, and nervous system for the tough road ahead. That way, he would step onto the starting line with a psychological edge which would help his performance tremendously.

Run Smarter Lesson 20

Many components need to align for you to perform at your best on race day. Hopefully, most of these components are already ticked off before race day begins. In fact, many runners calm their nerves at the start line by telling themselves that the hard work has already been done. The weeks of high mileage training and gruelling long runs are behind you. Now it is time to enjoy the moment and reap the rewards.

While this mindset is great to shake off pre-race jitters, some elements during the race can give you an added advantage. Below is a list of ingredients during the training phase that will contribute to peak performance.

Performance Checklist Before Race Day

- A well balanced training plan: Having the right balance in your training is essential, and the specifics will depend on the type of race you have set. Building a substantial base of low intensity running will set up most of your success for a marathon. For example, a runner who successfully runs 60 kilometres per week is likely to outperform a runner who has only accumulated 30 kilometres per week. In addition, an 80/20 intensity distribution will be an excellent balance for most endurance races.

- Strength and conditioning training: If you want to improve your running performance, strength training twice a week is a crucial component. Strength train with heavier weights in mind and ensure you progress safely. Do not become complacent once a certain weight range is achieved. Dedicating 10 to 15% of your strength training to power-based or plyometric exercises will also provide a helpful edge.

- Training with specificity in mind: Toward the back end of your running schedule, your running demands should begin to align with race specifics. Consider as many variables as possible such as the likely temperature, humidity, distance, elevation, terrain and racing time of day. Gathering this information will help you train and prepare for these conditions.

- Running technique: While there is no perfect running technique, correcting any apparent inefficiencies will provide you with an advantage. Ensure your cadence is within an ideal range and an overstride is absent.

- Footwear: Provided you have adapted to your racing shoes throughout your training cycle, lighter shoes will enhance running economy and performance. Carbon fibre shoes also appear to enhance running performance and can be considered.

- Adequate recovery: If recovery is enhanced, your body will adapt quicker and tolerate higher demands. Ensure sleep is optimised and daily stress is managed.

- Optimal taper: The ideal taper period provides the perfect balance between removing cumulative fatigue, rejuvenating psychological energy levels, and preserving running performance. Follow the recommended guidelines for a standard taper and elicit micro adjustments from season to season to find the right balance for you.

- Avoid illness or injury: Part of this involves luck, and some includes creating your own luck. While some illnesses are unavoidable, most can be dealt with quickly with a healthy immune system. If you are fit, healthy and recovered, you should be able to fight infections easier and return to training quicker. Similar to illness, running injuries are sometimes unavoidable. However, being strong, healthy and proactive with your rehabilitation will result in injuries being quickly managed without disruption in your training.

Ticking off these elements will provide the best running potential. However, sometimes, potential does not influence or impact reality. Truthfully, there can be a lot of factors that go right or go wrong during the event itself. There is simply no guarantee that your hard work will result in the best possible outcome. This chapter will discuss the physiological and psychological strategies to move that potential closer to reality.

Race Day Fuelling

Fuelling your body on race day is an art and a science. We all have different gut sensitivities and levels of tolerance. Based on individual preferences and sensitivities, the aim is to find an adequate fuel strategy designed to maintain an ongoing energy source. Energy is lost primarily through movement and heat when running, and these rates will change depending on the duration, temperature, humidity, intensity and several other factors. It is hard to determine the most efficient ongoing fuel strategy for optimal performance with so many variables.

Train Your Body and Train Your Gut

Where fueling is concerned, the main energy source mid race will come from carbohydrates. Commonly, runners provide their bodies with carbs in the form of energy drinks or gels. It can be tricky when trying to consume food, drinks or gels while running and it can even cause gastrointestinal problems. This is why training your gut to tolerate certain foods is important for optimal performance. In the same way your body needs to prepare for a race physically, so should your body practice race day fuelling. For example, for some runners, eating breakfast before a run can result in an upset stomach. As a result, they often resort to running on an empty stomach and fuelling with a coffee or water. While this strategy may be successful for a weekend training run, it will not be satisfactory if optimal race performance is your goal.

With this in mind, your focus should be on training your body and training your gut for race day. Start by eating small amounts of food before a training run. When your training plan progresses to longer runs, practice ingesting gels or energy drinks. This conversation came up when I interviewed sports dietician Chloe McLeod on episode 26 of the Run Smarter Podcast [158]. Chloe mentioned when training for her first marathon, she could only stomach half a gel at a time without feeling unwell. However, over time and with practice, she trained her gut to tolerate larger volumes. Come race time, Chloe could quite happily digest one whole gel packet, which resulted in more fuel and more energy available throughout the race.

If you are training your body to tolerate more food and still getting gastrointestinal stress on race day, you may need to consider the role of stress on the digestive system. For some, race day can generate a lot of nerves. The big crowds, unknown outcomes, anticipation and excitement can lead to a jittery state which hinders the gut's function. If you recognise this pattern of gut distress only on race day, and you're prone to nerves, practice calming strategies to assist with gut function.

Time Your Race Day Fuelling

For optimal performance, Chloe McLeod suggests a high sugar sports drink or carbohydrate gel throughout the race. This food source will assist in providing the body with the fuel required to perform at its best. Ideally, your intake should be established through trial and error during your long training sessions. However, Chloe mentioned some helpful guidelines during our podcast interview:

> *"I would always encourage runners to practice what they are going to be doing in a race in training sessions beforehand so they can work out what works best for them".*

> *"I often have runners say they can run a marathon and not need anything until they're 25 kilometres in. Yes, you can do that, but you could do it better if you had your gel or your sports drink earlier in your race to get better quality performance".*

> *"What I like to recommend for people is to start your intake early, because when you are fatigued, your gut isn't as good at absorbing carbohydrates".* [158]

Chloe explained that digesting your carbohydrate source earlier in the race will pay dividends in the back end. You'll encounter overall fatigue by this stage of the race, but your energy stores will not be depleted. This approach is much better than attempting to consume your carbohydrates too late while battling fatigue and concurrently struggling with digestion.

Sweat Science and Cramping

Another threat that runners face on race day is muscle cramping. If severe enough, it can cripple the muscle's ability to function and single handedly derail any performance goal. Identifying one sole mechanism of muscle cramping still eludes scientists and the reality most likely points to multiple causes. For instance, one theory for muscle cramping is due to a severe loss of electrolytes through your sweat. Sodium makes up most of the electrolytes in sweat, and a rapid loss without replacement can cause the muscle to lose function. This makes sense because cramping is particularly common when runners are pushed to their endurance limits involving high sweat rates. High temperatures or humid conditions can drastically increase the likelihood of muscle cramping.

The theory about a disturbance in electrolyte balance is warranted, and some very large studies have tested such theories with impressive results. For example, several studies in the early 20th century gathered large numbers of industrial workers operating in hot, humid conditions. They discovered the rate of muscle cramping was significantly reduced when adding salt to their drinking water [159]. However, we also know that cramping can occur without sweat loss. For example, foot cramps when walking barefoot or keyboard cramps in the hands are commonly observed. These occurrences gave rise to a second theory involving a primarily neurological origin.

The truth may lie between these two theories, and individuals may cramp for different reasons, prompting other remedies. That said, it is recommended that athletes try different treatment options to find a remedy that best suits them.

An important piece of advice for overcoming cramps is understanding the make-up of your sweat and your sweat loss rate. On the podcast, I interviewed Andy Blow, sports scientist and co-founder of Precision Fuel and Hydration, a company that works to help runners understand the mechanisms of sweating. Andy helps runners uncover two main sweat mechanisms as he explained in episode 194:

> "There are two main components of sweating that matter. The first is how much you sweat and the next is what is in your sweat. If we start with how much you sweat that is the easiest for the runner to measure themselves because you can do a pretty basic sweat rate test".

> "You do a training session of a given duration, and you weigh yourself immediately before and again immediately after your session. The difference in body weight will roughly be what you have lost in fluid. If you do that over a number of times in a number of different conditions you can start to gain a pretty strong appreciation for what your range of sweat rates are as an individual".

> "That can then paint a good picture of whether you will need to be more aggressive with your approach to hydration during long exercise or whether you'll be okay drinking to thirst or listening to your body". [160]

Not only do people sweat at different rates, but several factors influence an individual's sweat loss. Some common components include the weather, clothing, fitness level, exercise intensity and exercise duration. Weighing yourself before and after exercise, can help determine whether you fit into a low, moderate or high sweat rate. Andy continues:

> *"The sweat concentration test is more difficult and can be done with an advanced sweat test. Sodium is the predominant electrolyte you lose in your sweat, and the range in sweat sodium loss can vary hugely between people. At the lower end, some people are losing about 200 milligrams of sodium in every litre of sweat, and at the high end, some people are losing over 2,000 milligrams".*

> *"The sodium concentration is relatively stable and so an advanced sweat test generally only needs to be administered once while the sweat rate varies and ideally needs to be done several times under different conditions and at different exercise intensities".* [160]

Sweat Test Components

| Sweat Concentration | Sweat Rate | Duration | Your Net Losses |

After our interview, and courtesy of Andy Blow, we organised my own sweat concentration test. As luck would have it, Andy introduced me to Reece Noble, a local sweat tester who was happy to help me out. A few weeks later, Reece turned up at my house with a briefcase sized unit and opened it up on my living room table. As

Reece was setting up his fancy sweat device, I answered several sweat questions through an online survey.

I didn't think I had a high electrolyte concentration because muscle cramping had never impacted my performance. I couldn't recall a moment where I had to stop due to cramping throughout my basketball career, marathons, triathlons, and day long bike events. Reflecting back, none of my physical feats had been performed on hot, humid days. Therefore, I was quietly confident about the final result.

Once the set up was complete, Reece strapped electrodes onto my skin and turned on his machine. The electrodes are designed to trigger a sweat response. Once enough sweat is gathered, it is then injected into the sweat tester for calculation. To my surprise, I actually tested high on the sweat concentration scale. My concentration level showed that I was losing 1,269 milligrams of sodium for every litre of sweat.

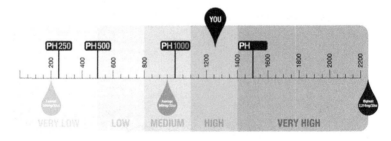

With my sweat concentration calculated, the next piece of the puzzle was to determine my average sweat rate. I followed Andy's instructions and weighed myself immediately before and after different training sessions across three weeks. Since each workout was 60 minutes or under, I decided to not drink water throughout the session. Each time I weighed myself, I would remove all clothing, dry off any remaining sweat and step on the scale. I then measured all the relevant details of the workout:

Workout #1:

- 30 minute run 17 degrees, 90% humidity, RPE 3–4
- Before: 69.4 kgs
- After: 69.2 kgs

Workout #2:

- 45 minute indoor ride 22 degrees, RPE 3–4
- Before: 69.0 kgs
- After: 68.7 kgs

Workout #3:

- 30 minute HIIT circuit, indoor at 22 degrees, RPE 3–4
- Before: 69.9 kgs
- After: 69.7 kgs

Workout #4:

- 45 minute indoor spin, 22 degrees, 6 RPE
- Before: 69.0 kgs
- After: 68.5 kgs

Workout #5

- 60 minute run, 9 degrees, 99% humidity, RPE 5.5
- Before: 69.4 kgs
- After: 68.9 kgs

Workout #6:

- 30 minute indoor spin, 22 degrees, 6.5 RPE
- Plus 30 min run, 16 degrees, 100% humidity, 4 RPE
- Before: 69.2 kgs
- After: 68.7 kgs

The above examples offer a variety of conditions. The data may have been more accurate if I had included sessions lasting over 60 minutes and RPE sessions over six. Nonetheless, the team at Precision Fuel and Hydration received my data and concluded:

> *"The body mass changes you recorded show you have a fairly low sweat rate of between 0.4 and 0.5 litres per hour. When compared to a vast amount of scientific research and a large personal database, we class a "moderate" sweat rate as anywhere between 0.7–1.85 L/hr".*
>
> *"I can see that you lose around 1269mg of sodium in every litre of sweat you produce, which puts you in the "high" sweat sodium category, more commonly known as a 'salty sweater'. You'll need to consider this when planning what fluids to drink, as you could be losing around 750mg of sodium per hour at a sweat rate of 0.6L/hr".*

Understanding your own measurements will give you a great race day template. However, micro adjustments may still be required. As mentioned earlier, people cramp for different reasons, under different circumstances, so the aim is to test and observe. If you try a particular fuelling strategy and witness a decrease in the severity or frequency of cramping, then you know you are on the right track. Do not take this as a rigid recipe, as each race and performance presents unique obstacles, and your fuelling strategy should reflect that.

The Most Effective Pace Strategy

A pacing strategy refers to your overall race pace throughout various segments. Pacing has long been of interest to scientists. They have characterised successful pacing trajectories and identified physiological, psychological, energetic, and environmental factors that influence pacing. Looking at the variables within a runner's control, certain strategies can be pre-planned and well executed on race day. For example, a runner could plan to run at a conservative pace for the first half of a marathon to be fresh on the back end. Commonly, inexperienced runners get caught up in the hype of race day and initially run too fast, burning all their matches and suffering the consequences later. Some adopt an even pace strategy or even switch to scheduled walks periodically throughout. The correct pacing strategy will make a huge difference in the outcome of a race, and if you decide to race without a plan, you are subject to many unknowns.

Andy Renfree and Brian Hanley wrote a chapter titled '*Strategic and Tactical Decision-making*' in the book '*The Science and Practice of Middle and Long-Distance Running*' [161]. This chapter mentions that an even pace or a negative split is associated with a better marathon performance. A negative split refers to the race's second half being completed faster than the first half. I spoke to Brian Hanley on episode 162 of the Run Smarter Podcast who mentioned successfully running at an even split is the desired outcome when considering all physiological factors [162].

This means, if I wanted to run a marathon in under four hours, my goal would be to split 5 minutes and 41 seconds per kilometre evenly. Another complexity is added, however, when hills are involved because maintaining an even pace uphill will lead to early burnout. The same can also be said for changes in weather throughout the race. In this case, Brian suggests running with even effort rather than speed. The ability to run with even effort presents many challenges for inexperienced runners but will provide the best template for success.

Once you have calculated an even pace for the race, it might be worth recalculating with a buffer for the back half. Adjusting for slower splits in the first half of the race may help preserve energy and reap dividends in the back half. In addition to these calculations is the psychological boost of passing people at the end. Imagine two scenarios in the final 45 minutes of a marathon. First, you are depleted, your legs are heavy and burning, your body is screaming to stop, but you are gobbling up exhausted runners like Pac-Man. In the other scenario, as your body is screaming to stop, runners are passing you like you are a 90 year old crossing the street. The first scenario creates a huge psychological boost and motivation, while the second fosters doubt and demoralisation.

In other words, starting slower to pass people at the end will deliver greater outcomes. Brian recommends only making slight adjustments with these factors in mind, as starting too slow will be near impossible to make up later on. Below is an example of a four hour pacing strategy.

Goal: 4 hour marathon
Even pace 5 minutes and 41 seconds
+ Attrition buffer 5 minutes and 44 seconds
+ Psychological boost 5 minutes and 48 seconds
= Splits first section 5 minutes and 48 seconds
= Splits middle section 5 minutes and 41 seconds
= Splits final section under 5 minutes and 30 seconds

The decision making process does take experience and will become more refined after every race attempt. Most of the advice focuses squarely on avoiding running out of the gates too quickly and destroying your performance later. Whether it is from getting caught up in the excitement of race day, getting overly competitive with a runner next to you or showing overconfidence, some runners are more prone to this mistake. In fact, Robert Deaner and colleagues published a paper that discovered runners with the greatest discrepancy between self-forecast and actual performance displayed greater slowing throughout their marathon race. Deaner stated:

> *"This correlation may arise because overly confident runners tend to start the marathon too fast, which leads to greater slowing compared to runners with more reasonable expectations and less aggressive starting paces".* [163]

Reading this paper immediately took me back to my first marathon experience. It was 2015 and my first year as a recreational runner. My sister and I were training for the Melbourne half marathon, which was scheduled for October. That gave us eight months of preparation, but my running distances had progressed beyond 15 kilometres within four months of training. Wanting to avoid complacency and keep my motivation levels high, I upgraded to the full marathon ticket. To help with my training, I booked a half marathon in July. It was the Run Melbourne festival, and everything on race day aligned perfectly. The temperature was cool with low winds, and I was excited to enter my first big race. I started with a conservative pace but gradually picked it up and finished in 1 hour and 41 minutes. I was so happy with the outcome. My average pace was 4 minutes and 48 seconds per kilometre, and I finished in the top 15 percentile in my category. I felt unstoppable.

Fast forward to the marathon, and I was high on confidence. I thought I could race under 3 hours and 40 minutes based on my past performance. My average pace needed to be under 5 minutes and 15 seconds to achieve this. I started with five minute splits in my ignorant, naive, confident state. Early in the event, I spotted the 3 hour and 45 pacer. I decided to stick with him for most of the race and pass him when the time was right. My strategy lasted 27 kilometres. I was averaging 5 minutes and 5 seconds without any hassle at that time. But between kilometres 27 and 29, I noticed a lot more people passing me. It was strange because I left like I was running at the same pace and effort, but my splits confirmed my fear. I was slowing down.

The pacemaker and his pack gradually faded into the distance while my energy levels crashed quickly. I started getting lightheaded, and my run turned into a shuffle. I pulled out an energy gel which I received in my race pack. At this point, I had never eaten a performance gel in my life. Up until this point, I had gotten by with drinking water. Even during the half marathon, I didn't stop at one water station. Desperate times call for desperate measures, and I sucked down half a mouthful of gel. It was disgusting, and I struggled to swallow the gel due to the thickness. Trying to get it down disrupted my breathing, so I threw the rest away.

Reality hit me. My optimism faded just as quickly as my energy levels. Every passing minute presented its own challenges. One hip flexor would tighten up, then my left foot would hurt, and then a dizzy sensation overtook all other feelings. I checked my split, and it was 5 minutes and 40 seconds. There was no denying I was in bad shape. I saw a few people walking, and the idea floated in my head. I never resorted to walking throughout my training, but my leg soreness turned into a whole body sickness. I made a judgement call and decided to walk. In my eyes, it was a humiliating defeat. I'll never forget looking down at my watch at that moment and focusing on the total distance I had covered. I still had 12 kilometres until the finish line!

The next hour was brutal. I was walking in intervals as runners flew by me. When I could gather the strength to run, people still passed me. I was holding on, struggling for my best possible time, but the pain was overwhelming. My energy levels picked up in the final two kilometres. I managed to run at a decent pace with the end in sight, but my estimated goal shattered into pieces. I stumbled over the line in 3 hours 58 minutes and 38 seconds. Overall I enjoyed the day, but it was a harsh wake up call.

Consider Race Day Cognitive Load

One major epiphany I encountered when talking with Brian Hanley was connecting the brain's energy source with the rest of the body. The brain uses glucose as an energy source and when you're overloading your brain's capacity with decisions, it depletes the available energy stores you may require later in the race. This is why being mentally fatigued increases your perception of effort. Looking back on my own race experience, I can come up with a long list of factors my brain needed to constantly monitor:

Brainpower required during a marathon:

- Did I eat enough food beforehand?
- Is my pace on target?
- Should I keep with the pack or go alone?
- Do I need to drink at this aid station?
- Should I change my speed on this upcoming hill?
- What time should it be at the halfway point?
- Am I picking my feet up enough?
- Is my cadence staying in an ideal range?
- Should I change my speed if it gets too hot?

While you're running, your stored glycogen is released as glucose that supplies the cells with energy. But your brain is one of the most important organs in your body and requires a lot of energy to operate at such a high capacity. With these constant monitoring systems in place, your brain works overtime and draws your energy stores away from the rest of the body. With this in mind, it is important to consider the cognitive load and pre-plan a strategy to preserve brainpower.

One strategy to reduce cognitive load is to use the race pacers to your advantage. This recommendation comes from Andy Renfree and Brian Hanley:

> "Although using pacemakers is often considered advantageous because they potentially provide a drafting benefit, their value might lie more in the way in which they reduce the psychological load on the lead runners who otherwise would have to focus intently on the pace throughout the race". [161]

For the most part, pacemakers try to adopt an even pace strategy that gives you the greatest chance for success. Additionally, if you follow a pacemaker throughout the majority of the course, you are taking away a lot of the guesswork and brainpower and putting trust into an experienced athlete. Another interesting and valuable piece of information highlighted by Andy and Brian was their recap of Kipchoge's sub two hour performance:

> "It is noteworthy that in the recent successful sub-two-hour performance by Eliud Kipchoge in Vienna, it was decided to adopt an even-paced strategy with the speed being controlled by a pace car. Indeed, it could even be argued that the use of a car in this way made Kipchoge's task somewhat easier because it reduced the need for self-regulation through decision-making, thereby reducing the cognitive load on the athlete". [161]

Five Strategies to Reduce Cognitive Load

1. Relaxation strategies: During scheduled long runs and a race, practise clearing your mind and entering a flow state of running. Relax the face and shoulders and swing your arms and legs effortlessly. Occasionally check your pace but avoid constant monitoring.

2. Distraction: Talking with other runners, appreciating the scenery, and listening to the crowd still require some brainpower, but at a lower level than constant decision making. Find the right times throughout a race to implement your own distraction techniques.

3. Pre-meditated decisions: Your training routine and past race performances will help you with future race decisions. These could include timing of aid stations, water intake and gel consumption. Cut out all the guesswork on race day and commit to a plan before stepping onto the starting line.

4. A well rehearsed race day: Analyse the terrain and elevation of the course. Anticipate and plan your pace or effort levels for different course sections. Wear the same clothing and gear as you would on race day. Do some practice runs at the same time of day, under the anticipated weather conditions to mimic race day as closely as possible. Once you have rehearsed all controllable elements, race day decisions are minimal and effortless.

5. Pre-planned contingencies: Expect the unexpected and plan accordingly. It is difficult to plan for all contingencies, but changes in weather conditions, blisters and cramping can all have pre-planned contingencies. If you have thought through these problems before the race, you are preventing mid race

troubleshooting and problem solving, which takes up a lot of brainpower.

Unshakeable Mindset

No matter the distance of your running race, psychology will play an important factor.

Most runners will have heard the story of Roger Bannister and the four minute mile. Before breaking this feat, most scientists considered the four minute mile impossible. However, in 1954, Roger ran the mile in 3 minutes and 59 seconds, defying the science and the critics. Even more interesting was what came afterwards! Roger only held the record for 46 days and over the next eighteen months, the seemingly impossible task would be broken 40 times.

This begs the question of what held athletes back from breaking this feat in the first place. Once one person did it, why did so many other runners suddenly possess the physical attributes? To truly understand these results, we need to explore the role of the brain in controlling your physical capabilities. Alex Hutchinson details this process in his book '*Endure: Mind, Body and the Curiously Elastic Limits of Human Performance.*' The book explains that runners slow down due to fatigue well before any physiological limitations are reached. For example, an athlete's heart rate is well below max, they display modest lactate levels, and their muscles can still twitch on demand.

Much like an internal temperature thermostat, your body controls the limits of your physical output. This 'effort gauge' will bring on the effects of fatigue well before you're in real physiological distress to keep energy in the tank for safekeeping. This is a snippet from the book Endure:

> *"It turns out, whether it is heat or cold, hunger or thirst, or muscles screaming with the supposed poison of 'lactic acid', what matters in many cases is how the brain interprets these distress signals".* [164]

Brain Training

It seems clear that some people can push themselves into deeper stages of discomfort. Is this through sheer determination? Is it from years of training? With the brain serving as a gatekeeper to our potential, is there anything runners can do to change the brain's calibration?

While it seems reasonable to train the brain to change its settings, simple brain training tasks lack transferability. For instance, Daniel Simons and colleagues discovered that brain training tasks designed to enhance attributes such as memory, attention and problem solving do not seem to assist in life outside of the tasks themselves. They concluded:

> *"We find extensive evidence that brain-training interventions improve performance on the trained tasks, less evidence that such interventions improve performance on closely related tasks, and little evidence that training enhances performance on distantly related tasks or that training improves everyday cognitive performance".* [165]

This would indicate that brain training should be specific to running. In other words, train the brain by training the body to get comfortable with being uncomfortable. The more time you spend at uncomfortable effort levels, the more comfortable your brain becomes with the situation. With enough practice and repetition, the threat level diminishes, and the calibration adjusts. Experiencing high effort levels for extended periods in training can transfer nicely into the marathon performance. Firstly, the brain is less likely to freak out at the current level of discomfort. Secondly, the brain will also have greater anticipation of effort levels to be experienced later in a race. These two factors are crucial components in the final decision of applied fatigue.

For example, if you anticipated your effort levels out of ten throughout a marathon, you would hope to start between three and five. By the end of the race, if you want to perform at your best, you're anticipating an effort level of eight to ten. With this in mind, you're consciously or unconsciously anticipating various effort levels at every stage. If you experience an effort level higher than anticipated, your brain will gently apply the fatigue handbrake to keep you on task. This will occur even within the first half of a race if your effort levels are above what was anticipated.

Maintaining a run through high levels of perceived effort seems like an effective strategy to prepare the body and the mind for a marathon event. Implementing three, five, and even 10 kilometre time trials will be a good starting point.

The Psychology of Distance Running

I believe that what you think, dictates how you feel, which dictates how you act. When it comes to distance running, you'll spend a long time alone with your thoughts. All it takes is for one unwanted thought to creep in, which can derail your performance. Too often, a runner will talk themself out of a great running performance and put it down to fatigue. The truth is, there will come a time within the marathon when it feels too tough to continue. Your legs will feel heavy, and your mind will say stop, and it's at these moments that psychological strategies can become extremely effective. Here are four strategies to help:

Strategy 1: Emotional Self-talk

The first step is not to attribute these physiological stress signals to negative emotions. For instance, a small seed of doubt can grow and manifest itself throughout the entire body:

Negative Response:

- "My legs are feeling heavy"
- "Maybe I started out too fast"
- "My training wasn't adequate enough"
- "Today is not my day"
- "I don't even know why I signed up for this"
- "These remaining kilometres will be brutal"

Instead, process the sensations as nothing more than sensations. This process will lower the brain's internal threat level and reduce the urgency to slow down. As Alex Hutchinson stated:

> "For a marathoner, leg pain and shortness of breath become neutral sources of information, to be used for pacing, rather than emotionally charged warnings to panic about". [164]

Neutral Response:

- "My legs are feeling heavy"
- "My legs are supposed to feel heavy"
- "Perhaps I could dial back the speed and reassess"

Once you have practised avoiding unwanted, negative emotions from surfacing, you can move one step further and deliberately attribute positive emotion. This final step may come naturally to some and take a lot of practice for others. But like any skill, it becomes easier over time.

Positive Response:

- "My legs are feeling heavy"
- "My legs are supposed to feel heavy"
- "Other runners are hurting too"
- "This is a great opportunity to test my resilience"
- "It is moments like this I'll look back on and be proud I pushed through"

Stacey Winter and Carla Meijen wrote a chapter titled 'Psychology of Distance Running' in the book 'The Science and Practice of Middle and Long-Distance Running', and they listed other strategies to help in these situations:

> "To help regulate emotions, runners have reported using goal setting, recalling of previous accomplishments and how they feel afterwards, emotional intelligence, and having a pacer. These have all been shown to benefit positive emotions within distance running".

Strategy 2: Smiling

Another of my personal favourites is the power one can generate from smiling. It is a simple strategy but can be very powerful. You can even choose to fake a smile when you are not in the mood, because your brain struggles to know the difference, and you can trick your physiology. When you leave a fatigued, sluggish, demoralised state and enter a happy state, your perceived effort levels diminish. Rather than fake a smile, I prefer the real thing. I can always find a runner to joke with, a funny marathon banner to read, crowd members to high five and any other situation to generate positive energy.

Once during a challenging trail run, I was looking for creative ways to boost positivity. These were single track paths, and runners were hard to come by at this stage of the race. Then I spotted an event cameraman who was taking photos of passing runners. Instead of my usual smile and thumbs up pose, I decided to climb the nearest tree for the cameraman to photograph. We both shared a good laugh, and after that, my mood shifted and turned my whole race around.

Strategy 3: Self-belief

Going back to what you think dictates what you feel, a big role will include your self-belief and internal dialogue. If you have unquestionable belief in your ability, quitting is never an option and seeds of doubt never enter your brain. Such a strong self-belief can arise through hard training sessions. We have already highlighted that hard training sessions help adjust the brain's calibration to perceived efforts. Still, during these moments of success, you are proving to yourself what you're capable of. However, most of us runners don't obtain such a high level of self-belief. Even if some of our training sessions are tough, there is still enough doubt to sabotage race day. In the same way that smiling can trick the body into feeling good, so too can internal dialogue trick your mind into a higher level of belief.

Repeating a phrase that triggers a deep seated drive is useful during a tough moment within a given race. Below are a few examples but the more personal you make it, the more powerful its effect.

Internal dialogue examples:

- "I am strong and capable"
- "Every kilometre builds resilience"

- "Hard moments build character"
- "Breathe in strength, breathe out weakness"
- "I welcome tough challenges"

Strategy 4: Imagery and Gratitude

During your long training runs, you can use two more methods to build a strong mental game on race day. First is the practice of gratitude. I was first introduced to the concept of gratitude miles by Amanda Brooks. Amanda is a running coach and author of *'Run to the Finish: The Everyday Runner's Guide to Avoiding Injury, Ignoring the Clock, and Loving the Run'*. Here is a snippet from her interview on episode 57 of the Run Smarter Podcast:

> *"There is so much science around how we feel, what we are thinking and how that translates to our body on a run. So, during my slow, easy run, I start going through a gratitude list. I always start small and think, 'thank you right toe for pushing off the ground. Thank you, left calf, for feeling good'. Then I start rolling into things that are in my life that I am thankful for. It really causes a shift in your body and your brain. Sometimes that alone can help turn your whole run around".* [167]

Lastly, during your long training sessions, you can practice vivid imagery. This strategy will again trick the brain, body and nervous system into believing race day has arrived in an attempt to create a sense of familiarity and, therefore, less panic when the real thing happens. The more vivid your imagery and the more senses you incorporate, the more benefit it'll have. For example, during a challenging run, when the legs are heavy and your brain tells you to stop, visualise this exact moment in your marathon. See the kilometre markers and the runners around you. Listen to the cheering crowd or the live music played. Taste your energy gels and experience every aid station. Remember, the more senses you incorporate and the more vivid the imagery, the more powerful it becomes. These strategies take time to develop, and you shouldn't expect to be a natural straight away. Once you've executed every strategy in this chapter, however, you'll be mentally prepared when stepping on the start line.

Constantly Working on Tightrope Skills

Much like running is a skill, so is developing a strong mental game. It takes repetition, a lot of the time, and unfortunately for new runners, it takes experience. Each race holds lessons to self-reflect on to help you learn and grow for the next one. Maybe in one race you learn to pace better and in another to fuel better. If you are learning and reiterating from each race, you'll be building better skills and strategies for future endeavours. This is the final factor we must consider with our tightrope walker. You could have set up all your equipment precisely and planned your journey to a tee, but sometimes, experience trumps a methodical novice. Tightrope walking can spark a lot of anxiety in inexperienced people, and these anxieties can impact performance.

It is also important to realise that sometimes you may do everything right and still fall off the rope, and that is okay. Every fall is an opportunity to learn and develop necessary skills. With self-reflection and patience, you can slowly build the necessary physical qualities and mental capabilities to handle the toughest of rope walks.

Chapter 20 Summary

1. Race day performance depends on a well balanced training schedule.

2. Reduce cognitive load within the race by pre-planning and removing as many decision making processors.

3. You can recalibrate the brain's fatigue handbrake by getting comfortable with uncomfortable training efforts.

Action Items

1. Conduct your own tests to identify your sweat rate.

2. You can choose to go one step further and do a sweat test to analyse your sodium concentration levels.

3. Based on your sweat results, test and tweak your fuel and hydration strategy to find a method that best suits you.

4. If gut issues are a problem on race day, train your gut to tolerate more fuel.

5. Avoid negative thought patterns and replace them with positive ones.

6. For an added psychological boost, implement imagery, self-talk mantras, and gratitude lists.

7. Finally, don't forget to smile.

CONCLUSION

Pete's Race Day

Everything had been leading up to this moment—the morning of the marathon. As Pete ate his usual banana and muesli breakfast, he was surprisingly calm. He had slept well the night before and was feeling fresh. He had studied the course layout, the drinking stations and the weather forecast. Fortunately, the weather predicted an unseasonably cool day with low winds. After breakfast, he walked to his bedroom to put on his racing gear. While getting dressed, he calmly repeated the game plan, the pacing strategy, and Steve's psychological strategies. Finally, with plenty of time to spare, he walked out the door on his way to the start line.

Approaching the start line on foot, a calm zen washed over Pete. He took a moment to reflect on the hard work that had got him to the start line. He thought about the strength training commitments, the early mornings, the journey to finding the right running shoe, the dedication to enhancing his recovery, and now the tactics and strategies developed to give him the best chance for success. All that was left was to embrace the moment, stick to the plan, and reap the rewards of his hard work.

Pete already had three marathons under his belt and was experienced enough to not start too fast with other overzealous runners. His internal dialogue kicked in, "I am only running against myself; my race, my pace." He shuffled his way to the starting line and took in the atmosphere. Some runners had dressed up in costumes, while others looked more serious and focused. He continued to shuffle deeper into his starting section. The pack of people became denser, and all he could do was wait for the countdown. Suddenly, the announcer's voice was heard through the loudspeakers. The countdown had begun, and the crowd joined in. Excitement filled Pete's body until the countdown reached zero. Within a few seconds, his wave of runners started shuffling forward. Moments later, the crowd of runners dispersed and he had the freedom to break into a jog. The last chapter of Pete's incredible journey had begun.

At the 10 kilometre mark, everything was going as planned. An average pace of 5 minutes and 45 seconds appeared on his watch. That was three seconds quicker than he had planned in this section of the race, but he was happy to continue without slowing down. It was a cool morning at 10 degrees celsius, which was perfect for Pete, but he knew the temperatures would start climbing and peak at 24 degrees later in the day. He stopped at every drinking station to take a bit of water, just like in his training. He aimed to take his first energy gel at 12 kilometres. The subsequent gels were scheduled for kilometres 20 and 30.

After digesting the first gel at 12 kilometres, Pete made a conscious effort to take in the atmosphere, the crowd and the scenery. This decision came as a distraction tactic and a way to embrace the experience and be grateful for every kilometre he completed. He entered a relaxed flow state and managed to maintain his target pace. Looking up ahead, he noticed the 24 kilometre marker. Even further in the distance, he could see the three hour and 50 minute pacemaker. He had his second gel and decided to keep the pacemaker within his line of sight throughout the middle section of the race.

Beyond 25 kilometres, the early signs of fatigue were kicking in. Pete decided that he'd casually go through a mental checklist for every five kilometres. This strategy offered a welcomed distraction but also helped his running efficiency. First, he would focus inward and ask "How is my breathing? How is my posture? Am I picking my feet up?" Next, he would focus outward, "Am I creating a quiet footfall?" Lastly, he would sing a predetermined song in his head. He chose "Monkey Wrench" by his favourite rock band, the Foo Fighters. This song would always fire Pete up when he needed a hit of energy. In addition, this song had a tempo of 175 beats per minute, an ideal cadence for Pete. This meant that while he was singing this song in his head, he could keep a steady pace and step to the song's rhythm. Another beep went off on his watch. He looked down and realised he had hit the 30 kilometre mark!

"Only 12 more kilometres to go," Pete thought to himself as he took his final gel. He was happy with how his body and gut were responding at this stage. His legs felt heavy, and the front of his hips was getting tighter, but the pacemaker was still in sight. He kept a close eye on this pacemaker. The tall, raised flag from the pacer's back was still in his sight line, but Pete could tell the gap was slowly increasing. He didn't think anything of this. His pace was ahead of schedule, and he was happy to see the pacemaker fade away into the distance. He repeated one more time in his head, "my race, my pace".

Ever since Pete had passed half way, he gradually picked up the pace. The legs continued to increase in heaviness, but he had anticipated this and visualised these moments over the past two weeks. Another split alert sounded from his watch. Ten kilometres to go! Pete's average pace was 5 minutes and 35 seconds. He felt he had more in the tank. The slower kilometres at the beginning were starting to pay off.

Pete decided to repeat his mental checklist every kilometre for the final ten. He was also in luck when he ran alongside another runner travelling at the same pace and in a similar amount of discomfort. A chat would be a welcome distraction, he thought to himself, as he struck up a conversation. They started chatting about running shoes and marathon bucket list races. Suddenly, three kilometres had flown by and Pete's new friend decided to start some walking intervals, so he was back running solo. His watch beeped for another split displaying 5 minutes and 48 seconds, Pete's slowest split yet. "Come on," he told himself, "only six kilometres to go."

The final stretch was upon Pete. He was hurting but expected as much and had vividly visualised every moment. He knew the next few kilometres would be the biggest struggle before the crowd got louder and the adrenaline rush of the finish line would kick in. Another split alert recorded 6 minutes and 5 seconds. He was losing pace, but his average was holding strong at 5 minutes and 38 seconds. A nice buffer for the final five kilometres. Then he brought out the secret weapon he hadn't used up until this point. His deep seated mantra that Steve, his sports psychologist, helped create. Pete's focus took him to why he was doing this in the first place. He took a calming, meditative, deep breath and whispered to himself, "my family is my fuel."

Pete repeated this "family is fuel, family is fuel," and he started visualising his family celebrating this marathon milestone with him. He visualised the relief, the sense of accomplishment and the confidence to tackle any future goal he set his mind to. Redirecting his focus from his legs to this celebratory moment transformed his attitude. It was so overpowering that he didn't even check his previous split time. The visceral reaction forced him to smile, laugh and almost cry. While he didn't check his watch, he did notice he was passing a lot more people. He was back in the zone.

Without warning, Pete looked up and saw the cheering crowd along with a marathon marker, indicating there were three kilometres to go. The crowd must have been three people deep along each side of the barricaded road. Spectators were holding up posters for loved ones and the cheers became louder. It was time for another strategy Pete had up his sleeve. Throughout the final stretch, he made a conscious effort to high five every supporter that had their arm out and to read all the funny posters. He read a sign that said *"that bad tinder date is behind you, run faster"* and *"you run better than the government"*. Pete laughed and showed his respect to the supporters and forgot all about his heavy legs. Then he heard some booming music off in the distance. It was the event village. The finish line was close.

Pete passed a marker that said one kilometre to go. He looked down at his watch, the average pace held steady at 5 minutes and 37 seconds. The total run time at this point was 3 hours and 52 minutes. A huge surge of energy rushed through his body. Now he knew he was going to finish in under four hours and nothing was going to stop him. His eyes started watering as he kept high fiving the crowd. He felt so grateful to be out here, grateful for his family and for his super-star coaching team Daniel, Jane, Claire and Steve. The crowd grew into a loud ball of energy as he could see the finish line in sight. With a final sprint, he squinted his watery eyes to read 3 hours 57 minutes and 7 seconds on the massive marathon clock as he crossed the line.

Pete couldn't believe how well the day went. The adrenaline lasted long enough to grab his medal and find a shady spot under a tree. He collapsed to the ground and gave his legs a shake. The final chapter in Pete's journey was complete and he would spend the rest of the day celebrating with his family.

Part 2 Final Summary

1. Increasing your performance starts with writing down specific goals and a realistic roadmap to success.

2. Heavy strength training twice a week and lighter running shoes have been shown to enhance running economy and improve running performance.

3. When racing, an effective taper, nutrition plan and mindset will give you a physical and psychological edge over your competitors.

Action Items

1. Write down your performance goals for the next 6 months.

2. Learn to run slow and implement an 80/20 intensity balance in your training.

3. Ensure your recovery strategies match the ever increasing training load. Enhance your sleep, downtime and nutrition.

4. When things don't go your way, don't be too hard on yourself. Learn, grow and have fun in the process.

ACKNOWLEDGEMENTS

When I started writing this book, I had no idea what it would take to get something published. Like most of my projects, I took it one step at a time and learned along the way. To date, it has been the hardest project I have ever completed, and none of it would be possible without the help I received along the way.

Firstly, to my sister Zoe, who asked if I could train with her for a half marathon event. Without her, I would never have discovered my love for running and my podcast, physiotherapy clinic and book, would never have existed. A big thank you also, to the love of my life, Megan. Writing this book took hundreds of hours, but your encouragement and unwavering support made the journey a lot smoother. Thank you for your positive attitude and help whenever I needed your opinion and for listening to my constant ramblings whenever I got excited about the next step in the book's development.

Thank you to Campbell Maffett, Michelle Linehan, Mani Alavi and Rachel Nolan for providing initial feedback on the first draft. Thank you to Laura Peil and Gillian Bronte for editing and Jill Riva, Paige Rundle and Stephanie Cassar for proofreading. As each one of you now knows, academic writing and sentence structure are not my strong suit. Thank you for your patience and expertise, and for formulating my draft into a readable, professional piece.

I would like to thank all my past podcast guests featured in this book and their approval for the use of their quotes. A special thank you to Chris Bramah, whose research and podcast appearance was featured heavily in this book. Your dedication to the science of running has furthered my professional wisdom and many other health professionals. Also, thank you to Richard Blagrove and Philip Hayes and their book '*The Science and Practice of Middle and Long Distance Running*', which was a big inspiration and serves as a cornerstone for running related research.

Thank you to Minhajul Islam and Verity Casey for the design and layout of the book. Without your assistance, my vision of a physical book would never be possible. Also, thank you to Matt Fitzgerald for the cover blurb. I have been blown away by your professionalism and willingness to be involved in this project. Your success and legacy as an author will continue to serve as an inspiration.

Last but not least, a big thank you to all the Run Smarter Scholars. Those who have been listening to the podcast and following the social media channels. Your encouragement and excitement for the launch of this book kept my passion and productivity high. Without your support, this book would not be possible.

ABOUT THE AUTHOR

Brodie Sharpe was born and raised in Melbourne, Australia and graduated from La Trobe University in 2012 with a Masters in Physiotherapy Practice. After working in a private practice for four years, he discovered a love for running, which grew into a career driven passion to educate runners on how to survive and thrive.

In 2019, Brodie followed his passion and launched the Run Smarter Physiotherapy Clinic, a niche online clinic to help serve runners worldwide. A few months later, he launched the Run Smarter Podcast which in two short years climbed in popularity into the top 1% of podcasts globally.

Brodie also became a qualified running coach in 2020, and has served as a professional speaker at health clinics, teaching physiotherapists, osteopaths, chiropractors and podiatrists how to best treat their runners. He is on a mission to bring clarity and control to every injured runner, by empowering and educating them through evidence based research. He aims to reach as many runners as possible and the Run Smarter Book is a natural extension of serving that mission.

REFERENCES

CHAPTER 2

1. Bramah C. Common overuse injuries in runners. In: Blagrove R, Hayes P. The science and practice of middle and long distance running. Routledge: Taylor & Francis Group, 2021: 28–46.

2. The Run Smarter Podcast: Episode 230: A deep dive into load vs capacity with Chris Bramah.

3. Soligard T, Schwellnus M, Alonso J, *et al*. How much is too much? (Part 1) International Olympic Committee consensus statement on load in sport and risk of injury. British Journal of Sports Medicine 2016; 50: 1030–1041.

4. Dorn T, Schache A, Pandy M. Muscular strategy shift in human running: dependence of running speed on hip and ankle muscle performance. The Journal of Experimental Biology 2012 1;215(Pt 11):1944–1956.

5. Fredette A, Roy J, Perreault K, Dupuis F, Napier C, Esculier J. The association between running injuries and training parameters: A systematic review. Journal of Athletic Training 2021; 3: doi:10.4085/1062–6050–0195.21.

6. Nielsen R, Parner E, Nohr E, Sørensen H, Lind M, Rasmussen S. Excessive progression in weekly running distance and risk of running-related injuries: an association which varies according to type of injury. The Journal of Orthopaedic and Sports Physical Therapy 2014; 44(10): 739–747.

7. Salzler M, Kirwan H, Scarborough D, Walker J, Guarino A, Berkson E. Injuries observed in a prospective transition from traditional to minimalist footwear: correlation of high impact transient forces and lower injury severity. The Physician and sports medicine 2016; 44(4): 373–379.

8. Cook J, Docking S. "Rehabilitation will increase the 'capacity' of your ... insert musculoskeletal tissue here...." Defining 'tissue capacity': a core concept for clinicians. British Journal of Sports Medicine 2015; 49: 1484–1485.

9. Hulin B, Gabbett T, Blanch P, Chapman P, Bailey D, Orchard J. Spikes in acute workload are associated with increased injury risk in elite cricket fast bowlers. British Journal of Sports Medicine 2014; 48: 708–712.

10. Hulin B, Gabbett T, Lawson D, Caputi P, Sampson J. The acute:chronic workload ratio predicts injury: high chronic workload may decrease injury risk in elite rugby league players. British Journal of Sports Medicine 2016; 50: 231–236.

CHAPTER 3

11. Hegedus E, McDonough S, Bleakley C, Baxter D, DePew T, Bradbury I, Cook C. Physical performance tests predict injury in National Collegiate Athletic Association athletes: a three-season prospective cohort study. British Journal of Sports Medicine 2016; 50(21): 1333–1337.

12. The Run Smarter Podcast: Episode 219: Predicting future injuries & early detection with Eric Hegedus.

13. Esculier J, Bouyer L, Dubois B. Is combining gait retraining or an exercise programme with education better than education alone in treating runners with patellofemoral pain? A randomised clinical trial. British Journal of Sports Medicine 2018; 52(10): 659–666.

CHAPTER 4

14. Zoë Slote Morris,1 Steven Wooding,2 and Jonathan Grant. The answer is 17 years, what is the question: understanding time lags in translational research. Journal of the Royal Society of Medicine 2011; 104(12): 510–520.

15. Hunter D. Osteoarthritis: time for us all to shift the needle. Rheumatology 2018; 1(57): iv1-iv2.

16. Bunzli S, O'Brien P, Ayton D, et al. Misconceptions and the Acceptance of Evidence-based Nonsurgical Interventions for Knee Osteoarthritis. A Qualitative Study. Clinical Orthopaedics and Related Research 2019; 477(9): 1975–1983.

17. The Run Smarter Podcast: Episode 32: Knee OA misconceptions with Kevin Maggs.

18. Alentorn-Geli E, Samuelsson K, Musahl V, Green C, Bhandari M, Karlsson J. The Association of Recreational and Competitive Running

With Hip and Knee Osteoarthritis: A Systematic Review and Meta-analysis. Journal of Orthopaedic and Sports Physical Therapy 2017; 47(6): 373–390.

19. Behm D, Blazevich A, Kay A, McHugh M. Acute effects of muscle stretching on physical performance, range of motion, and injury incidence in healthy active individuals: a systematic review. Applied Physiology, Nutrition and Metabolism 2016; 41(1): 1–11.

20. Baxter C, McNaughton L, Sparks A, Norton L, Bentley D. Impact of stretching on the performance and injury risk of long-distance runners. Research in Sports Medicine 2017; 25(1): 78–90.

21. Pepper T, Brismee J, Sizer P, et al. The Immediate Effects of Foam Rolling and Stretching on Iliotibial Band Stiffness: A Randomized Controlled Trial. International Journal of Sports Physical Therapy 2021; 16(3): 651–661.

22. 22 Nielsen R, Buist I, Parner E, et al. Foot pronation is not associated with increased injury risk in novice runners wearing a neutral shoe: a 1-year prospective cohort study. British Journal of Sports Medicine 2014; 48: 440–447.

23. 23 Knutson G. Anatomic and functional leg-length inequality: A review and recommendation for clinical decision-making. Part I, anatomic leg-length inequality: prevalence, magnitude, effects and clinical significance. Chiropractic and Osteopathy 2005; 13(1):11.

CHAPTER 5

24. 24 Larson P, Higgins E, Kaminski J, Decker T, Preble J, Lyons D, McIntyre K, Normile A. Foot strike patterns of recreational and sub-elite runners in a long-distance road race. Journal of Sports Sciences 2011; 29(15): 1665–1673.

25. 25 Ceyssens L, Vanelderen R, Barton C, Malliaras P, Dingenen B. Biomechanical Risk Factors Associated with Running-Related Injuries: A Systematic Review. Sports Medicine 2019; 49(7): 1095–1115.

26. 26 Bramah C, Preece S, Gill N, Herrington L. Is There a Pathological Gait Associated With Common Soft Tissue Running Injuries? American Journal of Sports Medicine 2018; 46(12): 3023–3031.

27. 27 The Run Smarter Podcast: Episode 61: Running Technique Insight for Injury Prevention & Performance with Chris Bramah.

28. 28 Poppa K, McDermott W, Hughes J, Baxter S, Stovitz S, Petita M. Bone strength estimates relative to vertical ground reaction force discriminates women runners with stress fracture history. Bone 2017; 94 22–28.

29. 29 Chan Z, Zhang J, Au I, An W, Shum G, Ng G, Cheung R. Gait Retraining for the Reduction of Injury Occurrence in Novice Distance Runners 1-Year Follow-up of a Randomized Controlled Trial. American Journal of Sports Medicine 2018; 46(2): 388–395.

30. 30 Schubert A, Kempf J, Heiderscheit B. Influence of stride frequency and length on running mechanics: a systematic review. Sports Health 2014; 6(3): 210–217.

31. Tenforde A, Borgstrom H, Outerleys J, Davis I. Is Cadence Related to Leg Length and Load Rate? Journal of Orthopaedic & Sports Physical Therapy 2019; 49(4): 280–283.

32. Dorn T, Schache A, Pandy M. Muscular strategy shift in human running: dependence of running speed on hip and ankle muscle performance. The Journal of Experimental Biology 2012 1;215(Pt 11):1944–1956.

33. Willson J, Ratcliff O, Meardon S, Willy R. Influence of step length and landing pattern on patellofemoral joint kinetics during running. Scandinavian Journal of Medicine and Science in Sports 2015; 25(6): 736–743.

34. Napier C. Science of Running: Analyse your technique, prevent injury, revolutionise your training. Dorling Kindersley, Ltd, 2020.

CHAPTER 6

35. Bramah C. Common overuse injuries in runners. In: Blagrove R, Hayes P. The science and practice of middle and long distance running. Routledge: Taylor & Francis Group, 2021: 28–46.

36. Buist I, Bredeweg S, Mechelen W, Lemmink K, Pepping G, Diercks R. No effect of a graded training program on the number of running-related injuries in novice runners: a randomized controlled trial. The American Journal of Sports Medicine 2008; 36(1): 33–39.

37. Nielsen R, Parner E, Nohr E, Sorensen H, Lind M, Rasmussen S. Excessive progression in weekly running distance and risk of running-related injuries: an association which varies according to type of injury. The Journal of Orthopaedic and Sports Physical Therapy 2014; 44(10): 739–747.

38. Damsted C, Parner E, Sorensen H, Malisoux L, Hulme A, Nielsen R. The Association Between Changes in Weekly Running Distance and Running-Related Injury: Preparing for a Half Marathon. The Journal of Orthopaedic and Sports Physical Therapy 2019; 49(4): 230–238.

39. The Run Smarter Podcast: Episode 231: Run like a pro, even if you're slow with Matt Fitzgerald.

40. The Run Smarter Podcast: Episode 144: Are you really running slow enough? with Zoe Sharpe.

41. Gabbett T. The training—injury prevention paradox: should athletes be training smarter and harder? British Journal of Sports Medicine 2016; 50: 273–280.

CHAPTER 7

42. Soligard T, Schwellnus M, Alonso J, et al. How much is too much? (Part 1) International Olympic Committee consensus statement on load in sport and risk of injury. British Journal of Sports Medicine 2016; 50: 1030–1041.

43. Ivarsson A, Johnson U, Andersen M, Tranaeus U, Stenling A, Lindwall M. Psychosocial Factors and Sport Injuries: Meta-analyses for Prediction and Prevention. Sports Medicine 2017; 47(2): 353–365.

44. Wiese-Bjornstal D. Psychology and socioculture affect injury risk, response, and recovery in high-intensity athletes: a consensus statement. Scandinavian Journal of Medicine and Science in Sports 2010; 20(S2): 103–111.

45. Holmer B, Lapierre S, Jake-Schoffman D, Christou D. Effects of sleep deprivation on endothelial function in adult humans: a systematic review. Geroscience 2021; 43(1): 137–158.

46. Fullagar H, Skorski S, Duffield R, Hammes D, Coutts A, Meyer T. Sleep and athletic performance: the effects of sleep loss on exercise performance, and physiological and cognitive responses to exercise. Sports Medicine 2015; 45(2): 161–186.

47. Milewski M, Skaggs D, Bishop G, Pace L, et al. Chronic Lack of Sleep is Associated With Increased Sports Injuries in Adolescent Athletes. Journal of Pediatric Orthopaedics 2014; 34(2): 129–133.

48. Johnston R, Cahalan R, Bonnett L, Maguire M, et al. General health complaints and sleep associated with new injury within an endurance

sporting population: A prospective study. Journal of Science and Medicine in Sport 2020; 23(3): 252–257.

49. Birrer D, Morgan G. Psychological skills training as a way to enhance an athlete's performance in high-intensity sports. Scandanavian Journal of Medicine and Science in Sports 2010; 20 (S2): 78–87.

CHAPTER 8

50. Dubois B, Esculier J. Soft-tissue injuries simply need PEACE and LOVE. British Journal of Sports Medicine 2020;54: 72–73.

51. Hansrani V, Khanbhai M, Bhandari S, Pillai A, McCollum C. The role of compression in the management of soft tissue ankle injuries: a systematic review. European Journal of Orthopaedic Surgery and Traumatologie 2015; 25(6): 987–995.

52. The Run Smarter Podcast: Episode 89: Rehab Success Stories with Michelle.

53. The Run Smarter Podcast: Episode 137: Running is Rehab: When doing is the fixing with Greg Lehman.

CHAPTER 9

54. Lauersen J, Bertelsen D, Andersen L. The effectiveness of exercise interventions to prevent sports injuries: a systematic review and meta-analysis of randomised controlled trials. British Journal of Sports Medicine 2014; 48(11): 871–877.

55. Messier S, Martin D, Mihalko S, et al. A 2-Year Prospective Cohort Study of Overuse Running Injuries The Runners and Injury Longitudinal Study (TRAILS). The American Journal of Sports Medicine 2018; 46(9): 2211–2221.

56. Ramskov D, Barton C, O'Nielsen R, Rasmussen S. High eccentric hip abduction strength reduces the risk of developing patellofemoral pain among novice runners initiating a self-structured running program: a 1-year observational study. Journal of Orthopaedic and Sports Physical Therapy 2015; 45(3): 153–161.

57. Verrelst R, Willems T, Clercq D, Roosen P, Goossens L, Witvrouw E. The role of hip abductor and external rotator muscle strength in the

development of exertional medial tibial pain: a prospective study. British Journal of Sports Medicine 2014; 48(21): 1564–1569.

58. Fredericson M, Cookingham C, Chaudhari A, Dowdell B, Oestreicher N, Sahrmann S. Hip abductor weakness in distance runners with iliotibial band syndrome. Clinical Journal of Sport Medicine 2000; 10(3): 169–75.

59. Habets B, Smits H, Backx F, Cingel R, Huisstede B. Hip muscle strength is decreased in middle-aged recreational male athletes with midportion Achilles tendinopathy: A cross-sectional study. Physical Therapy in Sport 2017; 25: 55–61.

60. Magnusson S, Langberg H, Kjaer M. The pathogenesis of tendinopathy: balancing the response to loading. Nature Reviews, Rheumatology 2010; 6(5): 262–268.

61. Bramah C. Common overuse injuries in runners. In: Blagrove R, Hayes P. The science and practice of middle and long distance running. Routledge: Taylor & Francis Group, 2021: 28–46.

62. Blagrove R, Hooper, D. Strength training for enhancing performance and reducing injury risk. In: Blagrove R, Hayes P. The science and practice of middle and long distance running. Routledge: Taylor & Francis Group, 2021: 207–222.

63. Saragiotto B, Yamato T, Hespanhol L, Rainbow M, Davis I, Lopes A. What are the main risk factors for running-related injuries? Sports Medicine 2014; 44(8): 1153–1163.

CHAPTER 10

64. The Run Smarter Podcast: Episode 81: Is exercise addiction detrimental to your running? with Heather Hausenblas.

65. Wiese-Bjornstal D. Psychology and socioculture affect injury risk, response, and recovery in high-intensity athletes: a consensus statement. Scandinavian Journal of Medicine and Science in Sports 2010; 20(S2): 103–111.

66. Madigan D, Stoeber J, Forsdyke D, Dayson M, Passfield L. Perfectionism predicts injury in junior athletes: Preliminary evidence from a prospective study. Journal of Sports Sciences 2018; 36(5): 545–550.

67. Maggs, K. Load vs Capacity and Injuries (YouTube). British Journal of Sports Medicine 2019. Published online June 12. https://www.youtube.com/watch?v=H1rp_v4Dr3g

68. Cheadle C, Kuzma C. Rebound: Train your mind to bounce back stronger from sports injuries. London, UK: Bloomsbury Publishing, Plc, 2019.
69. Domenech J, Sanchis-Alfonso V, Espejo B. Changes in catastrophizing and kinesiophobia are predictive of changes in disability and pain after treatment in patients with anterior knee pain. Knee Surgery, Sports Traumatology and Arthroscopy 2014; 22(10): 2295–300.
70. Wakefield C, Reed C, Heil J. Patient as Athlete: A Metaphor for Injury Rehabilitation. The Psychotherapy Patient 2021; 10(3): 21–39.
71. Johnson U. Psychosocial antecedents of sport injury, prevention, and intervention: An overview of theoretical approaches and empirical findings. International Journal of Sport and Exercise Psychology 2007; 5(4): 352–369.
72. Silva D, Willy R, Barton C, Christensen K, Pazzinatto M, Azevedo F. Pain and disability in women with patellofemoral pain relate to kinesiophobia, but not to patellofemoral joint loading variables. Scandinavian journal of sports medicine in sports 2020; 30(11): 2215–2221.
73. Bagheri S, Naderi A, Mirali S, Calmeiro L, Brewer B. Adding Mindfulness Practice to Exercise Therapy for Female Recreational Runners With Patellofemoral Pain: A Randomized Controlled Trial. Journal of Athletic Training 2021; 56(8): 902–911.
74. Dubois B, Esculier J. Soft-tissue injuries simply need PEACE and LOVE. British Journal of Sports Medicine 2020; 54: 72–73.
75. The Run Smarter Podcast: Episode 41: Train your mind to bounce back from injury with Carrie Cheadle.
76. Briet J, Houwert R, Hageman M, Hietbrink F, Ring D, Verleisdonk E. Factors associated with pain intensity and physical limitations after lateral ankle sprains. Injury 2016; 47(11): 2565–2569.

CHAPTER 11

77. The Run Smarter Podcast: Episode 74: Goal setting & getting results with Jake Lowe.
78. Locke E, Shaw K, Saari L, Latham G. Goal setting and task performance: 1969–1980. Psychological Bulletin 1981; 90(1), 125–152.
79. Burton D, Weiss C. The fundamental goal concept: The path to process and performance success. In: Advances in sport psychology. 3rd ed. Champaign, IL: Human Kinetics 2008, 339–376.

80. The Run Smarter Podcast: Episode 27: Common training errors with Tyson Popplestone.

81. Buist I, Bredeweg S, Mechelen W, Lemmink K, Pepping G, Diercks R. No effect of a graded training program on the number of running-related injuries in novice runners: a randomized controlled trial. The American Journal of Sports Medicine 2008; 36(1): 33–39.

82. Nielsen R, Parner E, Nohr E, Sorensen H, Lind M, Rasmussen S. Excessive progression in weekly running distance and risk of running-related injuries: an association which varies according to type of injury. The Journal of Orthopaedic and Sports Physical Therapy 2014; 44(10): 739–747.

83. Damsted C, Parner E, Sorensen H, Malisoux L, Hulme A, Nielsen R. The Association Between Changes in Weekly Running Distance and Running-Related Injury: Preparing for a Half Marathon. The Journal of Orthopaedic and Sports Physical Therapy 2019; 49(4): 230–238.

CHAPTER 12

84. The Run Smarter Podcast: Episode 228: Chad Miller's Training plan success story.

85. The Run Smarter Podcast: Episode 74: Goal setting & getting results with Jake Lowe.

86. The Run Smarter Podcast: Episode 49: How can I boost my running program with Jason Fitzgerald.

87. Casado A, Hanley B, Santos-Concejero J, Ruiz-P´erez L. World-Class Long-Distance Running Performances Are Best Predicted by Volume of Easy Runs and Deliberate Practice of Short-Interval and Tempo Runs. The journal of strength and conditioning research 2021; 35(9): 2525–2531.

88. Casado A, Tjelta L. Training volume and intensity distribution among elite middle and long-distance runners. In: Blagrove R, Hayes P. The science and practice of middle and long distance running. Routledge: Taylor & Francis Group, 2021: 118–131.

89. Seiler S. What is the best practice for training intensity and duration distribution in endurance athletes? International Journal of Sports Physiology and Performance. 2010; 5(3):276–91.

90. Kenneally M, Arturo C, Jordan S. The Effect of Periodisation and Training Intensity Distribution on Middle- and Long-Distance Running

Performance: A Systematic Review. International Journal of Sports Physiology and Performance 2017; 13(9), 1114–1121.

91. Esteve-Lanao J, Foster C, Seiler S, Lucia A. Impact of training intensity distribution on performance in endurance athletes. Journal of Strength and Conditioning Research 2007; 21: 943–949.

92. The Run Smarter Podcast: Episode 93: Heart Rate data insights with Chris Schneider.

93. The Run Smarter Podcast: Episode 123: Measuring your Power Output with Nathan Fenton.

94. Paquette M, Napier C, Willy R, Stellingwerff T. Moving Beyond Weekly "Distance": Optimizing Quantification of Training Load in Runners. Journal of Orthopaedic and Sports Physical Therapy 2020; 50(10): 564–569.

CHAPTER 13

95. Li F, Wang R, Newton R, Sutton D, Shi Y, Ding H. Effects of complex training versus heavy resistance training on neuromuscular adaptation, running economy and 5-km performance in well-trained distance runners. Peer J. 2019; 25(7): e6787.

96. Denadai B, de Aguiar R, de Lima L, Greco C, Caputo F. Explosive Training and Heavy Weight Training are Effective for Improving Running Economy in Endurance Athletes: A Systematic Review and Meta-Analysis. Sports Med 2017; 47(3): 545–554.

97. The Run Smarter Podcast: Episode 85: Optimizing S&C into your week with Trang Nguyen.

98. Bramah C, Preece S, Gill N. A 10% Increase in Step Rate Improves Running Kinematics and Clinical Outcomes in Runners With Patellofemoral Pain at 4 Weeks and 3 Months. The American Journal of Sports Medicine 2019; 47(14): 3406–3413.

99. Blagrove R. Strength and Conditioning for Endurance Running: Crowood Press 2015.

100. The Run Smarter Podcast: Episode 49: How can I boost my running program with Jason Fitzgerald.

101. Hamill B. Relative Safety of Weightlifting and Weight Training. Journal of Strength and Conditioning Research 1994; 8(1): 53–57.

102. Nielsen R, Buist I, Sørensen H, Lind M, Rasmussen S. Training errors and running related injuries: A systematic review. International Journal of Sports Physical Therapy. 2012; 7(1): 58–75.

103. The Run Smarter Podcast: Episode 14: Exercises & program planning for runners with Richard Blagrove.

CHAPTER 14

104. The Run Smarter Podcast: Episode 52: Is there a right & wrong running shoe? With JF Esculier.

105. Nielsen R, Buist I, Parner E, Nohr E, Sørensen H, Lind M, Rasmussen S. Foot pronation is not associated with increased injury risk in novice runners wearing a neutral shoe: a 1-year prospective cohort study. British Journal of Sports Medicine 2014; 48(6): 440–447.

106. Napier C, Willy R. Logical fallacies in the running shoe debate: let the evidence guide prescription. British Journal of Sports Medicine 2018; 52(24).

107. Nigg B, Vienneau J, Smith A, Trudeau M, Mohr M, Nigg S. The Preferred Movement Path Paradigm: Influence of Running Shoes on Joint Movement. Medicine and Science in Sports and Exercise 2017; 49(8): 1641–1648.

108. Hoogkamer W, Kipp S, Spiering B, Kram R. Altered Running Economy Directly Translates to Altered Distance-Running Performance. Medicine & Science in Sports & Exercise 2016; 48(11): 2175–2180.

109. Fuller J, Thewlis D, Tsiros M, Brown N, Buckley J. Six-week transition to minimalist shoes improves running economy and time-trial performance. Journal of Science and Medicine in Sport 2017;20(12):1117–1122.

110. Salzler M, Kirwan H, Scarborough D, Walker J, Guarino A, Berkson E. Injuries observed in a prospective transition from traditional to minimalist footwear: correlation of high impact transient forces and lower injury severity. The Physician and sports medicine 2016; 44(4): 373–379.

111. Warne J, Gruber A. Transitioning to Minimal Footwear: a Systematic Review of Methods and Future Clinical Recommendations. Sports medicine—Open 2017; 15; 3(1): 33.

112. The Run Smarter Podcast: Episode 80: Is a Carbon Fibre Shoe Right for Me? with Simon Bartold.

113. Farina E, Haigh D, Luo G. Creating footwear for performance running. Footwear Science, 11:S1, S134-S135.
114. Flores N, Rao G, Berton E, Delattre N. The stiff plate location into the shoe influences the running biomechanics. Sports Biomechanics 2021; 20(7): 815–830.
115. Joubert D. A Comparison of Running Economy Across Seven Carbon-Plated Racing Shoes. 2021. Faculty Publications. 33.
116. Kong P, Candelaria N, Smith D. Running in new and worn shoes: a comparison of three types of cushioning footwear. British Journal of Sports Medicine 2009; 43(10): 745–749.

CHAPTER 15

117. Saragiotto B, Yamato T, Lopes A. What do recreational runners think about risk factors for running injuries? A descriptive study of their beliefs and opinions 2014; 44(10): 733–738.
118. Behm D, Blazevich A, Kay A, McHugh M. Acute effects of muscle stretching on physical performance, range of motion, and injury incidence in healthy active individuals: a systematic review. Applied Physiology, Nutrition, and Metabolism 2016; 41(1): 1–11.
119. Baxter C, McNaughton L, Sparks A, Norton L, Bentley D. Impact of stretching on the performance and injury risk of long-distance runners. Research in Sports Medicine 2017; 25(1): 78–90.
120. Pepper T, Brismée J, Sizer P, Kapila J, Seeber G, Huggins C, Hooper T. The Immediate Effects of Foam Rolling and Stretching on Iliotibial Band Stiffness: A Randomized Controlled Trial. International journal of sports physical therapy. 2021; 16(3): 651–661.
121. Craib M, Mitchell V, Fields K, Cooper T, Hopewell R, Morgan D. The association between flexibility and running economy in sub-elite male distance runners. Journal of Medicine & Science in Sports & Exercise 1996; 28(6), 737–743.
122. Damasceno M, Duarte M, Pasqua L, Lima-Silva A, MacIntosh B, Bertuzzi R. Static Stretching Alters Neuromuscular Function and Pacing Strategy, but Not Performance during a 3-Km Running Time-Trial. PLoS One 2014; 9(6): e99238.

123. Herbert R, Gabriel M. Effects of stretching before and after exercising on muscle soreness and risk of injury: systematic review. British Journal of Medicine 2002; 325(7362): 468.

124. Herbert R, Noronha M, Kamper S. Stretching to prevent or reduce muscle soreness after exercise. Cochrane Database of Systematic Reviews 2011; 6(7): CD004577.

125. The Run Smarter Podcast: Episode 94: Understanding your Recovery Pyramid with Shona Halson.

CHAPTER 16

126. Saunders P, Pyne D, Telford R, Hawley J. Factors Affecting Running Economy in Trained Distance Runners. Sports Medicine 2004; 34(7): 465–485.

127. The Run Smarter Podcast: Episode 68: Understanding Running Economy with Christos Ziliaskoudis.

128. Dunn M, Claxton D, Fletcher G, Wheat J, Binney D. Effects of running retraining on biomechanical factors associated with lower limb injury. Human Movement Science 2018; 58: 21–31.

129. Moore I. Is There an Economical Running Technique? A Review of Modifiable Biomechanical Factors Affecting Running Economy. Sports Medicine 2016; 46(6): 793–807.

130. Doyle E, Doyle T, Bonacci J, Fuller J. The effects of running gait retraining on biomechanics, performance, pain and injury: a systematic review and meta-analysis. Journal of Science and Medicine in Sport 2021; 24(S70).

131. Anderson L, Bonanno D, Hart H, Barton C. What are the Benefits and Risks Associated with Changing Foot Strike Pattern During Running? A Systematic Review and Meta-analysis of Injury, Running Economy, and Biomechanics. Sports Medicine 2020; 50(5): 885–917.

132. Willson J, Ratcliff O, Meardon S, Willy R. Influence of step length and landing pattern on patellofemoral joint kinetics during running. Scandinavian Journal of Medicine and Science in Sports 2015; 25(6): 736–743.

133. Meardon S, Campbell S, Derrick T. Step width alters iliotibial band strain during running. Sports Biomechanics 2012; 11(4): 464–472.

134. Barton C, Bonanno D, Carr J, Neal B, Malliaras P, Franklyn-Miller A, Menz H. Running retraining to treat lower limb injuries: a mixed-methods

study of current evidence synthesised with expert opinion. British Journal of Sports Medicine 2016; 50(9): 513–526.

135. The Run Smarter Podcast: Episode 49: How can I boost my running program with Jason Fitzgerald.

136. Napier C. Science of Running: Analyse your technique, prevent injury, revolutionise your training. Dorling Kindersley, Ltd, 2020.

CHAPTER 17

137. The Run Smarter Podcast: Episode 208: What to do when injuries aren't getting any worse, or any better.

CHAPTER 18

138. The Run Smarter Podcast: Episode 92: Heart rate variability for measuring recovery with Simon Wegerif.

139. Sandercock, G. Monitoring Heart Rate Variability (HRV) is so much more valuable than just monitoring heart rate, ithlete, https://www.myithlete.com/what-is-hrv/

140. Dong J. The role of heart rate variability in sports physiology. Experimental and Therapeutic Medicine 2016; 11(5): 1531–1536.

141. Buchheit M, Papelier Y, Laursen P, Ahmaidi S. Noninvasive assessment of cardiac parasympathetic function: postexercise heart rate recovery or heart rate variability? American Journal of Physiology. Heart and Circulatory Physiology 2007; 293(1): H8–10.

142. Plews D, Laursen P, Stanley J, Kilding A, Buchheit M. Training Adaptation and Heart Rate Variability in Elite Endurance Athletes: Opening the Door to Effective Monitoring. Sports Medicine 2013; 43(9): 773–781.

143. The Run Smarter Podcast: Episode 94: Understanding your Recovery Pyramid with Shona Halson.

144. The Run Smarter Podcast: Episode 95: Understanding Nutrition for Optimal Recovery with Christie Aschwanden.

145. Aschwanden C. Good to go: How to eat, sleep and rest like a champion. London, UK: CPI Group (UK) Ltd, 2019.

146. Bonnar D, Bartel K, Kakoschke N, Lang C. Sleep Interventions Designed to Improve Athletic Performance and Recovery: A Systematic Review of Current Approaches. Sports Medicine 2018; 48(3): 683–703.

147. Vitale K, Owens R, Hopkins S, Malhotra A. Sleep Hygiene for Optimizing Recovery in Athletes: Review and Recommendations. International Journal of Sports Medicine 2019; 40(8): 535–543.
148. Leeder J, Gissane C, Someren K, Gregson K, et al. Cold water immersion and recovery from strenuous exercise: a meta-analysis. British Journal of Sports Medicine 2012; 46: 233–240.
149. The Run Smarter Podcast: Episode 79: The Good & Bad (mostly bad) of Massage Therapy with Alice Sanvito.

CHAPTER 19

150. Grivas, G. The Effects of Tapering on Performance in Elite Endurance Runners: A Systematic Review. International Journal of Sports Science 2018; 8(1): 8–13.
151. Mujika I, Padilla S, Pyne D, Busso T. Physiological changes associated with the pre-event taper in athletes. Sports Medicine 2004; 34(13): 891–927.
152. Neary P, Bhambhani Y, McKenzie D. Effects of different stepwise reduction taper protocols on cycling performance. Canadian Journal of Applied Physiology 2003; 28(4): 576–587.
153. Bosquet L, Montpetit J, Arvisais D, Mujika I. Effects of Tapering on Performance A Meta-Analysis. Medicine & Science in Sports & Exercise 2007; 39(8): 1358–1365.
154. Shepley B, MacDougall J, Cipriano N, Sutton J, Tarnopolsky M, Coates G. Physiological effects of tapering in highly trained athletes. Journal of Applied Physiology 1992; 72(2): 706–11.
155. Spilsbury, K. Tapering and peaking for an event or major competition. In: Blagrove R, Hayes P. The science and practice of middle and long distance running. Routledge: Taylor & Francis Group, 2021:132–144.
156. The Run Smarter Podcast: Episode 220: Finding the right taper & recovery week strategy with Jason Fitzgerald.
157. Taylor S, Rogers G, Driver H. Effects of training volume on sleep, psychological, and selected physiological profiles of elite female swimmers. Medicine and Science in Sports and Exercise 1997; 29(5): 688–693.

CHAPTER 20

158. The Run Smarter Podcast: Episode 26: Gut Health for Running Performance with Chloe McLeod.
159. Maughan R, Shirrefs S. Muscle Cramping During Exercise: Causes, Solutions, and Questions Remaining. Sports Medicine 2019; 49(2): S115–S124.
160. The Run Smarter Podcast: Episode 194: Understanding sweat science, hydration & cramping with Andy Blow.
161. Renfree A, Hanley B. Strategic and tactical decision-making in middle and long-distance running races. In: Blagrove R, Hayes P. The science and practice of middle and long distance running. Routledge: Taylor & Francis Group, 2021: 176–184.
162. The Run Smarter Podcast: Episode 162: Marathon PB tactics & strategy with Brian Hanley.
163. Deaner R, Addona V, Hanley B. Risk-Taking Runners Slow More in the Marathon. Frontiers in Psychology 2019; 10(333): 1–12.
164. Hutchinson A. Endure mind, body and the curiously elastic limits of human performance. CPI Group, Ltd, 2018.
165. Simons D, Boot W, Charness N, Gathercole S, Chabris C, Hambrick D, Stine-Morrow E. Do "Brain-Training" Programs Work? Psychological Science in the Public Interest 2016; 17(3): 103–186.
166. Winter S, Carla M. Psychology of distance running. In: Blagrove R, Hayes P. The science and practice of middle and long distance running. Routledge: Taylor & Francis Group, 2021: 66–75.
167. The Run Smarter Podcast: Episode 57: Learn to Love the Run you've got with Amanda Brooks.
168. Hettinga F, Edwards A, Hanley B. The Science Behind Competition and Winning in Athletics: Using World-Level Competition Data to Explore Pacing and Tactics. Frontiers in psychology 2019; 1(11): 1–16.

Made in United States
North Haven, CT
21 September 2022

24412911R00261